THE WOODLAND STEWARD

A Practical Guide to the Management of Small Private Forests

JAMES R. FAZIO

ILLUSTRATION & DESIGN
KRISTIN R. AUFDENBERG

The Woodland Press

Box 3524 University Station
Moscow, Idaho 83843

To
Jim, Dan, Walter, Julianna
and other woodland stewards of tomorrow

Today I have grown taller from walking with the trees.

—James Russell Lowell

CONTENTS

FOREWORD

Owning a piece of woodland is one of the major joys in the lives of millions of Americans. For many, it is the embodiment of a dream—a piece of land where one can go for work, play, inspiration and relaxation. A place where children (and sometimes parents) can learn of the wonders of nature. A place where many useful—and sometimes profitable—products can be obtained.

But to the thoughtful person, owning a piece of woodland is also a responsibility. That responsibility is often called stewardship—the need to provide nurture, care and protection to the land its resources. Good stewardship, however, involves more than good intentions. It demands skill, as well, and while the skills needed to manage woodlands are not terribly difficult, and can be learned by virtually anyone who wishes to learn them, they are not automatic, either. Even the person who has been fortunate enough to be "raised in the woods," where many of these skills are learned as a natural part of growing up, can profit from learning some of the technical factors that form the basis for good woodland stewardship.

That need is admirably met in this book, which sets forth a readable, straight-forward approach to planning and carrying out a good woodland program. In the following pages, readers will find information to help them better understand soils, landscapes, plants and animals. They will learn more about how a tree grows, and what people can do to help protect trees and improve their growth. They will learn how to become more than an owner of land; they will learn how to become a woodland steward. And that is an important distinction.

The welfare of people depends on the health of the land and its resources. People—and societies—that are good stewards of the land reap rewards. Those who exploit and waste it eventually pay a heavy price. That is the verdict of history, and it is the background upon which most conservation philosophies are based. Conservationists believe that good land stewardship is essential for the well-being of future generations.

But we do not need to wait for the future to reap the benefits of an informed and conservation-conscious citizenry. People who understand the need for good stewardship expect good land treatment from those who hold the privilege of private land ownership. Such social expectations largely remove the need for official regulations and government controls of land use.

A strong conservation ethic allows a much freer society where individual rights can be allowed because individual responsibility is practiced. Public awareness also undergirds the development and funding of appropriate land management and conservation programs on the part of government, affecting both the management of publicly-owned land and the programs that assist private landowners. In these situations, public knowledge and expectations are converted into political reality.

Thus, the lessons in *The Woodland Steward* are for each and every person, whether they own forest land, hope to become an owner some day, or simply want to understand what they are seeing as they drive down the road. For in the final analysis, no matter who holds the title to that land you see out there, the land will live longer than today's owner, as each of us is just a temporary part of the ongoing drama of life. What we leave behind, whether it improves the land or degrades it, is a legacy by which our children will remember us. Making that legacy a positive one should be our most important life goal.

R. Neil Sampson
Executive Vice President
American Forestry Association

PREFACE

Here at the start I want to confess a love affair with trees. Somewhere in my lost youth I gained this feeling from a family of farm and small town origin who with the passing of generations had moved into the city. But the links were still there. On holidays and special weekends, such as the opening of fishing season, we would return to the woods. There I was taught a few basics—this is moss, this is a seedling that comes from acorns like these, this giant tree was here when George Washington lived. I even learned a few names, or at least the difference between "pine trees" and "the other kind." Most of all, I learned to love the quiet of the woods. I came to know a fascination that has grown with time, and I came to an early understanding of myself, at least to the point of knowing that my life must be anchored in the woods.

We owned no land in those early years, but to my good fortune there was an odd area of woods that adjoined our backyard in the city. A speculator owned the woods, but he waited too long to develop and the deterioration of our neighborhood moved faster than he did. Unsuited for industry and too late to profitably offer housing, the parcel just sat there. It was about two city blocks in size, and served at once as dump, play area, lover's retreat, berry patch, hideaway, pet graveyard and who knows what else. But to me it was my second home. I used it living out childhood fantasies as Daniel Boone and for the real life adventures of adolescence. Looking back, I see now that I also used it—or it used me—to form my personal philosophy towards trees. For there in that urban woodlot, I used trees in much the same ways I do now. I made bonfires, built Tarzan-like shacks, gathered buckeyes for fun and walnuts to eat. I watched birds there and found solitude at times when I needed it most. I dug soil for my parents' garden and found cherries and apples and branches full of flowers. I used and enjoyed. I took but I also gave. I even drove off other boys with my BB gun if they came to the woods for the inane purpose of simply "chopping down trees".

Today little has changed, but it almost did. I went off to forestry college seeking a sure route out of the city and into a career in the outdoors. There, at one of the East's leading forestry schools, it would have been easy to let the cold facts of science and the emotionless formulas of forest finance overshadow the feelings that first drew me to the field. The forestry college where I am employed today still harbors a few of the kind of professors—who in turn clone practitioners—that could manage a shoe factory or a forest with equal feeling. But happily there are the others, too, and it was they who helped my philosophy mature. And there were books like Michael Frome's *Whose Woods These Are,* an eloquent portrayal of our national forests, that reinforced my feelings of caring at a time I was learning to manage and to exploit the forests for their wood.

In short, I learned stewardship—using, protecting, and passing along to future generations unimpaired. The idea of stewardship brought it all together with purpose and direction. And today I feel equally at home as a member of the Society of American Foresters and also a member of the Audubon Society and a trustee of The Nature Conservancy.

In writing this book, my wife Dawn and I travelled from Vermont to California. Wherever we went, it was thrilling to find landowners who shared our love of the woods and our view of using these treasures while guarding them jealously for tomorrow. Some of those people are portrayed in these pages. They represent a cross section of the four-and-one-half-million ordinary folks in the United States and Canada who own woodlands—farmers, shopkeepers, retirees, young people and middle-aged professionals of every hue. But the ones I sought out had something in common. For whatever reason, they are actively using their woodlands. They are also doing it with an enthusiasm and contagious optimism about the future of privately owned woodlands. More importantly, these people are harvesting more than crops from their land. They love their woodlands and are doing their best to be good stewards. They are taking from the land, while at the same time giving it their protective care. Without exception, they are gaining new avenues of learning, enjoying healthful exercise, having solitude when they need it and togetherness with family and friends at other times, and becoming refreshed for the tasks of their professions and other responsibilities.

Another confession I need to make is that I count myself within the ranks of wilderness enthusiasts. I believe in the preservation of some land areas as nearly unaltered by human activities as possible. A strong, rich and healthy nation should be able to recognize the value of natural diversity and see the benefits of wild places. It is inexcusable that samples of deserts, grasslands and forests should not be protected and passed on to future generations, complete with the total web of life they harbor. The array of wild places needs to include small bogs and desert springs, and sometimes whole mountain ranges with ecosystems large enough to allow the grizzly and the caribou to share our planet forever.

However, I feel just as strongly about the thoughtless waste of unmanaged lands where the axe and saw have already been felt. Second growth forest land is the majority of forest land in North America, and in the United States about half of it is in private ownership. In Canada, this figure is about ten percent. I have no argument with the landowner who decides he wants his own wilderness and consciously makes that decision because his goals are best met in that way. The few in that category should read no further and should give this book to a friend.

My concern is for people who want to do more with their woodlands but need to learn how to get started. These people are legion. Their opportunities are endless, and with care and devotion they can pass along their land to future generations to use and enjoy as they did. It is for these potential stewards that this book has been written.

James R. Fazio
Moscow, Idaho

ACKNOWLEDGEMENTS

When local publisher Ivar Nelson first had the idea for this book, the professional foresters he approached said it couldn't be done. Their concern was that the subject of woodland management is so complex and diverse that to attempt explaining it to non-professionals and writing about it on more than a regional basis would somehow do an injustice to the subject and to their profession. I hope they were wrong, and in the pages that follow I have attempted to interpret a subject that is dear to me and to many owners of non-industrial private woodlands.

The professionals were correct, however, that this would be no simple task. The subject is as complex as nature and people. Also, although I am a forester by training, in recent years I have mostly been behind an administrator's desk rather than working in the field. My forte is interpretation of the technical and I must look to the real experts to keep the facts straight and to sort through the often conflicting opinions about what is correct or best. Therefore, I relied upon many people in writing this book. It would not have been possible without them, and even with their help not everyone will agree with all that is written here. The remaining errors and some opinions that will inevitably rankle my professional colleagues are entirely my responsibility. For the vast amount of information that is accurate and, I hope, helpful, I wish to gratefully acknowledge the following specialists who reviewed the manuscript.

The two who carefully read the entire volume were Donald Hanley, extension forester working jointly for the University of Washington and Washington State University, and Fred E. Winch, Jr., consulting forester *per ex— cellent* of Bradford, New Hampshire.

Those who reviewed and corrected sections pertaining to their areas of specialization were: Ronald Mastrogiuseppe, ecologist at Redwoods National Park, Arcata, California; Don White, University of Idaho extension forester; faculty in the University of Idaho's College of Forestry, Wildlife and Range Sciences, especially Harold Osborne, Harry Lee, David Wenny and visiting professor Michael Frome; Kenneth L. Carvell, professor of forestry at West Virginia University; John Marker, national fire prevention officer for the USDA Forest Service, Washington, D.C.; William L. Hoover, associate professor of forestry at Purdue University; Dave Taber, extension specialist for the State University of New York college of Environmental Science and Forestry at Syracuse; Daniel J. Decker, wildlife extension specialist specialist for the New York State college of Agriculture and Life Sciences, Cornell University; Thom J. McEvoy, extension forest management specialist, University of Vermont; Alex Dickson, coordinator of continuing education in forestry, University of New Brunswick; William N. Darwin, Jr., timber harvesting specialist, USDA Forest Service, Atlanta, Georgia; and publisher Ivar Nelson, who contributed many of the ideas at the inception of this project.

I am especially grateful to Kristin Aufdenberg who went far beyond design and illustration in helping to make this book possible, and to others who came to the rescue when production problems nearly ended the project. These special friends of woodlands are Cort Conley, editor of the University Press of Idaho; author Michael Frome; R. Neil Sampson and the American Forestry Association; Walter and Ann Chapman; and the faculty and staff in the College of Forestry, Wildlife and Range Sciences at the University of Idaho.

Countless private and governmental organizations offered much of the information contained in these pages. To acknowledge all the sources of so much material would have rendered the book unreadable. I hope these contributors will be forgiving in view of the end result of bringing this information to the attention of landowners who can use it.

This book would be little more than another textbook if it were not for the living examples of good management based on interviews with these people in their woodlands. These are the true woodland stewards, every one of them an inspiration. I sincerely thank them for their time spent showing me their woodlands, their openness in sharing ideas and problems, and their hospitality in the good old fashioned spirit of neighborliness: George Freeman, Scott Barbour, Raoul Moore, Al and Daryl Kyle, David and Mary Utzig, Frank and Janet Lockhart, Walter and Ann Chapman, David Houston, and Evelyn Stock.

Finally, my deepest thanks to the one person who kept me at the task through good times and the lowest moments—my wife, Dawna. She shared the joys of our woodland visits and suffered the nuisances of mosquitoes and chiggers. She gave valuable ideas to the project, kept me from getting off track a time or two, and painstakingly read and re-read the entire manuscript looking for typographical gremlins. This book is as much hers as it is mine.

1 Trees
and
Your Future

The clearest way into the universe is through a forest.

—John Muir

During the springtime of my life, I lived for a while in a rented farmhouse not far from the woods where Aldo Leopold spent his happiest hours. There at his weekend retreat, on 120 acres of abandoned Wisconsin farmland, Leopold brought together his thoughts and experiences as a landowner, naturalist and philosopher. The result was his classic book on man–land ethics—*A Sand County Almanac.*

One evening I was walking an edge of one of the mile-long squares that mark off the farms and woods of central Wisconsin. It was one of those walks intended to erase the day's events, or to blot out "too much modernity," as Leopold would have said. I was thinking of Leopold that evening, as I often did when trying to put natural order ahead of the illogic that seems part of a bad day. That exercise focused my attention on the small woodlots dotting the pastures and potato fields and a passage from the *Almanac* kept coming to mind:

Every farm woodland, in addition to yielding lumber, fuel, and posts, should provide its owner a liberal education. This crop of wisdom never fails, but it is not always harvested.

These words have intrigued me, and they came back to me again as I set out to write *The Woodland Steward.* Just what are the benefits of owning a piece of wooded land?

Aldo Leopold believed that woodland ownership included the benefit of learning the basic principles of ecology. He died in 1948 while fighting a wildfire on his neighbor's farm, but had he lived he would have seen the Earth Day generation re-reading his *Almanac* to learn how the tinkerings of man were disrupting the machinery of nature. There are indeed ecology lessons in a woodlot, and some owners recognize this as part of their harvest.

There are other benefits as well. So many, in fact, that I believe they are bringing a new era to the woodlands of North America. It is an era of awakening to the real values of woodlands. As never before, people are looking to their land as a source of varied enrichment.

Part of this new era is economic. However, owning twenty, eighty, or a few hundred acres is no road to a fortune. Nor can anyone except the independently wealthy or a modern hermit expect to subsist on such property. What the small, private woodland does offer is an excellent source of supplementary income, or at least enough to pay the taxes while land values appreciate or to finance a vacation retreat. It may offer cash through the regular sale of small trees for pulpwood or fence posts. It may contribute income from an occasional harvest, which if done carefully will help the remaining trees grow better and raise the value of the forest. Or, it may provide savings through the supply of firewood or logs for a house.

But the new era promises something more. The renewed interest in woodlands has the potential of bringing needed management to large areas of neglected forest land. With our growing population constantly needing more wood, and especially with new markets developing for small-diameter trees, it is becoming practical to manage even the smallest woodlot. This in turn, offers hope that through care and good forestry, thousands of private woodlots can be converted to a state of health and vigor that will assure renewable timber supplies long into the future. For the national good, foresters have been trying for decades to encourage sound management on non-government lands, but it has been a losing battle. Now there is hope.

Another aspect of the new era is strictly personal, and it may be the most promising of all. Leopold's "liberal education" and "crop of wisdom" are proving to be more than ecology lessons. Growing numbers of people are discovering that there is far more to the enjoyment of woodland ownership than a sock full of dollars. This, indeed, is exactly the premise underlying this book.

In the pages ahead I try not to say what benefits you should seek from your land. That is for you to determine. If money is your only goal, fine. If it is not, the adventure of ownership offers endless enrichment in your life. But there are many dangers.

Few who own land realize what targets they are for persuasion and exploitation. Log buyers prowl the back roads and even scout by air, then suddenly appear at your door with an offer of cash. Large, well-known companies also come around, wanting to make you a member of their Tree Farm "family." Extension foresters, private foresters, and an assortment of government foresters send you mail or show up on your land offering advice.

In nearly every case, you will notice two common threads. One—the emphasis is on trees as a product. This means cash to you and satisfaction of a patriotic kind for helping to assure a flow of raw materials to our mills. Two—it is better to leave the planning, the technical aspects of growing and the harvesting to experts. The experts abound, and they are invariably personable people. In the press of other day-to-day concerns, taking cash offers and letting the experts make your decisions, may seem like a good deal.

For some, it is a good deal. But the scenario has two negative results. First, many small woodland owners reject the idea of other people on their land, so nothing is done and the woods are little more than a backdrop for the house or a piece of property once owned by a departed relative. The opposite result, equally uninspired, are agreements made with a handshake to sell off the timber, or to let experts manage the trees while the landowner sits by like an investor watching the big board.

The idea for this book was born when it occurred to me how much richer woodland owners would be if they took more of a personal interest in the trees on their property. Richer not only in dollars, but also in satisfaction. Although I won't say what a person should or should not do with his woodlands (within the bounds of ecological responsibility), I will attempt to provide a range of possibilities. I believe that the active management of woodlands for whatever purpose is well within the capability of any landowner. Certainly, the education of professional foresters takes up to five years and a whole bookcase of texts and references. You cannot expect to achieve their level of technical know-how. However, presented here are ideas, showing you how to get started, what to watch out for, and when to seek professional help. You will also find leads to more information about subjects you may want to explore in detail. Some of these are available through the mail from government sources at little or no cost. Others, particularly books, are too esoteric to be found in most local libraries or bookstores. In these cases, you can ask local foresters if they have a copy to loan (which is a good way to strike up a beneficial friendship), or you can order it through your bookstore.

There are several things you will not find in this book. The focus is on forests and forest trees, not fruit trees, shade trees, shrubs, or ornamentals. There are already many good sources on those topics. I also have not discussed the conversion of forest land to other uses. While this is an option that many landowners exercise, my personal feelings are best expressed by the song lyrics, "Lord, we don't need another mountain." Lord, we also don't need another shopping center. We don't need another drive-in movie, and the yellow arches that

sprouted in the woods I used to roam are the last ones I ever care to see. We also don't need more acres of slopes and marginally fertile soil converted to crops or cow pastures. We need trees. We need their friendly beauty, their gift of fresher air and their ever-renewable products that should not be replaced by plastic or other petroleum offsprings. Something is lost for humanity when woodlands are converted to other uses, and I'll have no part of it.

The other things you won't find are the techniques and equipment used by the forest industries. This is an area of high finance and high technology where corporate goals demand maximum profits, and where trees are often harvested like so many match sticks—sheared off at the stump, stripped of their limbs, cut to convenient lengths and bundled for transport—all by a single gargantuan machine. This is the world of high efficiency and volume production. It is fascinating in its own right, but in no way will it help you with *your* management problems or add to well-spent leisure in the peace of your woodlot.

A Bounty of Private Land

The ownership of small wooded tracts has gone through quite an evolution. In the history of North America, the forest was first loathed by white settlers, viewed as an impediment to progress and a refuge for all manner of evil. Woods not held by the government were owned largely by farmers, and the focus was on survival and earning a living. In the East, the land was cleared and tilled. What was not farmed was used in some way—to provide logs and lumber for homes and barns, or to furnish poles for fences and browse for livestock. Eventually many farmers left the land for the tempting salaries of city jobs. Thousands of fields reverted to woods, and the woods were often bought as sites for summer homes, weekend retreats or places to hunt game.

In the West, where the private ownership of small woodlands is less common, forests have been the appendages of ranches, homesteads and mining claims. Forests were cut as needed, usually cleared, and have only recently been seen as valuable assets in their own right.

The total amount of forested land in the United States and Canada is staggering. For lack of a better term, land is classified as "commercial" forest land if it is capable of producing at least 20 cubic feet of wood products per acre per year and is not officially withdrawn for wilderness or other non-commodity purposes. The amount of such land in the United States totals nearly half a billion acres, and as you can see in the chart, over half of it is owned by private parties not in the forest industries. In Canada, the amount of productive forest land (554 million acres) is roughly the same as in the United States, and about nine percent of it is privately owned by an estimated half million citizens.

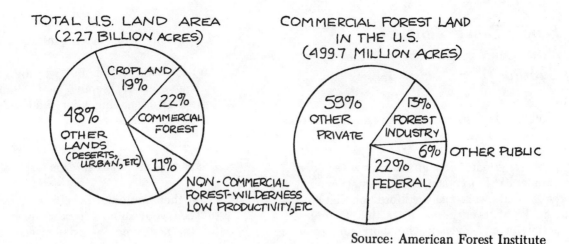

TOTAL U.S. LAND AREA
(2.27 BILLION ACRES)

CROPLAND 19%

22% COMMERCIAL FOREST

48% OTHER LANDS (DESERTS, URBAN, ETC)

11% NON-COMMERCIAL FOREST-WILDERNESS LOW PRODUCTIVITY, ETC

COMMERCIAL FOREST LAND IN THE U.S.
(499.7 MILLION ACRES)

59% OTHER PRIVATE

13% FOREST INDUSTRY

6% OTHER PUBLIC

22% FEDERAL

Source: American Forest Institute

Unfortunately, in both countries there has been widespread neglect of small, privately owned woodlands. The results are millions of dollars of lost income, increased imports, and greater pressure on public forests, including our relatively few remaining acres of forested wilderness.

I first became aware of the magnitude of this problem when I learned that in my own state of Idaho, of the 3,800,000 acres of privately-owned forest land, 3,110,000 acres need planting, seeding, thinning or some kind of improvement work. This is all too typical. In the South, for example, each year 700,000 acres of conifer forests lose much of their productivity because they are not adequately regenerated with desirable species after being logged. Cash is received and the land's future is forgotten. In fact, the Forest Industries Council has found that on private, nonindustrial land, only one out of nine harvested acres is being purposefully regenerated.

The situation on small, privately owned forests adds up to millions of people missing out on the personal joys of caring for their woodlands. It also means that our timber supplies are going to be in trouble within the next generation or two. One government source predicts that by 2030 there will be a 58 percent increase in the need for conifer products and a 207 percent increase in the need for hardwoods. These figures do not even include the spectacular increase in demand for firewood that began with the oil crunch of the early 1970s, nor do they reflect society's insatiable desire for other forest "products" such as camping, wildlife and other recreation. Coincidental with these demands is the shrinking of forested acreage — land lost forever to more and bigger highways, houses, shopping centers, dams and other appendages of civilization.

Distribution of Private Woodlands

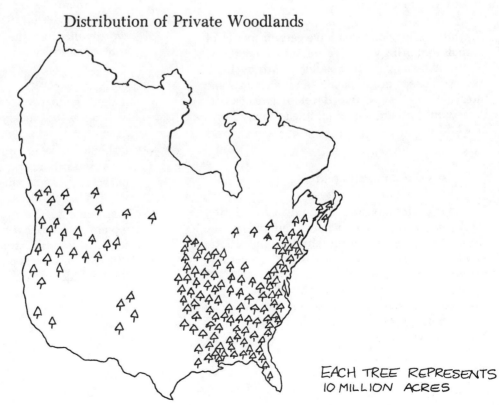

EACH TREE REPRESENTS 10 MILLION ACRES

Why People Don't Manage —
And Why
They Should

"I bought my land strictly as an investment and plan to sell it when the price goes up."

✔ If you are smart enough to know a good investment like land, you should be smart enough to realize that a well-managed forest on that land will make it even more attractive to many potential buyers. Even in the short run, some initial steps like improvement cuttings, plantings or thinnings can make a big difference in appearance and productivity. Cared-for land is a selling point!

"My property is for hunting. I don't give a damn about trees."

✔ Hunting for what? If it's squirrels — the number one small-game species in West Virginia — you'll need nut-producing trees and den trees. If it's deer, you need dense tree cover near open areas. Trees and wildlife are inseparable. Manage the one to get the other. And once you start, I think you will begin to realize that the fun of forest management extends your enjoyment of the land, and its wildlife, well beyond the hunting season.

"My property is a wildlife preserve, a sanctuary for animals and a retreat for me."

✔ That's fine, but don't you have certain species of animals that bring you more pleasure than others? Why not manage your woodlot to attract those species? Forests are dynamic, and without some intervention they often develop (we call it *succession*) into areas inhospitable to many forms of wildlife.

"We just want a place to retire."

✔ You don't plan to stop living when you stop working, do you? From what I understand, the three biggest threats to the physical and mental health of retirees are: lack of something stimulating to do; lack of exercise; and a feeling of no longer being important to society. Learning to manage your woodlot, and starting at it now, can solve these problems. I've talked to plenty of retirees who guarantee it!

"Land is my hedge against inflation."

✔ And it's a good one. But why be satisfied with staying even or keeping just a jump ahead of inflation? Managing your land will add to its value exponentially.

"Managing my small acreage just wouldn't pay."

✔ Well, there are other benefits — exercise, a hobby to keep your mind off other problems, family togetherness, and the challenge of learning, to name just a few. But in most cases, even from the economic angle, you are probably wrong, especially if you already own the land. It's just a matter of finding the best way to make your woodland pay — income from Christmas trees or high-value logs may someday buy your kids a college education or get you to Tahiti. The prices of wood products are going to go up, and now firewood, fence posts, and other small diameter products are making it worthwhile to thin young stands and manage acreages that were once too small to be profitable. Times are changing.

"Taxes work against me if I try to manage."

✔ This is a tough one in some areas. But tax laws are changing, too, and in many places they are becoming quite favorable to long-term management and estate planning. Since we live in a free country, it wouldn't hurt to get involved with these issues and help the politicians understand that tax structures making it worthwhile to manage forest land are in the best interest of everyone.

"I don't want my land raped by some logger. The beauty of my woods means a lot to me."

✔ I should hope so. But before you write off all loggers as land rapers, read the chapter on harvesting. And while everyone can't agree on what is beautiful and what isn't, it is my opinion that some of the most inspiring, cathedral-like woods are those that have been carefully managed to include tall, straight trees with plenty of diversity in species and sizes. They are definitely the healthiest forests, too.

"It's too much work."

✓ True, it is a lot of work. But thousands of people are finding that good old physical work is the missing ingredient that can restore healthy lives and bind families together. In a managed woodland children and parents can plan, work and profit together in ways they soon find are fun. In fact, throughout America the most successful small scale operations are usually family endeavors.

"I don't know enough about what to do."

✓ Great, this book is for you! And don't feel alone. Most owners of small woodlands face the same problem. Once you start learning a few basics you will find there is plenty you can do. You will also find there is plenty of help available, and plenty of other land owners—many who have joined together in forest owner associations—who started out exactly where you are and who are now enthusiastically enjoying a whole new dimension in life.

My goal is to help you toward the enjoyment and rewards of purposeful forest management. If you have the land—whether it's ten acres or five hundred—and the desire, there is no reason why you cannot gain more from your forest ownership. The options are endless, and so are the pleasures and rewards.

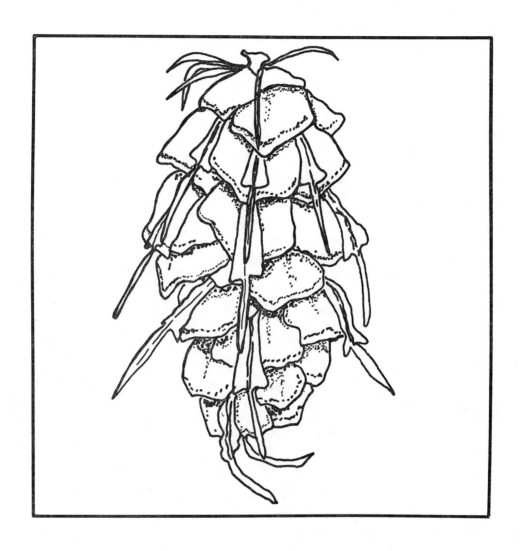

2 Know Your Land

The joy and appreciation of owning a woodland increases in proportion to familiarity with its community of life. "Dirt" soon seems like too lowly a term for soil. As you learn more about it, soil becomes a wonderful combination of bedrock and creatures and geological forces—all unique to the slopes and flat spots you claim as your own. Life that springs from this soil takes on names and meanings. Trees and shrubs are seen as associates, each an indicator that the other should be near. Some become recognized as products, perhaps worth far more in dollars than you ever imagined; others offer recreation. This living fabric—the soil, the trees, the open spaces and the water—can also open a new book about wildlife.

The mysteries of a forest can be revealed to the limits of your interest. Not to become its master, but rather to become a part of it. From that vantage point, to work with the forest is to bring into your life a richness that can be appreciated by few others than those with the privilege and responsibility of caring for wooded land.

Your Parcel of Land

If there is one great truth that can help us understand the land and its management, it is that nature is a highly organized system. What at first glance may seem like a random assemblage of trees and shrubs is actually a rather predictable community of life—both plants and animals— resulting from the effects of climate, soil, the presence or lack of moisture, and many other physical factors. In addition to making you savvy about the great outdoors, knowing about nature's systems helps tell you the limits of what you can or cannot expect from your land.

Biomes

The broadest classification recognized by scientists is the plant-animal community called a *biome*. In North America these are the zones you may have heard referred to as tundra, the northern coniferous or boreal forest, deciduous forest, desert, grassland, southern pine forest, tropical forest, and so forth. Certain plants and animals are typical of each biome, and for good reasons you would not expect to find them elsewhere. For example, moose are common in the northern coniferous forest, but you wouldn't expect to see one in the deciduous forests of the Ozarks. Likewise, the loblollies and sand pines of the southern pine biome would not survive or would grow poorly in the chaparral biome of southern California. Trying to grow tree species "off-site"—that is, out of the range of their natural tolerances—was once a common mistake and still brings disappointment to unwary planters.

Zones of a similar sort can be seen as elevation changes in mountainous areas. Feeling the combined effects of temperature, wind and precipitation, the plant and animal communities at the bottom of a mountain are often quite different than those at the summit. This is illustrated in the cross-sectional drawing of a California mountain.

Forest Types

The map on page 9 showing the distribution of forest vegetation provides another general way of classifying your parcel of land. However, more useful are two classification schemes called *forest cover types* and *forest habitat types*.

The *forest cover type* system is based on the names of trees that predominate in a particular area. To predominate, one species must make up at least 20 percent of the basal area (see p. 25). The forest cover type is then named after that tree. Sometimes there is more than one dominant species, in which case the type name may include up to three co-dominants. This is a relatively easy system to use, and the trained eye can soon classify a forest cover type without actually counting trees.

There are about 150 forest cover types recognized by the Society of American Foresters. Some examples from various regions of North America include:

Northern Coniferous Forest Region
Jack pine
Black spruce — tamarack

Northern Forest Region
Red spruce — balsam fir
Sugar maple — beech — yellow birch

Central Forest Region
White oak — black oak — northern red oak
White oak

Southern Forest Region
Loblolly pine
Longleaf pine — scrub oak

West-Middle Elevation, Interior
Lodgepole pine
Interior Douglas-fir

South Pacific, Except for High Mountains
Pacific ponderosa pine — Douglas-fir
Canyon live oak

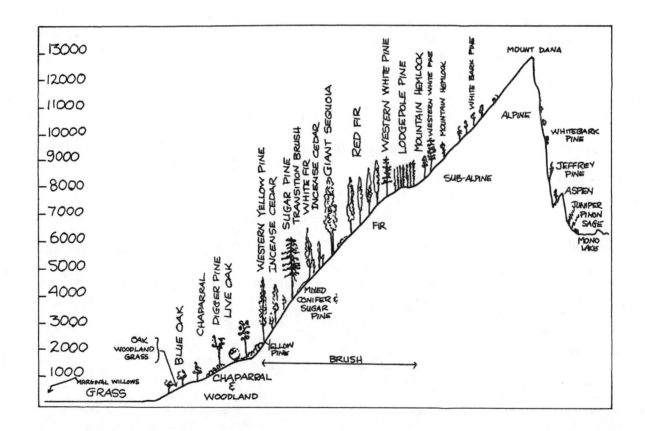

PLANT AND ANIMAL COMMUNITIES CHANGE WITH ELEVATION

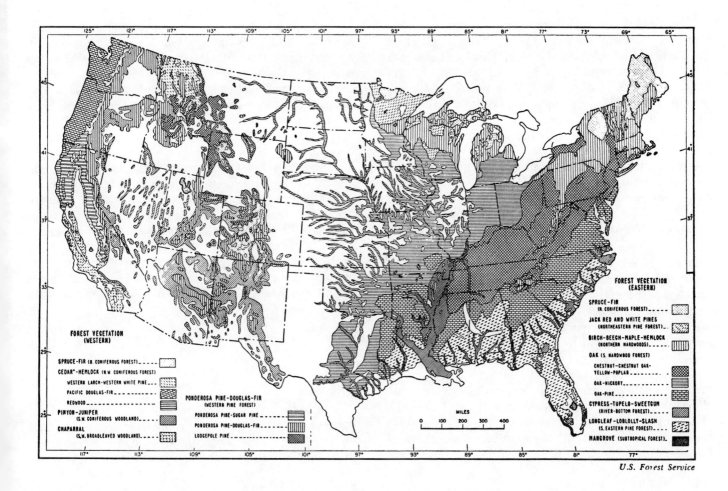

U.S. Forest Service

The *forest habitat type* system is one of the newest ways to classify forest land and is probably the most useful to anyone interested in growing trees. The major difference between this system and forest cover type system is that forest cover types describe the forest that currently occupies the site. But forests are dynamic. Anyone who has watched an abandoned field or pasture knows that grass and wildflowers soon are overtopped by shrubs which eventually give way to trees.

What may not be noticed is that over a long period of time (at least in human terms) the first community of trees may give way to a second type. With this, or in some stands after a series of such changes, a *climax* stage is reached, where a combination of species are able to reproduce themselves in their own shade. This final, stable condition theoretically can exist for as long as climatic changes do not alter the whole biome of which it is part. This fascinating process of change is called *succession*. It is a concept that forms the very foundation of forest management.

FOREST SUCCESSION IN THE SOUTHEAST

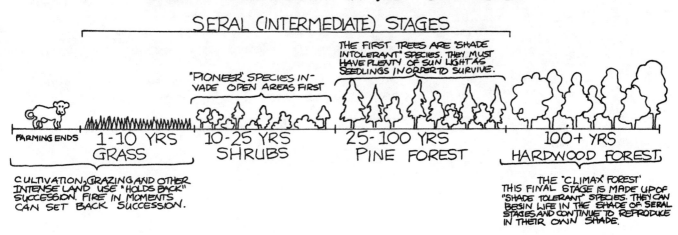

SERAL (INTERMEDIATE) STAGES

THE FIRST TREES ARE "SHADE INTOLERANT" SPECIES. THEY MUST HAVE PLENTY OF SUN LIGHT AS SEEDLINGS IN ORDER TO SURVIVE.

"PIONEER" SPECIES INVADE OPEN AREAS FIRST

FARMING ENDS

1-10 YRS GRASS

10-25 YRS SHRUBS

25-100 YRS PINE FOREST

100+ YRS HARDWOOD FOREST

CULTIVATION, GRAZING AND OTHER INTENSE LAND USE "HOLDS BACK" SUCCESSION. FIRE IN MOMENTS CAN SET BACK SUCCESSION.

THE "CLIMAX FOREST" THIS FINAL STAGE IS MADE UP OF "SHADE TOLERANT" SPECIES. THEY CAN BEGIN LIFE IN THE SHADE OF SERAL STAGES AND CONTINUE TO REPRODUCE IN THEIR OWN SHADE.

Forest habitat types are based not on what the biggest or most abundant trees are today, but rather on the prediction of what the forest on that particular site will be when it reaches the permanency of its climax stage. Of course, if it is an old stand already in climax, the job is easy. However, most of us own land that was cut over at one time, or burned, or farmed, or in some other way altered. Both natural disturbances and man's actions may set back succession. This happens each time you mow your lawn. On a large scale, it happens when we log a *seral*, or intermediate, stage in the stand's movement toward climax. In fact, forest management is actually little more than manipulating natural succession. It is the purposeful management of change.

The system of forest habitat types was developed primarily by a husband and wife team of scientists in the 1950s. Rexford and Jean Daubenmire pointed out that forests are potentially a predictable mosaic of plant associations that exist where they do because of climate, micro-climate, the relative richness of soil, and the amount of water held by the soil. However, since most woodlands today are not in their climax stage, there is a wide range of intergrading as species come and go while the forest progresses toward its specific climax type. Working in eastern Washington and northern Idaho, the Daubenmires identified 22 units, or habitat types, that they claimed as "the basic ecological subdivisions of landscapes."

At any point in succession on almost any forested piece of land, the habitat type can be named. The method used is similar to the use of a tree key as shown on page 14. One makes a series of decisions about characteristics of the soil (moist bottomland or dry upland?), the presence of shrubs or other "indicator" species (is snowberry or ocean spray represented?) and what trees (seedlings and saplings) are reproducing in the understory?

Scientists are constantly refining this system and working to expand the area where habitat types can be keyed by forest owners. Guides are available for areas of the Rocky Mountains and Pacific Northwest and in other regions where the system is believed to be workable, which is primarily in the northern latitudes. To find out if there is a habitat type guide available in your area, contact: Silviculturist, Intermountain Forest and Range Experiment Station, USDA Forest Service, Ogden, Utah 84401.

The Soil

Soil scientists fondly point out that all life on land depends on a rather thin layer of what most of us call dirt. Although this simplistic view ignores some other important considerations—air, water and sunlight, to name a few—it is true that soil is a major factor in determining what we can expect from the land. This is as true for forest land as it is for farmland, and your acquaintance with your property is not complete until you get to know your soil.

SOIL IS FAR MORE THAN DIRT

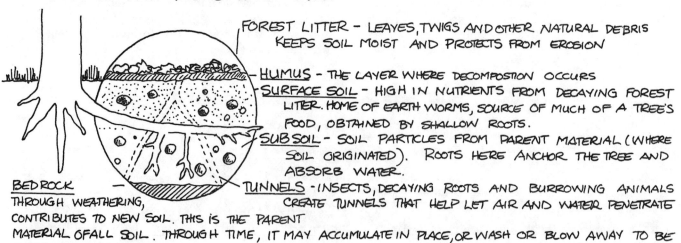

FOREST LITTER - LEAVES, TWIGS AND OTHER NATURAL DEBRIS KEEPS SOIL MOIST AND PROTECTS FROM EROSION

HUMUS - THE LAYER WHERE DECOMPOSTION OCCURS

SURFACE SOIL - HIGH IN NUTRIENTS FROM DECAYING FOREST LITTER. HOME OF EARTH WORMS, SOURCE OF MUCH OF A TREE'S FOOD, OBTAINED BY SHALLOW ROOTS.

SUBSOIL - SOIL PARTICLES FROM PARENT MATERIAL (WHERE SOIL ORIGINATED). ROOTS HERE ANCHOR THE TREE AND ABSORB WATER.

TUNNELS - INSECTS, DECAYING ROOTS AND BURROWING ANIMALS CREATE TUNNELS THAT HELP LET AIR AND WATER PENETRATE

BEDROCK - THROUGH WEATHERING, CONTRIBUTES TO NEW SOIL. THIS IS THE PARENT MATERIAL OF ALL SOIL. THROUGH TIME, IT MAY ACCUMULATE IN PLACE, OR WASH OR BLOW AWAY TO BE DEPOSITED ELSEWHERE.

- *Light Upland Soils*

  (Sandy, gravelly, or other well-drained soils)
  Jack Pine
  Virginia Pine
  Red Pine
  Lodgepole Pine
  Loblolly Pine
  Shortleaf Pine
  Longleaf Pine
  Ponderosa Pine

- *Upland Soils — More Moist*

  (Poor soils and moist, but well-drained — that is water doesn't stand in place)
  White Pine
  Sugar Pine
  Hemlock
  Douglas-fir
  Balsam Fir
  Red Spruce
  White Spruce
  Oaks

- *Swampy Mucks and Peats*

  Black Spruce
  Bald Cypress
  Eastern White Cedar
  Southern White Cedar
  Tamarack

- *Better Upland Soils*

  (Better soils, moist, but well-drained. Clays and loams)
  Birch
  Beech
  Cherry
  Elm
  Hickory
  Maple
  Aspen
  Sweet Gum
  Sitka Spruce
  Western Larch

- *Bottomland and Moist*

  (Cool, rich, silty, moist soils)
  Cottonwood
  Yellow Poplar
  Sycamore
  Western Red Cedar
  Port Orford Cedar
  Coast Redwood
  Walnut

Soil depth, fertility and water-holding capacity are some of the soil factors that influence what species will grow on a particular site and how well they can do if other conditions are favorable. Fortunately for most landowners, there is a wealth of information available about the hundreds of soil types. In the United States, county by county, scientists in the Soil Conservation Service of the U.S. Department of Agriculture are working toward the goal of mapping all the soils on private land. Much of the country has already been completed and the maps are available free from the agency's county offices. In Canada, information about the national soil survey can be obtained from the Canadian Department of Agriculture in Ottawa.

Soil maps are a fantastic planning tool. Using an aerial photo or fine quality map as the base, lines are drawn around areas where the soil has uniform characteristics. Each kind of soil is named and numbered. You simply locate your property on the map, find the number(s) for the one or more soil types located there, then look these up in an accompanying survey book. The information provided usually shows such things as:

- annual precipitation
- average temperature
- frost-free periods
- soil description
- problems with the soil and how they might affect erosion, roads, building construction, planting, etc.
- trees and shrubs with the best growth potential for the site
- suitability for farming, grazing, forestry, etc.
- potential production levels for farm crops or timber

Slope and Aspect

Closely related to soil are *slope* and *aspect*. Steep slopes usually mean thinner, rockier and poorer soils. They are usually prone to erosion and do not retain subsurface water for tree growth. They also limit road building, or make it prohibitively expensive, and create hazards for the use of logging or planting equipment.

The compass direction faced by sloping land is called *aspect*. This important feature affects air and soil surface temperature, and, most importantly, soil moisture. Trees that need cooler, moist sites occur mostly on slopes with northerly or easterly aspects; those that can thrive on warmer, drier sites can be expected on south- or west-facing slopes. When a species grows on all aspects, its success will often be influenced to a considerable degree by aspect. Usually you can expect faster growth on the moister aspects if all other conditions are equal.

Site Index — Predictor of Growth

For any site and major tree species, there is a measurement called *site index* that will show you how suitable that site is for tree growth. It is easy to make this measurement and, in combination with other information about your land, is an excellent way to help decide which species will grow best.

The illustration on page 12 shows how to obtain a site index. The basis for site index is the height attained by dominant or co-dominant trees. From tables that were developed after careful studies of each species, the figure (site index) you obtain is the height that trees of a given species are capable of attaining at a specified age, usually 50 years. For example, using the table, if you measure a dominant yellow-poplar and find it to be 30 years old and 58 feet high, the site index is 70. By age 50, dominant yellow-poplars grown in uncrowded conditions on that

FINDING THE SITE INDEX

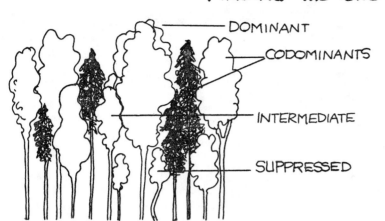

DOMINANT

CODOMINANTS

INTERMEDIATE

SUPPRESSED

1 FOR EACH SPECIES OF INTEREST IN A STAND, SELECT SEVERAL DOMINANT OR CO-DOMINANT TREES.

2 TAKE INCREMENT BORINGS ON EACH. (DRILL TO CENTER OF TREE, 4½ FEET ABOVE THE GROUND. INCREMENT BORERS ARE AVAILABLE THROUGH FORESTRY SUPPLIERS.)

3 REMOVE CORE AND COUNT RINGS TO DETERMINE THE TREE'S AGE (CORE MAY REQUIRE SANDING, WETTING AND MAGNIFICATION IF GROWTH RINGS ARE CLOSE TOGETHER OR VERY LIGHT.)

COUNT AS ONE YEAR

SPRINGWOOD (RAPID GROWTH)

SUMMER WOOD (DARKER, MORE COMPACT CELLS FROM SLOWER GROWTH DURING DRIER PART OF GROWING SEASON.)

4 MEASURE TOTAL TREE HEIGHT.

5 CONSULT A SITE INDEX TABLE FOR THE SPECIES YOU'VE MEASURED LOCAL FORESTERS HAVE COPIES. IN THE LEFT COLUMN OF THE SAMPLE FIND THE AGE OF YOUR TREE. GO ACROSS TO THE HEIGHT (ESTIMATE IF BETWEEN NUMBERS SHOWN) THEN UP TO FIND THE SITE INDEX. REPEAT FOR EACH TREE, THEN USE THE AVERAGE.

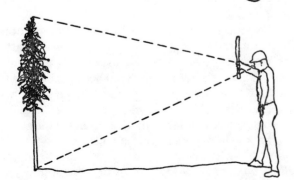

Yellow-Poplar: Height in Feet of Average Dominant Trees, by Site Index *

Age (yr.)	Site index					
	70	80	90	100	110	120
10	28	32	36	40	44	48
15	39	45	51	57	62	68
20	47	54	61	68	75	81
25	53	61	69	76	84	91
30	58	66	75	83	91	99
35	62	71	80	88	97	106
40	65	74	84	93	102	111
45	68	77	87	97	106	116
50	70	80	90	100	110	120

* At 50 yr. Source: U.S. Dept. of Agriculture

site could be expected to be 70 feet high. That height is relatively low and might suggest that other species found on the site and having higher site indices should be favorably considered in thinning, logging or future plantings.

Instead of index numbers, some tables simply show "poor," "medium," and "good," or site classes such as I, II and III (site I being best). Separate tables have been developed for use in plantations.

Your Trees

I had a friend once who talked to his trees. "Hello, Doug," he might say as we passed a Douglas-fir. "Larix, love ya!" he'd shout at a western larch. He even talked to wildflowers—"Well, *Delphinium barbeyi,* how nice to see you out!" His behavior was really disconcerting at first, but after awhile it became contagious. I envied my friend, because he was a good botanist. Finally I adopted his system of remembering plant names by addressing them occasionally. I do it a bit more quietly, however.

Getting to know the trees and shrubs on your land, and eventually the whole milieu of life under your stewardship, can be one of the greatest rewards of ownership. Names first, then life histories and growth characteristics (*silvics*), properties and uses of the wood, the tree's relationship to its surroundings and other life forms (*ecology*), all become part of a life-long pastime.

What's in a Name?

Many folks are repulsed by the Latin names they hear scientists spouting or perhaps see on interpretive trails. You can get along just fine without Latin names, but they do exist for a reason. They are part of a useful classification system called **binomial nomenclature.** Under this system, each plant is given a two-part name in Latin—the name of the genus it belongs to, and its very own specific name. The person who first describes the plant and publishes its name in the scientific journals gets to have his or her name added on at the end as the author citation. Some early botanist-explorers named so many that scientists simply use their intial. "L," for example, in *Acer saccharinum L.* stands for Linnaeus, an eighteenth-

century Swede who must hold the record for naming plants. In common usage, the third name often gets omitted.

Latin name:

Pinus	palustris	Mill.
↓	↓	↓
Genus	specific epithet, or adjective	Author citation (namer) (In this case, Philip Miller, an eighteenth-century English botanist)

Common names:
hard pine, heart pine, longleaf yellow pine, longstraw pine, southern pine, southern yellow pine

The beauty of binomial nomenclature when applied to trees is that the name is recognized by experts in any part of the world. With common names, different people have different names for the same tree even in the same state or locale. Each swears his is the right name, but there is no correct common name. Usually we learn to recognize a tree by several common names, but at times it can mean dollars and cents to be precise. For example, newspaper ads sometimes extoll "the amazing Robinia pseudoacacia." No other name is offered for what is billed as an exotic, fast-growing, flowering tree. After paying an excessive price, the buyer discovers he bought a black locust sapling, a common tree with sprouts easily transplantable from the woods over large areas of the U.S. and Canada. Loggers, too, may confuse the issue of buying and selling with terms like "bull pine" or "piss fir." So, if you want to be sure, or if you want to study trees and other plants, or if you plan foreign travel of an educational nature, it helps to learn the Latin, or scientific names.

Acer saccharum — Sugar maple, hard maple, rock maple
Acer rubrum — Red maple, soft maple, water maple, scarlet maple, white maple, swamp maple
Acer saccharinum — Silver maple, soft maple, white maple, river maple, water maple, swamp maple
Acer negundo — Boxelder, ash-leaf maple, three-leaf maple

Identification — Keys to the Unknown

For the beginner there are two ways to find out the name of a tree. One is to use a key. This is simply a series of questions about the tree's features that lead you through various alternatives until you arrive at the name and description of the specimen at hand. Keys can be purchased for trees, shrubs, insects, disease symptoms, twigs in winter, wildflowers, mushrooms and many other subjects.

Keying out unknowns can be fun if you have a key that is clearly written and includes definitions of terms and illustrations to help at the decision points. A good example is William M. Harlow's *Fruit Key & Twig Key to Trees and Shrubs* of eastern North America. The accompanying illustration shows a page in the key that would be reached after several previous separations. Having arrived at this point, you know you have a birch, and are finally guided to the specific one in hand.

Example of Winter Twig Key

Key to the Birches

1. Twigs with a wintergreen taste - - - - - - - - - - - - 2
1. Twigs lacking a wintergreen taste - - - - - - - - - - 3

   2. Buds sharply pointed, divergent, mostly glabrous; twigs brown to black, very aromatic. Sweet Birch *Betula lenta* L. See Figs. 85-86.
   2. Buds acute but not sharp to the touch, often appressed along the lower half, often hairy; twigs greenish brown; less aromatic. Yellow Birch *Betula alleghaniensis* Britton (*B. lutea* Michx.)

3. Buds short, tapering both ways from the middle; twigs grayish with very prominent warty lenticels; bark on older branches and trunk grayish white, usually close with few exfoliating strips. Gray Birch *Betula populifolia* Marsh. 1
3. Buds longer (see Figs. 1 and 2), tapering from the base to the apex; twigs brown to nearly black, usually with less prominent lenticels; bark of tree salmon red, or chalky white, exfoliating in thin papery strips - - - - - - - - - - - - - 4

   4. Twigs and buds mostly glabrous; the former nearly black; bark of tree chalky white. Paper Birch *Betula papyrifera* Marsh. 2
   4. Twigs and buds somewhat hairy; the former reddish brown; bark of tree salmon red. River or Red Birch *Betula nigra* L.

(Used by permission of Dover Publications, New York, NY.)

To help you identify unfamiliar species, tree keys often ask about shapes, color, arrangement of parts, and even taste.

Identifying by Sight

The other method of learning trees is simply to be told by someone who knows, or to skim through an illustrated identification book matching up features. This method is usually easiest, for out of the hundreds of species in North America, it is likely that only a few major species will be found in your woodlot. Once identified, it is just a matter of practice until you can spot these old friends a mile away.

There are seven characteristics most commonly used in rapid identification. For any one tree, usually two of these will be so noticeable that if you know those key features you won't have to search your memory further. For example, after Scotch pine grows more than about 8 or 10 feet tall, it develops unique, orange-colored bark over its upper half. So any conifer (the so-called *evergreens* or needle species) I see with an orange top I instantly recognize as Scotch pine. In the open, Scotch pines are recognizable for a country mile.

Following are the seven features to look for and a few tips about each, arranged in the order I find most useful when trying to figure out a new species or recall an old acquaintance.

LOCATION

First you need to look at range maps and learn what relatively few species can be expected to live wild in your locality (backyards and plantations are a different story — anything might show up there!). Next, learn to associate species with sites. On dry, southern slopes you expect certain species; in moist coves and along creeks others commonly show up. This is a rapid way to screen out many possibilities.

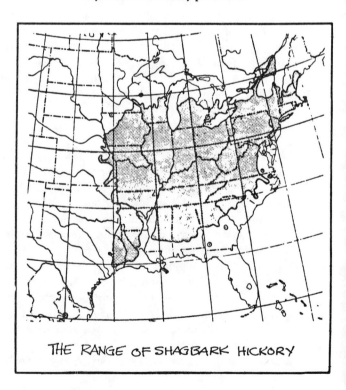

THE RANGE OF SHAGBARK HICKORY

LEAVES

The best clue to a tree's identity. Leaves range from the impressive 30-inch bigleaf magnolias to the tiny scales of cedar.

Needles are leaves. Trees with needles are commonly called softwoods, conifers, or evergreens. Some, however, are not always "ever" green; the needles of larch, or tamarack, are shed each winter, fooling some owners into thinking the tree has died.

The broad leaves of *deciduous* trees are usually shed each autumn. Some, however, like holly and the live oaks, remain green year round.

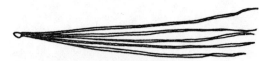

GYMNOSPERM

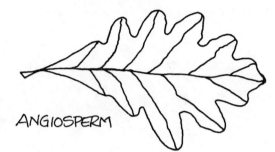

ANGIOSPERM

What else to look for:

OPPOSITE OR ALTERNATE
ARRANGEMENT ON TWIGS

MAPLES   YELLOW-POPLAR

SIMPLE OR COMPOUND

SWEETGUM   BUCKEYE

KINDS OF COMPOUND LEAVES

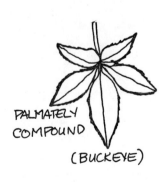

PALMATELY
COMPOUND

(BUCKEYE)

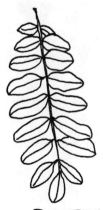

PINNATELY
COMPOUND
(BLACK LOCUST)

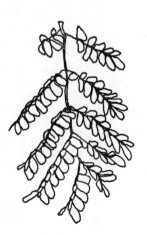

BIPINNATELY
COMPOUND
(HONEYLOCUST)

15

Margins

Leaf margins often provide an overlooked, but unmistakable, "fingerprint" that separates species otherwise similar in appearance.

ENTIRE (SMOOTH)
SERRULATE (VERY FINELY TOOTHED)
SERRATE (TOOTHED AND POINTING TOWARD TIP OR APEX
DOUBLY SERRATE (DOUBLE TOOTHED)
DENTATE (LARGE TOOTH THAT POINTS OUTWARD
CRENATE (SMALL ROUNDED LOBES
SINUATE (LOBED)
UNDULATE (WAVY)
INCISED (DEEP CUTS)

Other Features

Other less helpful identifying features are the shape of the leaf's base and apex (tip), and its overall shape and size. In pines, an important feature is the length of its needles and the number of needles in a fascicle (bundle).

A FASICLE

THE NUMBER OF NEEDLES IN A FASICLE IS IMPORTANT IN IDENTIFYING PINES

SCALE-LIKE

COMMON ON CEDARS & CYPRESS

AWL-LIKE

COMMON ON SOME JUNIPERS

BARK

This isn't very helpful on younger trees, but on many older ones it gives a prominent clue to identity. It is also sometimes used to judge the *vigor* of a tree.

Color
Varies from very dark to almost white, with yellow or orange hues being common clues to some species.

Configuration

DOGWOOD

PERSIMMON

EASTERN WHITE PINE

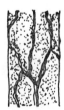

RED PINE

Texture

BEECH

SYCAMORE

SWEET BIRCH

YELLOW BIRCH

FRUIT

When a tree's fruit is available, there is usually no better aid to identification. Not only its appearance, but sometimes its arrangement on the branch is important, such as whether a cone grows straight up or hangs down.

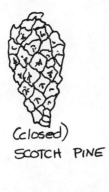

(closed)
SCOTCH PINE

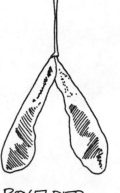

BOXELDER

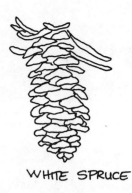

WHITE SPRUCE

BLACK OAK

RED OAK

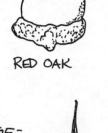

LODGE-
POLE
PINE

(closed)

ASH

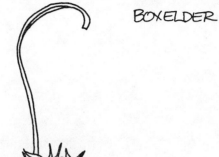

SWEET GUM

DOUGLAS-FIR

BALSAM
FIR

Best Guides to Tree & Shrub Identification

Trees of North America by C. Frank Brockman. Golden Press, New York.
280 pages of full-color leaves, fruits and other critical features useful for identification throughout U.S. and Canada. Descriptions and range maps next to illustrations. Convenient size for the field.

Knowing your Trees by G.H. Collingwood and W.D. Brush. The American Forestry Association, Washington, D.C.
105-page booklet in black and white featuring 51 major species. Good descriptions and photos of these relatively few species, including tips for growing them. Inexpensive; sometimes free during membership drives.

Textbook of Dendrology by William M. Harlow and Ellwood S. Harrar. McGraw-Hill Book Co., New York and Toronto.
This 561-page textbook is understandable and readable for laymen, but is technical enough to be highly useful for the serious tree aficionado.

Fruit Key and Twig Key to Trees and Shrubs by William M. Harlow. Dover Publications, New York.
Two keys in one 106-page book of convenient field size. Easy to use and fully illustrated with photographs.

Trees and Shrubs of the United States by E.L. Little, Jr. and Barbara H. Honkkala. USDA Forest Service, Washington, D.C.
Inexpensive booklet from U.S. Government Printing Office. Lists available publications by various categories, the most useful being tree guides specific to each state.

A Field Guide to Trees and Shrubs—Northeastern and Central North America by George A. Petrides, The Peterson Field Guide Series, Houghton Mifflin Co., Boston.
One of nearly two dozen pocket-sized field guides on subjects ranging from birds to seashells. Well-illustrated and written expressly for laymen.

TWIGS

In the winter on deciduous trees, twigs provide a distinct "fingerprint." Twig keys are available. The features of twigs also reveal fascinating insights into the life of trees.

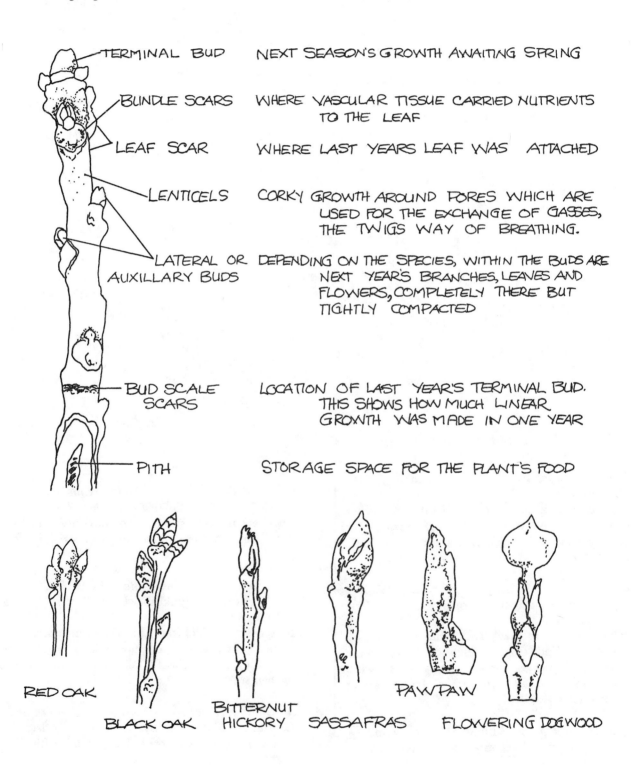

TERMINAL BUD — NEXT SEASON'S GROWTH AWAITING SPRING

BUNDLE SCARS — WHERE VASCULAR TISSUE CARRIED NUTRIENTS TO THE LEAF

LEAF SCAR — WHERE LAST YEARS LEAF WAS ATTACHED

LENTICELS — CORKY GROWTH AROUND PORES WHICH ARE USED FOR THE EXCHANGE OF GASSES, THE TWIGS WAY OF BREATHING.

LATERAL OR AUXILLARY BUDS — DEPENDING ON THE SPECIES, WITHIN THE BUDS ARE NEXT YEAR'S BRANCHES, LEAVES AND FLOWERS, COMPLETELY THERE BUT TIGHTLY COMPACTED

BUD SCALE SCARS — LOCATION OF LAST YEAR'S TERMINAL BUD. THIS SHOWS HOW MUCH LINEAR GROWTH WAS MADE IN ONE YEAR

PITH — STORAGE SPACE FOR THE PLANT'S FOOD

RED OAK

BLACK OAK

BITTERNUT HICKORY

SASSAFRAS

PAWPAW

FLOWERING DOGWOOD

SIZE & SHAPE

Silhouettes can sometimes help identify a tree, especially at a long distance, if it is growing by itself away from the influences of surrounding trees.

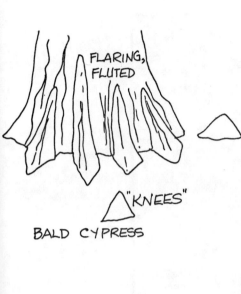

FLARING, FLUTED

"KNEES"

BALD CYPRESS

FLAG TOP

EASTERN WHITE PINE

LOMBARDY POPLAR

ROUND HEAD

WHITE OAK

GROWING IN OPEN

DROOPING LOWER BRANCHES

PIN OAK

WESTERN LARCH

LODGEPOLE PINE

SUBALPINE FIR

ENGELMANN SPRUCE

19

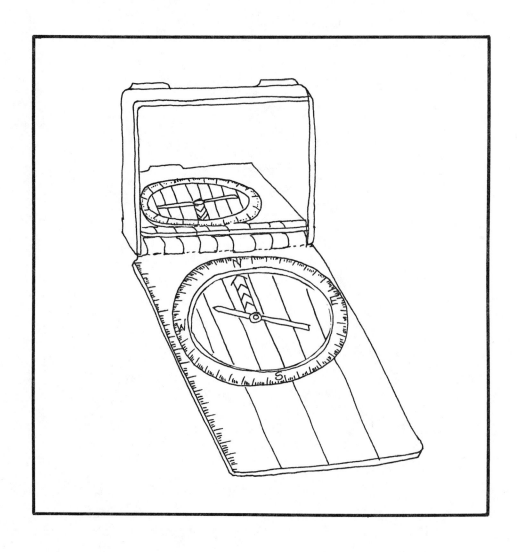

3 Taking Inventory

Nature tells her secrets not to those who hurry by, but to those who walk with happy heart and seeing eye.

—Patience Strong

John Burroughs, the nature writer, once said, "Be imaginative with facts, but don't imagine your facts."

Accurate information is the foundation of good decisions. In forest management, the best way to obtain facts is by inventorying the woods and systematically compiling information. Regardless of your plans, the sooner you take inventory, the better prepared you will be to carry out or improve upon your original ideas.

Forestry people call the inventory a *cruise*, and the process, *cruising*. Specifically, cruising or inventorying is the determination of the kinds and amounts of wood growing on a piece of land. This has evolved into a somewhat precise system of measurements. Old-time timber cruisers were so skilled they could walk through a forest, eye the trees, and say what volume of lumber would result from a timber sale. A lot of sales were made on that basis and many were probably fair and accurate. But it's a risky way to go, especially if you are the seller. Even today many unwary landowners sell their trees, called stumpage, while taking the word of a buyer—often the logger—on how much volume is involved. This foolishness has cost many folks dearly.

In its simplest form, an inventory can be conducted by almost anyone. I suspect this could be an enjoyable recreational activity as well as a most useful project. However, in talking with landowners and extension foresters, I found that very few people do their own inventories. Instead, they turn to professional foresters, particularly private consultants who charge for their services.

Using a professional is fine for people who do not have the time or interest to do a cruise themselves. However, inventorying should not frighten away the layman. Those who do it themselves will find that a systematic inventory provides an unexcelled opportunity for gaining a better understanding of the land and its vegetation. Either way, a forest inventory allows us to quantify what we own, which in turn can guide future actions and help us ask the right questions when discussing our ideas with experts.

Maps and Aerial Photos

A map of your land helps in planning the inventory, displaying the results and planning future strategies. A surveyor's plat received at the time of purchase is a good start, but you may need to add creeks, roads, rock outcroppings, the location of buildings and any other prominent features of the site. After locating known boundary lines and corner markings (described in your deed), other features can be added with the help of a compass and measuring tape or pacing.

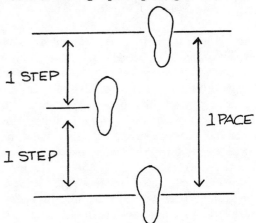

Pacing

Pacing is a rapid and reasonably accurate way to measure distance.

Calculate the length of your pace by walking a measured course of about 300 feet in an open area. Walk *normally*, and always begin pacing with the same foot, counting each time the opposite one strikes the ground. Divide 300 by the number of paces to determine the length of your pace.

Topographic maps can help, especially if your tract is a large one. Even for parcels as small as ten acres, topo maps can be blown up to a convenient scale and the contour lines transferred to your plat or working map. The county courthouse, library or a surveyor's office is the place to ask about which "quad" covers your location, and where you can purchase it locally. Otherwise, contact:

National Cartographic
Information Office
U.S. Geological Survey
507 National Center
Reston, VA 22092
(Phone: 703-860-6045)

Map Distribution Office
615 Booth Street
Ottawa, Ontario K1A 0E9
(Phone: 613-995-4510)

CORRECTING
FOR SLOPE

Correcting for Slope

Since map distances are always expressed as though areas are flat planes (horizontal distances), measuring on the ground on slopes requires a correction factor. For precision work, you measure the distance on the slope and the degree of slope, then look up the horizontal distance in a surveyor's table. In pacing, try to mentally allow for slope. Going uphill, you'll need to count perhaps 3 or 4 steps to equal one horizontal pace. Going down, figure less than 1 step to the pace.

All of the United States and Canada are also covered by aerial photographs. These amazing 9 x 9-inch squares were taken at an elevation of 8,000 to 18,000 feet. At these elevations a few inches on the photo can represent a mile on the ground. The photos were shot so that they overlap, which means when two are viewed side by side with stereo glasses, the scene appears three-dimensional. It works on exactly the same principle as the old-fashioned parlor stereoscope or the newer Viewmaster. The stereo glasses, which are available through forestry supply dealers listed in the appendix, also magnify the scene, allowing a clear view of objects as small as fences, fallen logs and outbuildings. The glasses and photos will fit easily into a large pocket for use in the field.

For a few dollars you can have a fixed platform high above your property. Like a hovering hawk, you can peer down on ridges and valleys, see the size and shape of fields or other openings, pinpoint prominent landmarks, and possibly even determine the composition of your woods. With a little study you can distinguish hardwoods from conifers, plantations from natural regeneration, large trees from small, habitat types, and much more. By inking in boundaries or using a transparent overlay, you can have a new version of a map, with the detail and precision possible only through photography.

To obtain copies of aerial photos in your area, try the Agricultural Stabilization and Conservation Service or the Soil Conservation Service in your county in the United States. If these folks can't help, or if you live in

Canada, here is a way to buy photos directly from the source:

1. Write to the following address and ask for the leaflet: "How to Order Aerial Photographs"

   National Cartographic
   Information Center
   U.S. Geological Survey
   507 National Center
   Reston, VA 22092
   (Phone: 703-860-6045)

   National Air Photo
   Library
   615 Booth Street
   Ottawa, Ontario KIA 0E
   (Phone: 613-995-4510)

2. Complete the form they send you and return it with a topo map or other map with your property clearly sketched in on it. Indicate black and white, 9x9-inch photos in the appropriate places on the form or in your letter.

3. They will then advise you about which and how many photos are needed to provide coverage of your land and how much they will cost. For black and white, the cost is modest.

4. Order the photos and send the required prepayment to the same address shown above.

Measuring Your Trees

Knowing how to measure trees comes in handy in a variety of ways. It is essential, of course, in taking inventory. It is also essential in the sale of standing trees, whether for a few or an entire stand. It can be useful in determining how many house logs are available for the dream home, or how much custom-sawed lumber you might expect from some given number of trees. You may even have a champion big tree you want to measure.

In most cases, tree measurements are taken to determine merchantable wood content. This involves first determining its dimensions. Next the dimensions of useable trunk are converted to a unit called board feet, an estimated amount of rot or other visible defects is subtracted, and a net amount of useable wood results. This is explained in more detail later, but for the purpose of inventory, the two important measurements that must be taken are diameter and height.

22

Diameter

By general agreement, a tree's diameter is measured at *breast height*, or 4½ feet above the ground (on the uphill side). This is expressed as diameter at breast height, or DBH. Exceptions are made when an irregularity or unusual swelling occurs at this point, or when the tree forks less than one *log* (usually considered to be 8 or 16 feet) above the approximate stump height. In these cases, measure at the nearest point that represents a more typical diameter of the tree, and treat forked trees as two.

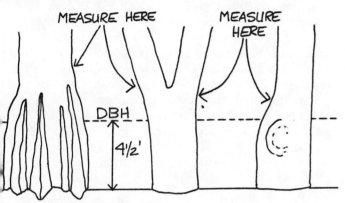

EXCEPTIONS TO THE RULE OF MEASURING DBH AT 4½ FT.

Diameter is sometimes measured with large calipers, but more commonly a Biltmore stick is used. Directions for this method are included with the illustration.

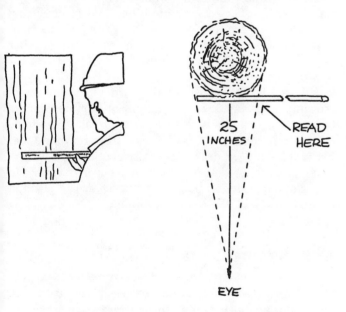

Using a Biltmore Stick to Measure Diameter

1. Hold the stick 25" from your eyes. This will probably come naturally. It's the most comfortable distance for most people and is why the calibrations were made for that distance. But check with a measure tape until you get the proper distance.
2. With the left end of the stick in your line of sight to the left edge of the tree, without moving your head read the scale where your line of sight intersects it when looking at the right edge of the tree.
3. On trees that are oblong instead of round, take two readings and use the average.

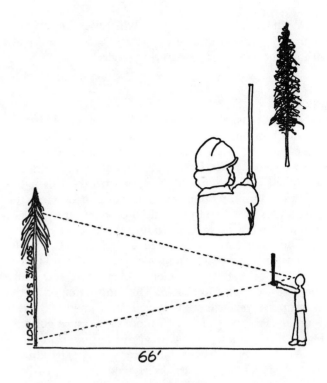

Using a Merritt Hypsometer

1. Pace out 66 feet (1 chain in forester's lingo) from the tree, and level with it — neither uphill nor downhill from its base.
2. Hold the hypsometer vertically and 25 inches from your eye.
3. With the bottom of the stick in your line of sight to where you estimate the tree would be cut (stump height), read the scale where your line of sight intersects it looking at the minimum useable diameter (usually 4"-6") near the top of the tree.

A more accurate method is to measure the circumference with a specially graduated diameter tape. The units allow you to read in inches of diameter. Or you can use a regular cloth measuring tape, then convert circumferences to diameters using the table below (or the formula, Circumference ÷ 3.1416 = Diameter):

Circumference	Diameter (inches)	Circumference	Diameter (inches)
1'½"	4	7'4"	28
1'7"	6	7'10½"	30
2'1'	8	8'5"	32
2'7½"	10	8'11"	34
3'2"	12	9'5"	36
3'8"	14	9'11½"	38
4'2½"	16	10'6"	40
4'9"	18	11'0"	42
5'3"	20	11'6½"	44
5'9"	22	12'½"	46
6'3½"	24	12'7"	48
6'10"	26	13'1"	50

(These figures are rounded because diameters are commonly recorded in two-inch categories.)

With some practice, you will soon be able to accurately judge diameters to the closest two inches without the aid of any measuring device.

Height

Height is usually measured in terms of merchantable logs and half logs. Sixteen feet is standard in the West, with eight-foot lengths used more often in the East. The measurement is taken from the estimated stump height to the highest usable point on the tree's trunk. This is the tree's minimum top diameter. It is determined before the cruise and is based on the potential products or by agreement with whoever is going to buy the logs.

The illustration on page 23 shows a Merritt hypsometer being used. This scale is usually found on the other side of a Biltmore stick. Other tools—far more expensive—are also available. The most common is the Relaskop, a versatile, hand-sized instrument of great accuracy. Professionals use this tool to measure not only height, but diameter, basal area, distance and slope.

As with diameters, before long you will be able to estimate height, in logs, fairly accurately without instruments. This speeds up cruising considerably and is a skill that is easily improved with practice. By measuring 8-and 16-foot lengths and painting them on a flag pole or tree near home, you can more clearly visualize these units. Be careful, however, and be sure to check your unaided estimates regularly, especially when measuring large or high-value trees.

Timber Cruising

A timber cruise can do several things. Primarily it quantifies the amount and kind of lumber that could be sold, or the volume of pulpwood, poles, firewood or other potential products you own. It also allows you to add on your map forest types or various size classes, ages or other conditions of interest. Even if you do not plan to sell your trees, a cruise can help you determine whether to thin, what wildlife habitats exist, and whether your forest is young and vigorous or old and declining. In short, a cruise provides facts. The information you gather depends on your needs, but in most cases a cruise focuses on measuring volumes of wood.

In small woodlots, a one hundred percent or *total* cruise may be best. This means that you count and measure every tree on your land, or at least every tree above a certain size. It is the most accurate way of estimating wood volumes and *stocking* levels (the number of stems in various size classes). However, unless you have plenty of time and patience, it is only practical on areas of less than about ten acres.

When the property to be cruised is more than ten acres, or is smaller but very uniform in composition, or when time is of the essence, a *sample* cruise should be made. This is merely a count and measurement of the trees on representative plots of known size throughout the forest. Sample cruising is a bit more complex than total cruising, and greater care must be taken in measuring distances and in using the map. Judgment is also needed

so you get a truly representative sample of your whole forest. In fact, if you know from aerial photos or general reconnaissance that there is a lot of variation in the total forest (such as different forest types, old growth and second or third growth areas, etc.), it is best to map out these different areas and plan completely separate cruises on each parcel. Incidentally, these zones of similarity are called *stands*. They are the basic management unit of the forest, and the forest or woodlot may or may not be composed of one or more stands.

If you want to plan and conduct your own cruise, detailed procedures are provided in the appendix (page 199). The suggested cruise procedure uses the direct measurement of trees and is easy to understand. However, there is another method that is popular with professional foresters because it is faster. This method is variously called *variable plot*, *point sampling*, or *prism cruising*.

In this method, inexpensive prisms are used that have been ground to reflect light at known angles. The cruiser stands at the plot center and views each tree around him. As shown on page 26, he counts all trees that have trunks not visually separated by the prism. These are considered "in" the plot. He counts every other one that is borderline.

By multiplying the prism's *basal area factor* times the number of "in" trees, a figure is obtained that estimates the *basal area per acre*. Basal area is the cross-sectional area of trees at breast height, expressed in square feet. This can be used in planning timber sales, but it is especially important when discussing *stocking*, or stand density. These terms are often used in discussing whether there are too few, too many, or just the right number of trees per acre for optimum growth. For timber sales, basal area is usually converted to board feet for negotiating purposes.

There is nothing especially difficult about prism cruising, and any forestry equipment supplier carries these useful little tools. A local forester can suggest the correct one to buy for the size of trees in your area. Perhaps the biggest drawback in prism cruising is that on steep ground it is necessary to make corrections. On slopes under about 15 percent, however, it is a fast and accurate method of estimating volume.

Determining Growth and Yield

When a cruise is completed, you know what exists in your forest today. That is the essential first step. However, to make management decisions, or even to understand woodland dynamics if you choose to do nothing, it is equally important to be able to predict how the stand will grow and change in coming years.

As with any prediction, this is a tricky business at best. So many factors and local variables are involved in predicting growth and future yield that professional judgment is definitely needed at this point. But don't be discouraged. If you wish to take this next step in knowing your land, you can determine growth and yield yourself

THE UNITS OF WOOD

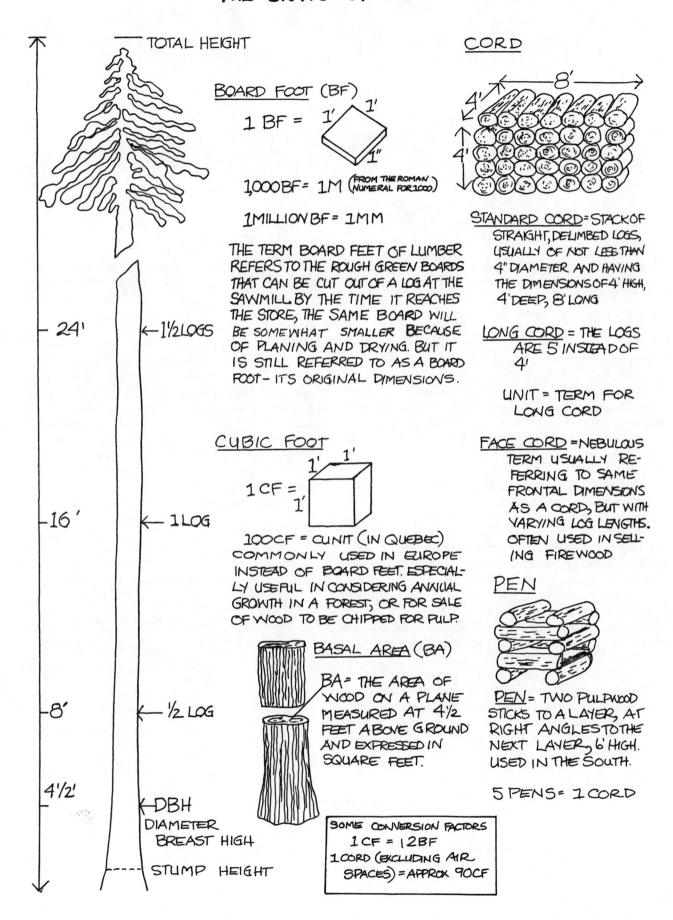

TOTAL HEIGHT

BOARD FOOT (BF)

1 BF = [diagram 1' × 1' × 1"]

1,000 BF = 1M (FROM THE ROMAN NUMERAL FOR 1000)

1 MILLION BF = 1 MM

THE TERM BOARD FEET OF LUMBER REFERS TO THE ROUGH GREEN BOARDS THAT CAN BE CUT OUT OF A LOG AT THE SAWMILL. BY THE TIME IT REACHES THE STORE, THE SAME BOARD WILL BE SOMEWHAT SMALLER BECAUSE OF PLANING AND DRYING. BUT IT IS STILL REFERRED TO AS A BOARD FOOT — ITS ORIGINAL DIMENSIONS.

CUBIC FOOT

1 CF = [cube 1' × 1' × 1']

100 CF = CUNIT (IN QUEBEC) COMMONLY USED IN EUROPE INSTEAD OF BOARD FEET. ESPECIALLY USEFUL IN CONSIDERING ANNUAL GROWTH IN A FOREST, OR FOR SALE OF WOOD TO BE CHIPPED FOR PULP.

BASAL AREA (BA)

BA = THE AREA OF WOOD ON A PLANE MEASURED AT 4½ FEET ABOVE GROUND AND EXPRESSED IN SQUARE FEET.

CORD

STANDARD CORD = STACK OF STRAIGHT, DELIMBED LOGS, USUALLY OF NOT LESS THAN 4" DIAMETER AND HAVING THE DIMENSIONS OF 4' HIGH, 4' DEEP, 8' LONG

LONG CORD = THE LOGS ARE 5' INSTEAD OF 4'

UNIT = TERM FOR LONG CORD

FACE CORD = NEBULOUS TERM USUALLY REFERRING TO SAME FRONTAL DIMENSIONS AS A CORD, BUT WITH VARYING LOG LENGTHS. OFTEN USED IN SELLING FIREWOOD

PEN

PEN = TWO PULPWOOD STICKS TO A LAYER, AT RIGHT ANGLES TO THE NEXT LAYER, 6' HIGH. USED IN THE SOUTH.

5 PENS = 1 CORD

24' ← 1½ LOGS

16' ← 1 LOG

8' ← ½ LOG

4½'

← DBH
DIAMETER
BREAST HIGH

STUMP HEIGHT

SOME CONVERSION FACTORS
1 CF = 12 BF
1 CORD (EXCLUDING AIR SPACES) = APPROX 90 CF

PRISM CRUISING

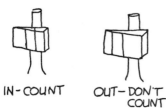

IN-COUNT   OUT-DON'T   BORDERLINE-
            COUNT   COUNT EVERY
                         OTHER ONE

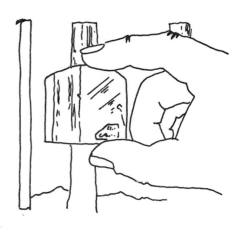

PRISM CRUISING IS A FAST METHOD OF OBTAINING AN ESTIMATE OF BASAL AREA IN A STAND OF TREES.

through study and careful measurements. But by all means, also obtain local, professional advice.

When forestry was introduced from Europe around the turn of the century, the heart of this scientific approach to forest management was *sustained yield*. It remains so today. Sustained yield means that forest growth should balance all losses over some period of time and, ideally, at a maximum level of production. Technically speaking, *growth* refers to wood produced expressed in whatever unit you prefer — cubic feet, board feet, cords, etc. But not all of this growth accumulates over the years ready for harvest. Insects, rot, wind and other natural elements claim their toll. What is left for cutting is termed *yield*.

A knowledge of your forest's growth and yield capabilities can be essential to management, especially if a continued flow of forest products is among your goals. This information gives you the best clues as to how much may be harvested at various intervals on a regular basis. It is like determining how much interest you can use from your savings account without eating into the principal.

Here are some commonly used methods of determining growth and yield. For specific "how-to" information a qualified local forester should be consulted. You may also want to study these methods in a good forestry text.

The *comparison*, or general observation approach involves locating a stand elsewhere similar to yours in terms of forest type, age, site, etc., where measurements have already been made. The growth and yield figures are then assumed to be the same in your stand. Well-managed government, industrial and university forests are the best hope for such data. In a few fortunate localities, extension foresters have even designated some areas as demonstration forests. Still, finding a forest exactly like yours will not be easy, and the use of this method is crude at best.

If you have an even-aged stand and if site curves and yield tables are available for the species involved, the *yield table* method is a cheap and quick way to estimate growth and yield. You simply find the site index of your stand, locate it on a set of site curves and read what it

would be at a point in time specified on an accompanying yield table, say at 50 years. Then this figure is found on the yield table and cross-tabulated with the actual age of the stand. The resulting figure is the normal yield expected for that species on an annual, per acre basis.

Unfortunately, even if you find the curves and tables, the yield table method assumes your stand is fully stocked, that is, contains the optimum number of trees per acre for ideal growth. This means locating yet another table for your locale, *a stocking table*, and making any necessary adjustments by comparing, as a percentage, the basal areas in your woodlot with the optimal figures, by species, on the tables.

The *growth percentage* method is an easier technique and builds on data collected from your cruise. But during the cruise, you must take increment borings on a representative sample of trees in each diameter class. A sample of fifty to one hundred trees of each species will help assure accuracy. From each boring:

1 . Count the number of annual rings in the last inch of tree growth
2 . Measure the bark thickness
3 . Subtract *twice* the bark thickness from the tree's DBH

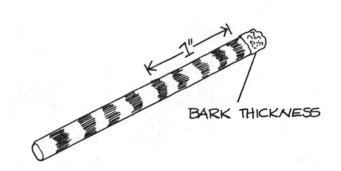

BARK THICKNESS

26

4. Use the following table to determine the tree's average annual recent growth:

d.b.h. (i.b.) inches	Number of annual rings per last radial inch of growth											
	1	2	3	4	5	6	7	8	9	10	11	12
						Percent						
2		340.0	144.4	83.3	57.1	37.5	32.0	29.4	24.2	22.2		
3	680.0	122.7	68.9	44.4	32.4	28.9	25.6	19.5	16.7	14.0		
4	295.4	77.5	45.0	30.0	22.5	19.2	16.0	13.0	11.5	10.1		
5	177.5	56.3	33.3	23.6	18.2	15.2	12.4	10.5	8.8	7.9	7.1	6.2
6	125.2	44.1	26.4	18.8	14.6	12.0	10.1	8.8	7.7	7.1	6.5	6.0
7	96.3	36.4	22.5	16.1	12.1	9.8	8.5	7.2	6.3	5.9	5.1	4.2
8	77.5	30.7	19.1	13.6	10.8	9.0	7.7	6.7	5.8	5.1	4.5	4.0
9	65.5	26.6	16.6	12.2	9.7	7.8	6.7	6.0	5.3	4.7	4.2	4.0
10	56.1	23.3	14.7	10.7	8.3	6.9	6.0	5.3	4.5	4.0	3.6	3.4
11	49.3	21.1	13.4	9.8	7.6	6.3	5.6	4.7	4.1	3.8	3.4	3.1
12	44.0	18.9	12.1	8.9	6.9	5.5	4.9	4.3	3.7	3.4	3.0	2.9
13	39.7	17.5	11.2	8.2	6.5	5.2	4.6	3.9	3.5	3.1	2.8	2.7
14	36.2	15.9	10.3	7.6	5.9	4.9	4.2	3.5	3.2	2.9	2.6	2.4
15	33.1	14.8	9.5	6.9	5.5	4.5	3.9	3.3	2.9	2.7	2.4	2.2
16	30.6	13.8	8.8	6.5	5.2	4.2	3.7	3.2	2.8	2.5	2.3	2.1
17	28.4	12.9	8.4	6.1	4.8	4.0	3.5	3.1	2.7	2.4	2.1	2.0
18	26.6	12.0	7.9	5.8	4.6	3.8	3.3	2.9	2.5	2.3	2.0	1.9
19	24.9	11.4	7.4	5.5	4.3	3.5	3.1	2.7	2.3	2.1	1.9	1.8
20	23.5	10.8	7.1	5.2	4.1	3.4	3.0	2.6	2.2	2.0	1.8	1.7
21	22.1	10.2	6.8	4.9	3.9	3.2	2.9	2.4	2.1	1.9	1.7	1.6
22	21.0	9.8	6.4	4.7	3.7	3.1	2.7	2.3	2.0	1.8	1.6	1.5
23	20.0	9.3	6.1	4.5	3.5	2.9	2.6	2.2	1.9	1.7	1.5	1.4
24	19.0	8.9	5.8	4.3	3.4	2.8	2.5	2.1	1.8	1.7	1.5	1.4

U.S.F.S., Region 1, Foresters Field Handbook

For each species and diameter class in your cruise data, you can then multiply the corresponding average growth percents. This will give you the approximate increase in diameter you can expect in the future. The actual increase in board-foot volume will be exponentially greater.

The only fly in this wise management ointment is that we have ignored natural mortality—losses from such things as pests, competition, and weather. Some percentage must be deducted. Again, put this on your list of questions for an experienced forester, as the figure ranges too widely among localities for any generalizations to be worthwhile.

Finally, there is the *continuous forest inventory* (CFI) method. This is the most accurate method of determining yield, but it also requires the most work and a long period of time. In essence, CFI is a diary of forest growth and yield, not a prediction. The CFI method requires establishing a series of permanent 1/5- or 1/4-acre plots laid out the same way you would design a cruise. The greater the number of plots, the higher the accuracy. Mark the plot centers with a pipe or reinforcement rod with the top brightly painted so it can be easily found in the future. The volume for each plot is measured as in any cruise (but perhaps more carefully), and this is repeated at some interval, usually five to ten years. The figures are converted to growth-per-acre to represent the whole forest.

The volume of any cutting in a plot between one measurement period and another must be added to the standing volume to present an accurate growth figure. On the other hand, this is the only method that does not require estimating natural mortality. That, of course, will already have been subtracted by nature.

Growth and yield figures are excellent aids to help determine how much wood you can remove on a sustained-yield basis, how the stand is responding to thinning or other treatments, and whether or not it is better to cut now or wait for higher market prices and allow more wood to accumulate. This is important information to have, and it can vary widely on different sites. For example in California growth ranges from 100 bf/acre/year on some sites to as high as 2000 bf/acre/year on others. Growth and yield measurements in your woods may even be a clue to whether or not it is economically feasible to manage for forest products. One old rule of thumb is that land with a yield of under 20 cubic feet/acre/year (240 bf) is below the limit of economical feasibility. But great arguments rage over exactly where that limit lies, and it would depend to a great extent on the location and species involved, and the landowner's goals.

The various methods of measurement in this chapter and appendix section on cruising present ways of quantifying what is in your forest. It should help you become acquainted with your land, develop guidelines for its future management, and provide a basis of communication with foresters or potential purchasers of your products or property. Put the data to work for you in any way that will help meet your goals. And be sure to obtain plenty of advice. But in the end, remember it is all intended only to aid in your decisions.

Computer Aids

To the computer-gadgeteer it should be obvious that the large volume of data and number of variables in cruising are what computers are made for. But computers have been slow coming to the aid of small landowners. Some like it that way, others do not.

Since the early 1960s, computers have been used by some foresters to convert field data into final tables. In the mid-seventies, standard programs were developed for consultants and managers who did not have programming experts at their disposal. Now we are finally seeing some services and software available to the part-time forest manager.

At the most basic level, computers in the forest may be hand-sized programmable calculators. For the computer-minded, these instruments can make the compilation and display of cruise data much easier. Units are now available that are weatherproof; the computer folks call it "environmentally sealed." In some cases, the data recorders can be taken inside and plugged into office or home computers for the permanent storage of data, or data printout, graphing, and analysis. Most forestry suppliers carry these units.

Computers are definitely heading for the woods. To those of us who go there to seek refuge from the Electronic Age, this is akin to an infestation. But to many it means the recreational challenge of learning a new computer game, or relief from the tedium of dot tallies, tables and summations. At their best, computer programs will help predict the outcome of decisions. They will help you decide if the cost of thinning will pay off in enough extra growth, and if so, when. They can chart out the best time to harvest, keep your expense records for you, and even help you decide what harvest method to use. To find out what programs are locally available, contact a service forester.

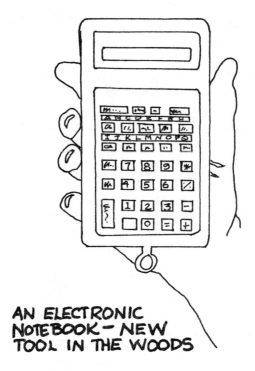

AN ELECTRONIC
NOTEBOOK — NEW
TOOL IN THE WOODS

Two Helpful Reference Books

Foresters Field Handbook. Division of State
and private Forestry, USDA Forest Service
(contact the regional office nearest you).

This is a pocket-sized notebook intended
primarily for foresters, but you may be able to obtain
one if the supply is sufficient. Each Forest Service
region produces a version of this handy reference that
contains volume tables, site index curves and other
technical data.

Forestry Handbook edited by Karl Wenger. Society of
American Foresters, 5400 Grosvenor Lane, Bethesda,
MD 20814.

This, too, is for the pros, and it is not
cheap, but it is one of the best single sources of volume
tables for most merchantable species. Moreover, it is a
compact encyclopedia of information ranging from
tools and inventorying to fences and wildlife.

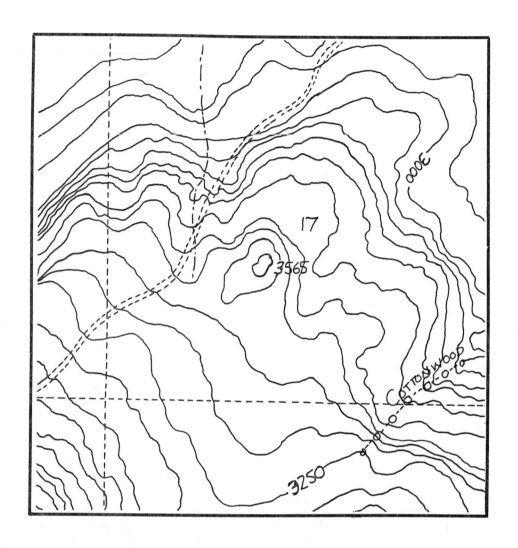

4   Planning

*When all is said and done, the final deci-
sions about your land must come from you.*
—The Woodland Steward

High in the mountains of Norway are little farms called seters. They were originally used for fattening the family goats and cows during the brief Nordic summer. Generation after generation used the seters and some are still in use today as farms, but now most are personal vacation retreats for skiing in the winter and hiking or relaxing in the summer. Although their use has changed, the seters remain a family treasure. It is difficult to find one for sale.

In the U.S. and Canada, the picture is quite different. Minnesota's Itasca County illustrates the situation, as a recent study found that most of the properties in this woodland setting change hands on the average of every six years.

It does not require much analysis to see that a high turnover rate in woodland ownership portends a bleak outlook for the care and management of trees. One solution to the problem is to help landowners establish goals and objectives for their land. This process asks a landowner (or better yet, a prospective landowner) to think carefully about what he wants from the experience of ownership and what is necessary to obtain his goals. The limitations of any piece of property, as well as personal limitations such as time, skills, or finances of the owner will then be brought to light. I believe it is important to go through this process before trying any of the ideas presented in this book.

Goals and Objectives Point the Way

Goals are long-term desires. In the case of forest ownership, they should reflect your ultimate reasons for owning the land. Some goals are mutually achievable; others conflict. When goals are incompatible, they should be recognized as such as early as possible.

Since your goals affect everything else you do with a piece of land, some honest introspection is a necessary first step to successful woodland management. Here are a few typical goals:

- To have a way of supplementing annual income

- To have a sound financial investment as a tax shelter or hedge against inflation
- To have the opportunity to see birds and other wildlife
- To have a place to relax in peace and quiet with nothing to do but read, or visit with family and friends
- To have a change of pace from the daily routine—a change of scene, the chance to learn new things, a way to assure some healthy exercise.

There is no such thing as "right" or proper goals, and none that are "wrong," so long as they respect the resources and do not violate someone else's rights. Goals are a very personal matter, but the importance of identifying your goals cannot be over-emphasized.

Once you have a clear understanding of your goals, the next step is to learn enough about your land to set reasonable objectives. Knowing your soils, cover and habitat types, wildlife and tree species, wood volumes, and similar features will certainly help. The resulting objectives should then be *realistic*, *achievable*, and *measurable*. For example:

Goal: To supplement annual income
Objective:

- To harvest, on a sustained basis, enough products each year to cover my expenses and earn 15 percent on my initial investment

Goal: To see wildlife
Objectives:

- To develop an acre of open marshland around part of my creek so ducks and other waterfowl begin using my property

- To protect at least two hollow trees or snags per acre

- To create diverse cover types to increase numbers and varieties of songbirds

A hunter might have different or additional objectives:

- To increase the rabbit population
- To provide additional hiding cover for deer (or browse for elk, nut trees for squirrels, etc.)

Objectives are like the rungs on a ladder. The goal is the top of the ladder, the rungs make certain you have a way of getting there. Through planning, specific techniques can be decided upon to help you meet your objectives and ultimately your goals. The bird watcher can dam part of his creek, fell or girdle the trees, put up wood duck houses and plant marsh grasses to develop his marsh. He can locate den trees and post "Wildlife Home" signs to protect them from firewood gatherers. The hunter might pile limbs and brush after firewood cuttings or logging operations to make homes for cottontails, or plant a species appropriate to his site for deer cover.

Objectives not only guide management actions, they also provide a way to measure success and failure. If your only objective is annual income in excess of costs, and five years later your costs still exceed income, it may be a clue that a different investment is called for. Or it may be that a different approach to managing your land is needed. Similarly, in our hunter example, if wildlife does not increase, something different should be tried before too many years go by without the landowner realizing his goal. Even goals like "peace and quiet" or "learning and healthful exercise" have well thought out objectives that lead to success.

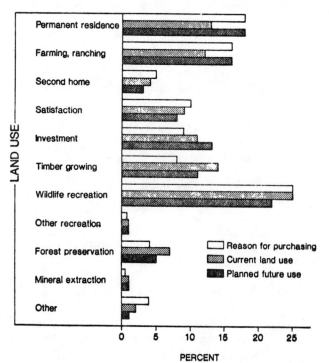

SOME REASONS WHY PEOPLE BUY FOREST LAND — AND HOW THEY CHANGE

LAND USE

- Permanent residence
- Farming, ranching
- Second home
- Satisfaction
- Investment
- Timber growing
- Wildlife recreation
- Other recreation
- Forest preservation
- Mineral extraction
- Other

☐ Reason for purchasing
▨ Current land use
■ Planned future use

0 5 10 15 20 25

PERCENT

SOURCE: ELLEFSON; PALM AND LATHNER, JOURNAL OF FORESTRY, APRIL 1982

There is no shame in changing one's goals, objectives, or management techniques. As the years pass, preferences change, new ideas emerge, health or family circumstances change. The chart on land use shows some of the reasons why people buy forest land and how their goals for it change over the years. The chart is based on a study in Minnesota, but it is probably typical for many other areas of the U.S. and Canada. It is especially interesting to see that general satisfaction and the thrill of owning a second home decreased with time, whereas timber production, investment potential, and forest preservation all increased over the years.

Help is Available

In the management of woodlands there is plenty of opportunity for the do-it-yourselfer. But even the most self-reliant landowner occasionally needs advice, and most people need all the help they can get. Happily, in most forested areas of the U.S. and Canada there is probably more assistance available than you will ever need.

Services and Incentives — United States

Government policy, as reflected both in state and federal legislation, is that society's interests are best served by having a continuous flow of products and recreational benefits (including wildlife) coming from private as well as public land. Because of this philosophy, private landowners can benefit from the many assistance programs set up at taxpayers' expense to encourage forestry and wildlife management. In fact, so many programs have resulted from this policy that sometimes the most difficult decision is deciding which source of help is best for you. Even so, surveys have shown that one big reason owners of nonindustrial forest lands do not manage their property is that they are unaware of the assistance available.

To help you quickly locate agencies that can offer assistance, refer to the chart on page 34. Cooperative Extension or a local state forestry office are the best places to start. Both specialize in providing information to landowners, and they are probably the most unbiased sources of help. That is, they will help you obtain what you want from your land. Cooperative Extension usually has offices in every county, and best of all, both agencies provide most of their services free or at very low cost.

Low cost loans are another kind of aid to promote woodland management. Farmers and certain other rural landowners who are unable to obtain reasonable credit elsewhere may be eligible to borrow funds from the Farmers Home Administration (FmHA). Three types of "Loans for Forestry Purposes" are made to individuals:

- Farm Ownership Loans — For developing or buying forest land or refinancing debts against forest land
- Soil and Water Loans — for developing or improving forest resources

- Operating Loans—for normal costs of producing, harvesting, and processing forest products

Farm ownership and operating loans may be used for income-producing recreation enterprises. However, they are limited to operators of family-size farms. Soil and water loans may be made to individual farm owners, partnerships, corporations, tenants, and nonprofit associations.

Another potential source of a loan for woodland management is the Federal Land Bank. Tree farmers may receive low cost loans up to 85 percent of the appraised value of their forests, but it must be on a large enough tract for profitable management. Reforestation of bare land is also covered, but additional securities are required in that case.

Cost sharing is one of the better incentives to help foster forestry practices that will improve a woodland. Some states offer cost sharing programs and a local forester, usually employed by the government and called a "service forester," is available to tell you about these. The two most common programs are both federal. They are administered by the Agricultural Stabilization and Conservation Service (ASCS) which usually has local offices in the federal or county office building.

Most parts of the United States are covered by the Agricultural Conservation Program (ACP). This is the more flexible of the two programs because it includes such practices as wildlife habitat improvement, fish ponds, and soil erosion control, as well as forest management. Depending on local rules and available funds, you may be able to have up to 50 or 75 percent of your costs paid for by the government! You can serve as the labor for the projects, or labor can be contracted, but all jobs will be inspected and must meet specifications before payments are made. Merchantable crops removed during an allowable improvement activity (such as firewood from a thinning) are permissible, but the costs of their removal must be deducted from any assistance request. Also, before you even apply, you must have a plan so that the work can be shown as fitting into worthwhile objectives for your land.

The other program is appropriately called the Forestry Incentives Program (FIP). It was authorized by Congress in 1973 to share the cost of tree planting and timber stand improvement (precommercial thinning, pruning, site preparation for natural regeneration, etc.). The federal share in this program also ranges up to 75 percent. The only problem is that not all counties are included. Coverage is based on a government survey that determines potentially productive timber land in private ownership. Check with ASCS, Cooperative Extension or your service forester to see if your land is in an eligible county. If so, you still must meet other criteria:

1. Own no more than 1,000 acres of eligible forest land (unless the Secretary of Agriculture determines it is in the public interest to grant an exception for a larger unit, not to exceed 5,000 acres).

2. Be a private forest landowner. Any individual, group, association or corporation may be eligible provided they are not primarily engaged in the business of manufacturing forest products or providing public utility services of any type.
3. Own land that is suitable for planting or seeding, or for improved forest management.
4. Own land that is capable of producing marketable timber crops and that meets minimum productivity standards established for this program in the landowner's state. At least a 10-acre tract of eligible forest land is required for FIP.

This brings us to the tax angle. Someone once wrote that an unwise tax is as deadly to growing trees as fire, insects, or disease. Despite government incentives to encourage forest management, taxes in some areas of the country place burdens on forest landowners that actually discourage forestry or long-term ownership. Generally, the problem exists in the form of *ad valorem* property taxes. These are the taxes used primarily for the support of town or county government.

You should find out as much as possible about how your land is supposed to be assessed. Check your assessment carefully, perhaps even hiring a private appraiser to see if you are receiving fair treatment. Sometimes previous farm land that has grown into forest land is still being taxed as a farm. Sometimes improvements that no longer exist are included in the assessment. In some areas, there is even a tendency (illegal as it is) to assess absentee landowners at a higher rate than locals. The moral of this story is to watch closely, gather facts, and formally protest any assessment that is inaccurate or unfair. You might also promote or support such tax reforms that allow for scenic easements (that is, legally give up development rights to guarantee that the scenery or current use will not be altered), that substitute severance or yield taxes for at least part of the annual property taxes (so you pay when timber is cut, not when it is growing and no income is being derived), and that use "current use" instead of "potential use" tax levels. Any method that encourages keeping land tree-covered should be considered.

Federal income tax laws have generally become quite favorable to the forest owner. Two areas of tax law are of particular interest. One is Public Law 96-451 which provides tax credits for reforestation. If you hold one acre or more of commercially valuable timberland and plan to plant trees for some long-term product (pulpwood, lumber, poles, etc.), you should look into the provisions of this law. In short, for any reforestation expenses (site preparation, seedlings, labor, etc.) up to $10,000, you can receive a 10 percent tax credit. This amount is subtracted from the taxes you would otherwise owe the government. Happily, you can also use the entire amount of your expenses as a deduction spread (amortized) over a seven-year period. These tax benefits certainly sweeten the prospects of a plantation on your land!

Services Available to Private Forest Owners in the United States

Key
- ••• Best Source
- •• Usually Available
- • Sometimes Available
- ▲ Advice Only

Source of Help	Usual Local Location	Literature — Self-help Information	Workshops, Instruction	On-site Inspection or Review (advice)	Management Plan	Set up Cost-sharing	Boundary Survey	Cruise Timber	Contracts for Timber Sales	Advance Cash for Timber	Mark Timber	Administer Logging	Planting	Stand Improvement, Pre-Commercial Thinning	Wildlife Habitat & Fish Ponds	Comments
Agricultural Stabilization & Conservation Service	Federal or County Office Bldg. (See CES or State Forestry if not available)					••										
Consulting Foresters	Check Yellow Pages of phone directory	•••	•••	•••	•••	•	•••	•••	•••		•••	•••	••	•••	•	Relatively expensive but provide the most individual attention. Like lawyer, represents your best interests.
Cooperative Extension Service	County Office Bldg. & Land Grant University (See Appendix)	•	•••	•	• ▲								• ▲	• ▲	• ▲	Foresters not always available locally.
Industrial Foresters	Forest Product Companies (Pulp & paper, lumber, specialty items, etc.)			••	•		•	•••	•••	•	•••	•••	•	•••		Their goal is to assure source of raw materials for their company.
Soil Conservation Service	Federal Office Bldg.	••	••	•••	•••								••• ▲	•• ▲	••• ▲	U.S. Dept. of Agric.
State Forestry Service	State Capitol and various local offices	•••	•••	••	••	•	•		• ▲		•		•• ▲	••	• ▲	Name varies in differnt states.
U.S. Forest Service	National Forest Headquarters & Ranger Stations	••	•													Also have National & Regional offices that house Branch of State & Private Forestry. Also Experiment Stations.

However, one of the few pitfalls to be aware of is the so-called recapture provision. This means you pay back the deducted amounts if you sell your property within ten years. Also, fruit trees, ornamentals, shelterbelts and Christmas trees do not qualify for these tax breaks.

The other area of tax law that can be of special help is the capital gains treatment of income from timber sales. You pay less to Uncle Sam if the income can be counted as long-term capital gain instead of ordinary income. To qualify for this treatment, you must be able to show that your trees are being grown for long-term growth and investment. For example, you cannot claim capital gains treatment if you sell your timber within one year of acquiring it. You must also be able to show a "retention of economic interest" in a sale of timber. The clearest way to do this may be to sell on the basis of actual cords or board feet harvested, rather than simply on a lump sum basis. These and other provisions can be found in Internal Revenue Code Sections 631a, 631b, and 1231. Check the wording of any sale agreements with a tax consultant *before* making a sale. It is very easy to jeopardize your basis for capital gains treatment.

There are other ways that tax laws can work for you as you grow and improve your woodlot if you plan in advance. Deductions and investment credits, for example, are possible for just about anything from a shovel to insurance premiums—if you are involved in a profit-promising activity rather than using your land solely as a hobby. Expenses associated with a timber sale are also deductible, including cruising costs, tree marking expenses, consultant fees and temporary road construction necessary for the sale and not usable for more than one year. Estate and gift tax procedures are particularly important for passing woodlands along to future generations.

Since tax rules are complicated and subject to change and individual circumstances, I cannot overemphasize the importance of seeking regular advice from a qualified tax consultant (one familiar with rural land and forestry). Also, some forestry consultants specialize in tax problems.

Worth Writing For

A Guide to Federal Income Tax for Timber Owners. USDA Forest Service. Agriculture Handbook 596, US Government Printing Office, Washington, DC 20402.

Services and Incentives — Canada

With as much as 30 percent of Canada's wood products being produced on private woodlands, it is not surprising that the government is showing an increasing interest in helping woodlot owners manage their land better. Actually, the roots of this interest can be traced back to 1871 and 1883 when legislators in Ontario promoted roadside and shelterbelt planting. Early in this century, the effort expanded to reforestation of overcut "wastelands," including the creation of the first provincial nursery.

In the 1950s and 1960s, assistance programs of other kinds began to flourish, and today many of the provinces have a variety of services, loan programs, and tax incentives that offer valuable help to all who care about their woods. The major programs are summarized on page 36. For more information contact ministry officials or a forestry school in your province.

Worth Writing For

Private Land Forests: A Public Resource, Ministry of Natural Resources, Toronto M7A 1W3

Selecting a Consulting Forester

In the U.S., when you get beyond the stage of gathering information or planning, you either do most of the work yourself or turn to private sector foresters. Even in Canada, where in some provinces there are government services for almost every task, there are times when a woodland owner would feel more comfortable with a consulting forester looking after his interests.

Most consulting foresters are willing to do as little or as much of the total management of your woodland as you desire. A good consultant will advise you and represent your best interests. But even so, the more informed you are, the better prepared you will be to make the ultimate choices and not be led astray from your personal goals.

As in any profession there are good consultants and poor ones. I have seen the results of both and strongly urge you to select one with the same care you choose an attorney or a doctor. A good starting point is to obtain a copy of the Association of Consulting Foresters' *Membership Specialization Directory.* The 350 members of this professional organization can be located in the directory by state and they are described by their education and experience, size of staff, kind of equipment owned, and the kind of services performed. Members in this organization are screened and must have considerable experience and a degree in forestry from an approved university. They adhere to a rigid code of ethics which is included in the directory. To obtain a directory, write: Association of Consulting Foresters, 5410 Grosvenor Lane, Suite 120, Bethesda, MD 20814.

There are many good consultants who are not full-time or for some other reason do not belong to the association. In this case, here are some points to consider in your selection—and don't be shy about asking for answers, preferably in writing:
- Education and experience. Does he or she have a degree from a college accredited by the Society of American Foresters? How many jobs similar to yours has he performed?
- Check references and talk to previous clients.

SERVICES AVAILABLE TO OWNERS OF SMALL
PRIVATE FORESTS IN CANADA

Province	Private Forest Land as a Percentage of Total Forest Land	Assistance Programs Available
Alberta	3	* Alberta Dept. of Agriculture tree nursery (near Edmonton) provides free seedlings for shelterbelts and windbreaks, and at a small cost for Christmas trees.
British Columbia	5	* Taxation Tree Farm program. for a commitment to practice forest management in a government-approved manner, landowner receives a lower property tax. A plan and annual report of activities are required. Contact Ministry of Forests.
		* Woodlot License. Allows owner to combine private land with up to 988 acres of Crown land to form and operate a management unit.
		* Extension services available from Ministry of Forests.
Manitoba	2	* Planting stock for sale by provincial nursery at Hadashville.
New Brunswick	53	* Dept. of Natural Resources extension foresters offer educational programs, advice, and assistance to landowners in forming self-financed action groups.
		* Forest Products Commission and regional landowner marketing boards negotiate prices and delivery schedules.
		* Univ. of N.B. and Maritime Forest Ranger School offer continuing education programs and literature.
		* Private companies also offer assistance: Fraser Co. of Edmonton has demonstration woodlots, provides nursery stock at subsidized cost and promotes awards; MacMillan Rothesay Ltd. of St. John pays an extra amount over regular price of cordwood for use in silviculture. Georgia Pacific Corp. and St. Croix Pulpwood Ltd. foresters offer free advice and planning.
Newfoundland	13	* Technical advice from Dept. of Forest Resources and Lands.
Nova Scotia	72	* Private Land Forestry Assistance Program for tracts between 50 and 5,000 acres. Includes cost sharing for 60-100% of costs for access roads, boundary lines, fire pond construction and silvicultural operations. A management plan and 10-year agreement required.
		* Group Venture Forest Management Program. Allows 10 or more woodlot owners to form companies or cooperatives for costs averaging and other benefits of larger scale operations.
		* Scott Maritimes Ltd. Pulp & Paper Co. provides management for owners who then sell products to company.
Ontario	10	* Subsidized planting stock for sale to owners of 5 acres or more.
		* Woodlands Improvement Act provides for planting and stand improvement under 15 year agreement.
		* Advisory Services Program includes answering queries, providing advice and marking timber for harvest.
		* Managed Forest Tax Reduction provides a rebate of 50% of municipal taxes for qualifying woodlots.
Prince Edward Island	94	* Forest Resource Management Incentive Program for areas 25 acres or larger. Provides free planting stock, and payments for actual cost of such things as road construction, stand improvement, boundary surveys, and marketing. 5-year agreement needed.
Quebec	10	* Federation of Wood Producers negotiate with product outlets for all members covered by joint plan.
		* Forest Owner Groups pool resources to form a profit-oriented company. Members are paid for their work, including fringe benefits, but recieve only 1/3 of what is sold from their land.
		* Private Land Forest Assistance offers financial and technical assistance to associations and boards, and loans to owners.
		* Free planting stock for 1 acre or more.
		* Various tax breaks.
Saskatchewan	3	* Planting stock available from Prairie Farm Rehabilitation Administration nursery at Indian Head.

- Know his rates or commission in advance and exactly how much time and what services you will receive.
- Look for potential conflicts of interest. The consultant may be expected to receive a percentage of any timber sales he manages, but he should not otherwise profit from it or work for both seller (you) and a buyer.
- Is he attentive to your objectives? Beware of anyone who can see only dollars in your woodlot.

Developing a Plan

I have emphasized the need to know yourself and your land well enough to set realistic goals. The trees you have, the capability and limitations of your land, the time and money you wish to invest, and the satisfactions that mean the most to you are all considerations that will lead to joy or disappointment from the experience of owning a woodlot. Success will depend on how thoroughly you think this through, and, to no small degree, how well you document the results of these explorations.

A written plan helps put enough detail into this exercise to make it useful. A plan is also usually required before financial assistance is made available, and it can help document your intentions if you face a tax audit.

There is no such thing as a standard plan. Its format and content should meet your particular needs. For professional assistance, the Soil Conservation Service or your local service forester is the best bet. If you would rather do it yourself, here is a suggested list of what should be included:

1 . *Descriptive Information*
The name of your tract, owners, legal descriptions and date of the plan.
2 . *Goals and Objectives*
Be as specific as possible, using the guidelines presented earlier. (You may want to delay completing this section until you have inventoried and weighed your alternatives.)
3 . *Resource Map*
As a base, use your legal plat, a topo map, or aerial photos. These can be adjusted to a convenient scale if necessary. Show clearly such things as:
a . property boundaries
b . ridges, streams, marshes and ponds
c . roads
d . developments (buildings, springs, picnic sites, etc.)
e . cover types or habitat types
f . soil classes if more than one
g . current or past land uses (plantations, cutting areas, wildlife habitat projects, etc.)
To keep your map from being too cluttered, you may want to put items e, f or g on transparent overlays.

4 . *Inventory Data*
These are the facts upon which your decisions can be based. The results of cruise data, growth and yield studies, and the condition of regeneration (understory) are especially important. This should be clearly displayed in summary form, along with a brief description of how the cruise was conducted (plot sizes, percent cruise, minimum sizes tallied, excluded species). Special products or features should be noted, such as concentrations of sassafrass, berry patches, or large quantities of pine stumps suitable for distillate wood. If wildlife is of interest, den trees, wildlife habitat, salt licks, deer yards, and other pertinent features should be included.
5 . *Special Features/Problems*
Special conditions might exist that are not included elsewhere but should be described. These might be the conditions imposed by easements, boundary line or trespass problems, fire control efforts, hazards, and others. Key these to the map when possible.
6 . *Alternatives*
Regardless of your goals, you will probably be faced with more options that you can reasonably pursue, even under a "multiple-use" philosophy. In this section, briefly describe your alternatives, listing the advantages and disadvantages of each.
7 . *Management Actions*
Based on the best data and best advice available, and your goals, a plan of action should be laid out. This ties in closely with your objectives. In fact, it may be wise not to set specific objectives until this point in the process. Management actions should include what products (if any) will be harvested, and when, where and how. Cutting zones may add another overlay to your map, or lend themselves to a separate one. Treatments should also be described, such as thinnings, pruning, and how regeneration is to be achieved. Planned developments such as roads, trails, ponds, and recreation facilities should also be included.

Boundaries and Roads

"Good fences make good neighbors," wrote Robert Frost, and woodland managers would be well advised to heed his point. Although fences are not always practical, a clearly marked, undisputed boundary line is essential.

The most judicious approach is to insist on a survey with marked lines and property corners *before* you purchase the land. Then check with the neighbors to make sure they agree that the boundaries are in the right places. Disputes are all too common, even when one or more competent surveyors have done the job, and better to let the seller pay for a settlement than to acquire a continued legal headache and ill-feelings with neighbors.

When the property line is known, mark it clearly. Blazes, paint marks or small metal signs nailed to trees on or close to the line are the best ways to establish the boundary. Property corners should be identified with metal stakes driven deeply into the ground by a licensed surveyor. Their locations should be pinpointed using at least two "bearing trees." Each tree is clearly marked with the compass bearing and distance to the corner so it can be re-established if "lost." The same information is recorded on your map or property description.

Clearly marked boundaries should be a first step in woodland management. They are well worth the time and effort for reducing trespass, confining logging and firewood cutting, and generally preventing problems with neighbors.

A BLAZE

GOOD BOUNDARIES MAKE GOOD NEIGHBORS

PAINTED MARKS

PROPERTY LINE
NO HUNTING

NAIL FIRMLY, BUT ALLOW SPACE FOR TREE GROWTH

METAL SIGNS

A good road system is something else to think about early in planning for the future of your woodland. Unless a private wilderness is your goal, a road system is important for almost anything you want to do with your land—fight fires, carry out thinnings or improvement cuttings, grow Christmas trees, produce maple syrup, and even to improve habitat for most wildlife species. Good roads are especially important when harvesting timber and are discussed in more detail in Chapter 8.

Forestry and Financial Considerations

The trickiest part of planning for the future of your woodland is weighing the many financial options. There are the usual business decisions about investing time, equipment and materials, which are further complicated by choices of how to use your land or money and the optimum time and methods for harvesting your trees. Help with the latter is provided on page 89, but in all cases the best you can do is know past trends, be alert to current conditions and get information from impartial investment counselors.

In managing a woodland, the three main financial considerations are:

1 . *Product Prices*

Based on your inventory and the availability of local markets, it is easy to determine the value of your trees. But the prices offered for pulpwood and various species of sawlogs vary like any other commodity, so it is more difficult to be sure what prices for them will be in the future.

Your best estimate of future prices must then be weighed against growth and yield data from the past. For example, if you have a large number of high-value species in a small diameter class (say, 10 inches), they will be adding a large volume of wood if allowed to grow. Especially with proper thinning, they may add from 8 to 10 percent to their volume annually. Letting them stand is probably the wisest investment. On the other hand, large diameter trees add growth slowly—perhaps only from 1 to 3 percent if 20 inches or greater. These have probably passed the point of diminishing returns from a purely financial standpoint.

2 . *Costs*

Another balancing act is required when you estimate the costs needed to produce your logs (or other products) and compare them with anticipated income. Some costs are unavoidable. These are fixed costs such as taxes and loan payments. Other costs are optional, such as for precommercial thinnings, fertilizing, erosion control, and weeding around seedlings in a plantation. Whether to invest in these practices will be a matter of weighing costs (extended over time) against how much or how fast the treatments will result in increased yields.

3 . *Alternative Investments*

Toughest of all is to decide — is this worth it to me? Your entire investment is always comparable with other options such as subdividing for building lots or selling your land and putting the money in treasury bonds, an apartment house, or the stock market. The rising value of land, the potential income, your annual costs in dollars and time all enter in this comparison. But most of all it comes back to your goals again. Overall, are your trees providing you with what *you* want from your land?

To help with these decisions, use professional assistance such as an investment counselor, a tax consultant who knows forest land (many do not) and a lawyer who knows land and commercial law.

In the end, how you manage your land rests with you. Know thyself well and this will make the rest easier — and even fun!

5   The Science and Art
of
Growing a Forest

There is something nobly simple and pure
in a taste for the cultivation of forest trees.
—Washington Irving

It is tempting to say that a battle rages in your forest. Authors often use this analogy to explain the competitive forces that are at work in the woods. While this may read well, it erroneously lends human terms and emotions to a process that is strictly a matter of physics and chemistry. In the science and art of growing trees, the smart owner recognizes this and tries to understand what is going on. Then, like a gardener on a large scale, he can manipulate the factors involved to produce what meets his objectives.

In forestry jargon, producing and tending the forest is called *silviculture* (tree-culture). This is the heart of *forest management*, a term with broader inclusions such as finance, personnel management and fire protection. In its most useful sense, silviculture requires a knowledge of what each species needs in order to reproduce and grow. This foundation of silviculture is termed *silvics*—the characteristics, life histories and ecology of trees.

Silvics Is A Key to Decisions

Silvics can serve as a guide to making the best decisions in your woodlot. If you know the characteristics of your trees you can start a new and vigorous generation whether on an old farm field or under the canopy of a forest nearing maturity. If you are working with seedlings on bare ground, it is important to know their natural resistance to drought and frost. If you want to favor a certain species' under a canopy, you will need to know that specie's tolerance to shade in deciding how much of the overstory to remove.

Silvics is seeing the trees, not just the forest; knowing the characteristics of each species in your woodlot and those of species being considered for planting. A few characteristics of some common trees are summarized in the appendix in chart form, but nothing can take the place of reading detailed descriptions of the species that grow on your land.

Best Guides to the Silvics of Trees

Silvics of Forest Trees of the United States compiled by H.A. Fowells. Agricultural Handbook No. 271. U.S. Forest Service (U.S. Government Printing Office), Washington, D.C.

This 762-page classic is encyclopedic in its coverage. Arranged by species, information includes climate, soils, and growing sites specific to a species, as well as a list of other plants you might expect to find associated with the particular type of tree, its rate of growth, its enemies, its response to release cuttings, and in some cases what yields might be expected on various sites. A rich bibliography is included for each species, plus an appendix full of national maps showing annual rainfall, soils, vegetation types, and temperature ranges.

*Comparative Autecological Characteristics of
    Northwestern Tree Species* — A Literature Review by Don Minore. Pacific Northwest Forest and Range Experiment Station, U.S. Forest Service, P.O. Box 3141, Portland, Oregon 97208.

Don't let the professorial title scare you. If you live in the Northwest, it will be worth your time to wade through the jargon and Latin names to obtain the useful information summarized from scientific studies.

Two others:
    The Textbook of Dendrology by Harlow and Harrar described on page 17 provides some of the more important silvical information about many major tree species.

Woodlands for Profit and Pleasure by Reginald D. Forbes (The American Forestry Assn., 1319 18th St., N.W., Washington, D.C.) contains a list of eastern trees similar to the one on page 190. Forbes' list includes far more species — even small trees or shrubs such as staghorn sumac, and mountain-laurel — and also shows soil pH where the trees grow and their place in succession.

A MOST MARVELOUS MECHANISM

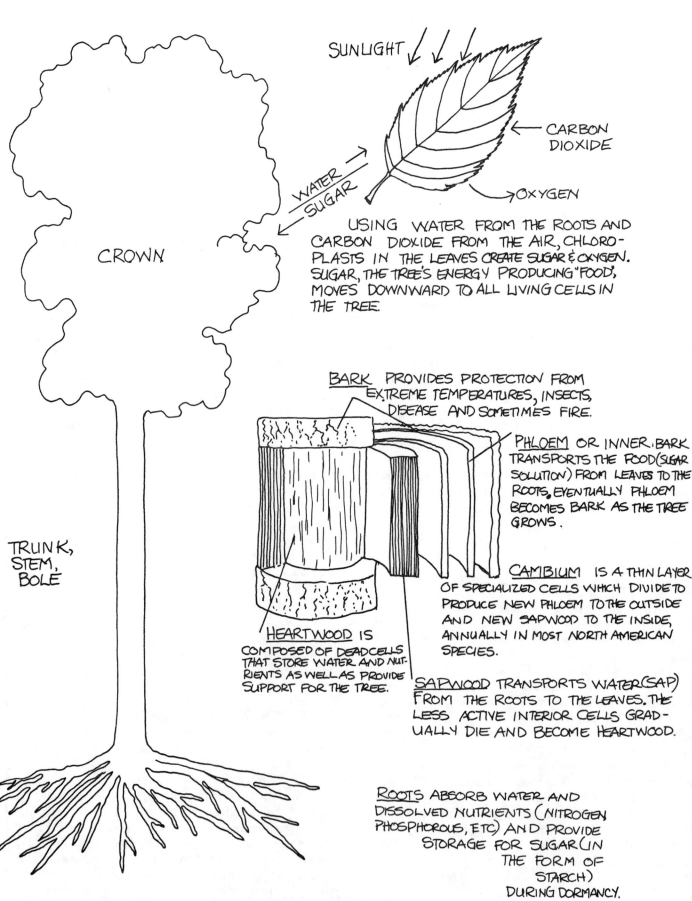

SUNLIGHT

CARBON DIOXIDE

OXYGEN

WATER
SUGAR

CROWN

USING WATER FROM THE ROOTS AND CARBON DIOXIDE FROM THE AIR, CHLORO-PLASTS IN THE LEAVES CREATE SUGAR & OXYGEN. SUGAR, THE TREE'S ENERGY PRODUCING "FOOD", MOVES DOWNWARD TO ALL LIVING CELLS IN THE TREE.

BARK PROVIDES PROTECTION FROM EXTREME TEMPERATURES, INSECTS, DISEASE AND SOMETIMES FIRE.

PHLOEM OR INNER BARK TRANSPORTS THE FOOD (SUGAR SOLUTION) FROM LEAVES TO THE ROOTS. EVENTUALLY PHLOEM BECOMES BARK AS THE TREE GROWS.

TRUNK, STEM, BOLE

CAMBIUM IS A THIN LAYER OF SPECIALIZED CELLS WHICH DIVIDE TO PRODUCE NEW PHLOEM TO THE OUTSIDE AND NEW SAPWOOD TO THE INSIDE, ANNUALLY IN MOST NORTH AMERICAN SPECIES.

HEARTWOOD IS COMPOSED OF DEAD CELLS THAT STORE WATER AND NUT-RIENTS AS WELL AS PROVIDE SUPPORT FOR THE TREE.

SAPWOOD TRANSPORTS WATER (SAP) FROM THE ROOTS TO THE LEAVES. THE LESS ACTIVE INTERIOR CELLS GRAD-UALLY DIE AND BECOME HEARTWOOD.

ROOTS ABSORB WATER AND DISSOLVED NUTRIENTS (NITROGEN, PHOSPHOROUS, ETC) AND PROVIDE STORAGE FOR SUGAR (IN THE FORM OF STARCH) DURING DORMANCY.

Silvicultural Systems

A silvicultural system is simply the method selected to grow and reproduce the forest in a way that combines the biological needs of the species and the personal objectives of the owner. Unfortunately, one sometimes excludes the other. In fact, on public lands such as national forests, major conflicts often arise when foresters select a silvicultural system that is inconsistent with the public's idea of what the land should provide.

There are many variations on the systems outlined in the following pages. Sometimes trying to consider all the natural and economical factors involved can be frustrating. Here is where the experience of a forester comes in handy, so it is a good idea to ask for a professional judgement before making your final decision.

Silvicultural systems range from the relative simplicity of clear-cutting and planting to the more complicated methods of selecting individual trees to cut in an attempt to maintain diversity and a steady supply of maturing timber. Silviculture usually relies on two kinds of cutting during the life of a stand. These are: *intermediate cuttings* to improve or maintain the desired composition and structure of the stand and vigor of the trees intended as the final crop; and *reproduction* or *harvest cuttings* that end the growing period for one stand of trees and provide for the establishment of the next crop.

The array of silvicultural options can be diagrammed like this:

Silviculture

No Treatment	Intermediate Cuttings		Harvest Cuttings	Intensive Planting/ Culture of Single Purpose Stands
• Wilderness, preservation of special sites	• Cleaning • Thinning • Improvement cutting • Sanitation cutting • Salvage cutting	Even-aged management Uneven-aged management	• Clearcutting • Seed-tree system • Shelterwood system • Coppicing • Single-tree selection system • Group selection system	• Christmas trees, holly, etc.

A Word About Wilderness

Many traditional foresters would turn red with anger at the very mention of wilderness under the heading of silviculture. We are not suggesting that a laissez-faire approach to woodland management is a silvicultural system in the sense it is usually used, but it *is* an option. A landowner has every right to elect this option, and there are many good reasons to do so.

Wilderness, whether a vast area like Yellowstone's backcountry that is part of the National Wilderness Preservation System, or a tiny bog near New York City, provides the opportunity for certain kinds of recreational and inspirational experiences that are part of a nation's well-balanced use of land and natural resources. It also provides for the survival of animal species such as the grizzly bear and mountain lion that need large areas of land for survival. Some areas protect delicate relationships. For example, when The Nature Conservancy preserved a bog near Seattle to assure a growing place for the inconspicuous northern bog violet, the rare and violet-dependent *Boloria selene* butterfly was also given a hold on life. Wild areas make valuable contributions as natural gene pools, and as benchmarks for comparison studies of tree growth, genetics, and pollution.

Whether it is a small private area or a large, government-owned tract, wilderness is a legitimate use of the land. Unfortunately, the commodity-oriented education of many foresters blinds them to this. They claim it is wasteful, stupid, or even unpatriotic and should not be considered. Be aware of this bias when seeking advice on land management.

Also be aware that even wild areas in our modern society require management. If you wish to protect a bog, fencing may be necessary. Or more subtle threats may need to be countered, such as depletion of the ground water that feeds the bog. Even domestic dogs and cats can wreak havoc on areas intended as wild sanctuaries.

Keep in mind that nature does not stand still. It may be your intent to keep the woods as they are, but this is not nature's way. Without direct intervention, succession will continue, insects and disease will take their toll and possibly alter the composition of the forest, fire will make its mark, and other forces of nature—and man—will continue to shape your forest. If you accept this, you can sit back and observe and enjoy whatever changes occur. Otherwise, you may be disappointed as beautiful white birches give way to invading maples, or the vigorous young pine stand you bought becomes dense, stunted and dark.

Intermediate Cuttings

In most managed forests, there are advantages in making certain types of cuttings long before the trees mature or are ready for a final harvest. During this period between establishment of the stand and final harvest, most silvicultural work is called timber stand improvement (TSI). Intermediate cuttings are at the heart of TSI. They are intended to improve the existing stand, speed the growth of crop trees, and sometimes provide early income for the owner. They are *not* cuttings made for regeneration purposes.

Intermediate cuttings are not difficult to understand. The tricky part is knowing how much to remove and how much investment to make in TSI before it becomes uneconomical. This will be discussed in the following chapter when we address the mechanics of caring for your trees. First we need to look at the range of treatments and how they differ in what they can do for your woodlands.

Cleaning

This treatment is appropriate very early in the life of some stands. It is necessary when the desired seedlings or saplings are mixed with undesirable species that might become dominant. This often happens in young pine stands. They may quickly become overtopped by hardwood species if cleaning is not done. Selective chemicals are sometimes recommended for cleaning, but with enough energy and help, machetes or brush cutters can also do the job. The result is a young stand that is "clean," or free of undesirable species, at least long enough for the favored species to get a head start toward precious sunlight and soil moisture.

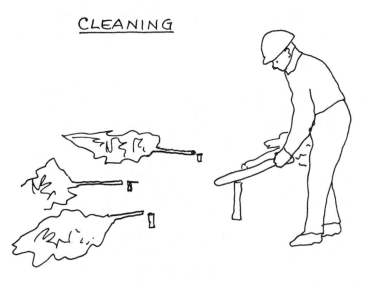

CLEANING

Thinning

Thinning is the removal of surplus trees from an immature stand, usually beyond the sapling stage. The idea is to concentrate growth on properly spaced, most promising future crop trees. It may mean the removal of the same species as the crop trees, or undesirables, or both.

When trees are thinned too early in the life of the stand to provide a source of income, it is called precommercial thinning. Sometimes, however, thinning is a very important source of products such as firewood, charcoal, posts and poles. Since thinning is so important to good forest management, so potentially lucrative to forest owners, and so universally needed in North American forests, it is covered in some depth in the next chapter.

THINNING

Improvement Cutting

Improvement cuttings are made to improve the stand by removing undesirable species and trees with defects in shape or condition. Terminology muddies the water, since an improvement cut also provides many of the benefits of a thinning. For all practical purposes, the operation is often one and the same. Improvement cuttings are usually needed in stands that have been neglected, which is common in small, privately owned woodlots.

REMOVE THIS TREE

REMOVE THIS TREE

IMPROVEMENT CUTTING

Other Intermediate Cuttings

There are other intermediate cuttings that can become important depending on local conditions and the species involved.

Weeding is the removal of all woody or herbaceous growth that may be competing with desired seedlings. It is no different than agricultural or garden crop operations and is usually done in nurseries, Christmas tree plantations and similar intensively managed operations.

A *liberation cutting* is the removal of older, overtopping and inferior trees from a stand of younger trees. Sometimes the large, overtopping trees are called "wolf trees." In areas where wolf trees are scattered and of low value, they may be girdled and left to die in place as illustrated. This is a quick and inexpensive technique, and while the dead tree yields its light and soil moisture to the younger crop trees, it continues to provide homes for cavity-nesting birds and mammals, food for woodpeckers, and a perch for birds of prey.

Sanitation cuttings are sometimes necessary to remove diseased or insect-infested trees in order to prevent spread. If the infestation kills commercial-sized trees, a *salvage cutting* may be necessary. This is an unplanned harvest to make the most, economically, of an unfortunate situation. Forest fires, ice storms, hurricanes or other disasters may also make salvage cutting necessary.

Pruning can technically be considered an intermediate cutting even though only branches, rather than entire trees, are removed. This practice is described in the next chapter.

Harvest Cuttings

Harvest cuttings are one of the most controversial aspects of forest management. They are also the main difference between modern forest management and the days of rape-and-run timber barons. Ideally, the harvest cut can also be referred to as *regeneration cutting,* for the intent should be as much to provide for the new stand as it is to make a profit from harvesting the old.

As can be seen in the diagram, a bewildering array of questions need to be answered before an intelligent choice of a cutting method can be made. Controversies on public lands continually result from ignoring some of these questions. On small, private lands, the problem is often that the forest is not large enough or in the right condition to permit one kind of cutting system rather than another, or that the owner is simply unaware of all the choices. On both public and private land, this results in more weight being given to immediate economic considerations than to the others, which fundamentally is no different from what happened when the timber barons

WOLF TREE

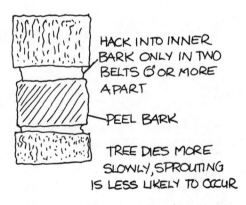

TWO WAYS TO GIRDLE A WOLF TREE OR OTHER UNWANTED TREES

HACK WELL INTO SAPWOOD

HACK INTO INNER BARK ONLY IN TWO BELTS 6" OR MORE APART

PEEL BARK

TREE DIES MORE SLOWLY, SPROUTING IS LESS LIKELY TO OCCUR

roamed the land. When immediate, maximum income becomes the driving force, silviculture crumbles. The trees are cut and sold, and the land is sold or neglected. At best, the forest faces a long period of recovery, ugliness and unproductivity.

For the landowner who wants to balance cash income with other benefits, careful consideration should be given to the choice of a method for harvest cutting. There are four principal systems, all with variations or combinations. In their simplest form, they are described below.

CONSIDERATIONS IN SELECTING A HARVEST (REGENERATION) CUTTING METHOD

Reproductive Needs
Is the desired regeneration shade tolerant or intolerant? And competitive species? What relative rates of growth are involved?

Landowner Objectives
What is most important — aesthetics, rapid growth of a new stand, immediate high income or continual income, wildlife, etc.?

Climatic Hazards/Soils
Is the site subject to heavy frosts, high winds, salt spray, drought? Is the soil suitable for the regeneration planned? Is the soil stable enough for roads and to withstand erosion?

WHICH ? SYSTEM TO USE

Socioeconomics
Are markets and labor available? Do you have the skill and expertise necessary? What about equipment and capital?

The Existing Stand
The species, size, age and vigor affect the sucess of some systems and how heavy the harvest cut should be.

Fire
Is fire going to be needed as a management tool to reduce logging debris or control brush or disease? Is wildfire a serious potential?

Insects and Disease
Are there infected or susceptible trees that should be removed? Is a solid canopy needed to protect the under-story from weevils?

Wildlife
Are certain wildlife species to be favored? Are the numbers of types of wild-life such that they will interfere with forest repro-duction?

Clearcutting

Used correctly, clearcutting is a legitimate and useful silvicultural method. European foresters have used it for centuries to provide a sustained flow of wood products, and it is popular with American and Canadian foresters in the great coniferous regions of this continent. As a cutting method, it is less popular with the general public, as witnessed by the explosion of public outcry when clearcutting was tried in the hardwoods on the Monongahela National Forest of West Virginia beginning in 1954.

With enough land and under ideal conditions, clearcutting small parcels one at a time can be considered a method of sustained yield forestry. That is, by the time the last trees in the property are cut, trees on the first harvested parcel have reached maturity. Usually, only the government and large forest industries have areas of land large enough to support this type of management.

Clearcutting, however, that is not intended as part of a continuously yielding forest is still an option. That is, all or part of your land might be clearcut with the realization that a long period of time will pass before a mature crop is again ready for harvest. In the southern pine region, this may be as short as 20 years for a yield of pulpwood (less in the case of hybrid poplars), but in most other regions it will take much longer.

One of the two biggest disadvantages of this method, especially in highly visible hilly areas, is the aesthetic impact. The second is the problem of getting seedlings established quickly so they are able to cope with the invasion of grass, brush and undesirable tree species that are typical on clearcuts. Both can be prevented. The first requires the careful design of cutting boundaries to reduce the unnatural appearance of straight lines, and the avoidance of highly visible prominences or hillsides facing living areas. As for successful regeneration, intensive management (site preparation, planting, weeding, cleaning or thinning) must be considered part of the responsible use of this method, even though it may be expensive and time-consuming in the years following the harvest cut.

CLEARCUTTING

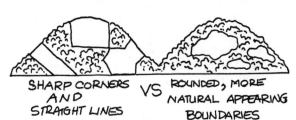

SHARP CORNERS AND STRAIGHT LINES VS ROUNDED, MORE NATURAL APPEARING BOUNDARIES

Clearcutting Advantages...

1. Best for regeneration of shade intolerant species. (e.g.: Douglas fir, oaks)
2. Concentrates logging in time and location, making it more economical (high immediate income).
3. Damage to remaining trees from logging, windfall or other environmental factors is not a problem.
4. Best for converting an area to a different species (e.g.: from hardwoods to pine).
5. Economical way to regenerate species needing fire as part of its management (to open cones, control disease, etc. (e.g.: jack pine, lodgepole pine).
6. Economical way to regenerate species with light, wind-blown seeds available from edges of clearcut. (e.g.: yellow-poplar, paper birch, loblolly pine).
7. Easy and economical to plant.
8. Simple and easy to plan and supervise; minimum of technical decisions.
9. Excellent for birding and for many forms of wildlife.
10. Provides forage for livestock.

Disadvantages...

1. May be aesthetically unpleasant.
2. Usually no merchantable products for a long period of time.
3. Invites the invasion of grass, weeds, shrubs and aggressive tree species that may be unwanted.
4. Changes microclimate, increasing impact of wind and extremes of temperatures.
5. May create short-term (3 to 5 years) erosion problems, especially in fine textured soils such as clays. The risk of landslides and snowslides may also be increased.
6. Under some conditions, large amounts of logging wastes may create risk of fire, insect or disease problems before slash disposal can be carried out.
7. If relying on natural regeneration, there is a high risk that seeds will be inadequate to start the new stand, or be unevenly distributed.

Seed Tree Method

The seed tree method is essentially a clearcut in which a scattering of selected trees is left to assure a seed crop for regeneration. A few years later, these parent trees are harvested. Depending on the species and characteristics of the site, from 1 to 10 trees per acre are usually left, representing something less than 10 percent of the merchantable volume. Since they will be the source of the future stand, proven seed producers with the best genetic attributes (height, form, vigor) are selected.

One variation of this method is to allow small groups to remain instead of scattered, individual trees. This helps with the problem of wind blowing over isolated trees and may help guarantee cross pollination and seed production.

A second variation is to leave trees with defects, then skip the future harvest of seed trees. This reduces damage to the new stand but requires extremely careful selection to be sure none of the seed trees have *genetically*-linked defects. That is a difficult distinction to make. Another advantage of this method is that it provides trees for woodpeckers, songbirds and birds of prey.

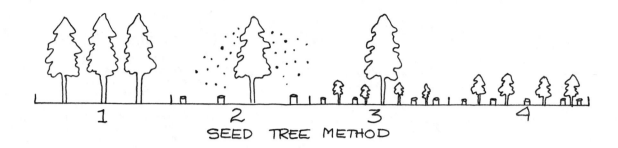

SEED TREE METHOD

SCATTERED SEED TREE METHOD

GROUP SEED TREE METHOD

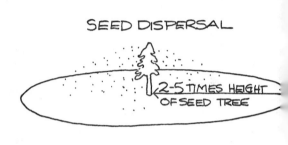

SEED DISPERSAL

Seed Tree Advantages...

1. Same as clearcutting except a seed source of the preferred species is assured.
2. The supply of seed is more uniformly distributed than in clearcutting.
3. Genetically superior parent trees can be selected.
4. Income can be spread over two periods; there will also be some volume increase on the trees left temporarily for seed production.
5. Slightly more aesthetic than clearcutting, and beneficial to a wider range of wildlife.

Disadvantages...

1. Mostly the same as clearcutting except for improved seeding and less risk of needing to plant.
2. Because of shock and windfall, there can be a loss of merchantable lumber before the follow-up harvest.
3. Cannot be used in shallow soils, with shallow-rooted species (Ex.: spruces), or with species having wood of low strength (Ex.: eastern white pine).
4. Restricted to species that produce large numbers of light seeds, and that are able to germinate and grow in open conditions (Ex.: longleaf and most other southern pines, yellow-poplar).

Shelterwood Method

The shelterwood system combines some of the advantages of clearcutting with those of the seed tree method, and adds some of its own. Consequently, it is a rather popular method with considerable flexibility to meet the needs of many species and sites, as well as the landowner's objectives.

The best application of shelterwood cutting is with species that need partial shade in the early stages of their growth. By adjusting the number of seed trees that are left in the canopy, the amount of shade can be regulated to meet the needs for successful regeneration of the desired species. The older trees are not only a source of seed, they provide shade and shelter for seedlings and protection for the site. Also, when viewed from a distance, a more natural appearance is retained until a new stand is well on its way toward replacing the old.

This system has at least three steps, all of which yield saleable products and spread income over a period of 10 to 20 years.

The first step is a *preparatory cut*. Similar to a late thinning, the intent in this cut is to remove weaker trees and provide more growing space for future seed trees. About 25 to 30 percent of the trees are removed. This allows the remaining trees to spread their crowns and increase their root systems, thereby becoming more windfirm and generally more vigorous. A side benefit, of course, is that they will also put on more wood volume and increase in value. Usually, 3 to 10 years are needed for the desired results.

If continuous thinning has been part of the history of the stand, the preparatory cut in the shelterwood system may be omitted. On the other hand, in thick, neglected stands, two or more preparatory cuts may be necessary before nicely spaced, vigorous seed trees cover the land.

48

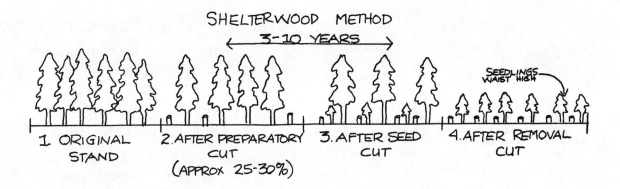

SHELTERWOOD METHOD
← 3-10 YEARS →

SEEDLINGS WAIST HIGH

1 ORIGINAL STAND   2. AFTER PREPARATORY CUT (APPROX 25-30%)   3. AFTER SEED CUT   4. AFTER REMOVAL CUT

The second step is the *seed cut*. This removes all but the very best seed trees and simultaneously opens up the canopy enough to allow seedlings to get established. The seed cut should be made in a year when the desired species produce an abundant seed crop. The best time for the cutting within that year comes after the seed has matured and before it is dispersed. Spacing of the parent trees might vary from 30 to 40 feet or more, depending on the species and site. Closer spacing will be needed in frost pockets or on south slopes; wider spacing is best on more favorable sites. The shade tolerance of undesirable, competitive species should also be considered. Previous local experience provides the best clues for fine-tuning this method of regeneration cutting.

The third and final step is the *removal cut*, or *overstory removal*. This is made after regeneration is assured, usually when the new trees are about waist high. If some final shading is needed, the removal cut can be made in two or more stages. However, this is uneconomical and increases the chances of damaging the new saplings when taking out the old trees.

Variations of the shelterwood method include doing the removal steps in a succession of strips. Another more complicated variation is sometimes used when a forest has large clumps of different size trees resulting from thinning, or old openings. This is called the group-shelterwood method. The stand is mapped on the basis of its condition and the shelterwood cuttings are adjusted accordingly.

Shelterwood cutting has been especially successful in the reproduction of both eastern and western white pines; red pine; loblolly, shortleaf and pitch pines in the South; ponderosa pine, especially in the Black Hills portion of its range; Douglas fir in the Rocky Mountains; and eastern hemlock. It has even been used to advantage in stands of heavy-seeded species, especially oaks, and a one-cut variation in spruce-fir forests has long been a common practice.

Shelterwood Advantages...

1 . Many the same as the seed tree method, but with even greater assurance of natural regeneration.
2 . Protects site, seedlings and visual qualities of area. Can be used to meet specific needs, including controlling competition.

3 . The first harvest cut also acts as a thinning in that the seed trees have less competition for several years and can add significant wood volume.
4 . Genetically superior trees can be selected to regenerate the new stand.
5 . If markets are available, cash income is more frequent.

Disadvantages...

1 . Unless regeneration is much too dense, logging, slash disposal and site preparation must be done with care to spare desirable trees.
2 . Logging and management costs are higher.
3 . Markets must exist for small-size logs as well as for lumber.
4 . More complex than clearcutting or seed tree methods.
5 . Only slightly better than clearcutting or seed tree methods for regenerating shallow-rooted species or stands on thin soil.
6 . Requires roads to be efficient.

Selection Cutting — The Dauerwald

Selection cutting is what many people consider "ideal" forestry. In this method, individual trees or small groups are cut at continuous intervals as frequent as five years. This yields the closest thing to a regular income from trees, especially if they are of lumber or veneer quality. At the same time it can leave the woods looking whole and beautiful. Unfortunately, it is one of the most difficult methods to execute properly, and many people who think they are practicing selection cutting are actually "high-grading" their forest and reducing its future value.

In true selection cutting, the stand will contain *all* ages of trees. Perpetuating this condition is called uneven-aged forest management. German foresters think of it as the *Dauerwald*, or "continuous forest." Its advantages are obvious, but it is not without drawbacks. Being aware of these problems can help you practice this method correctly, or may help underscore some of the reasons why the even-aged methods are also "ideal" forestry under the right conditions.

There are two principal kinds of selection methods— single-tree selection and group selection.

In the *single-tree method*, each tree is examined and

SELECTION CUTTING

SELECTION CUTTING ALLOWS CONTINUOUS, UNEVEN-AGED MANAGEMENT

GUIDELINES TO SINGLE-TREE SELECTION CUTTING

In selection cutting, the volume removed should be equal to the volume grown since the last harvest. *Remove the oldest trees (largest diameter) except:*

1. valuable species if still growing rapidly
2. when standing in groups of smaller trees that might be injured or wind thrown if the older one is cut
3. if it is needed nearby as a source of seed
4. if it is important aesthetically or as a wildlife den
5. if its removal would seriously reduce soil stability

Remove trees below the diameter guideline when:

1. defective, very slow-growing, or likely to die before the next harvest
2. severely exposed and likely to be wind thrown after the harvest (e.g., tall, thin trees, especially if shallow-rooted)
3. accidentally broken or severely damaged during logging
4. too dense, or when necessary to release more valuable or vigorous species
5. attempting to alter species composition

harvested as it matures or passes the "point of diminishing returns." This is when its growth slows to the point where more money would be earned by selling it at its current volume than waiting for more wood to be added. Usually this age is determined using the average of many trees in the stand. A specific diameter is then used as a guideline after this age has been determined. This guideline, however, must be considered flexible, as it is often beneficial to remove some additional trees below the diameter limit.

Essentially, the single-tree method combines harvest cuts with improvement cuts and thinnings. The removed trees provide growing space for younger ones. Selection cutting is especially beneficial when trying to regenerate shade- tolerant species such as sugar maple or beech in the East or redcedar in the West.

In *group-selection*, saleable trees of *all* sizes are taken from small areas of about ¼ to ½ acre. From the standpoint of logging, this is more economical than selecting individual trees. Man-hours and equipment can be concentrated in fewer places rather than being spread out over the entire forest. If small enough, the openings still protect the aesthetics and ecological diversity of the forest. However, when they exceed ¼ acre or their width is more than the height of the surrounding trees, they begin to resemble small clearcuts. When this happens, the greatest advantages of selection cutting may be lost.

There are two big problems with selection cutting. The first is the difficulty of balancing the volume of wood removed with the volume being added by the smaller, younger trees that are left. The second involves the kind of trees that will and will not be favored by such a harvesting method. Simply taking out large trees and making improvement cuts is not enough. As one forester

said "affairs may drift aimlessly into chaos as a result of lack of attention to regeneration and distribution of age classes." This has happened in forests of every type in America. Owners have yielded to the temptation of taking the biggest and the best. They think it is selection cutting, but it is really high-grading. To do otherwise requires careful inventories, a sound knowledge of the site and the silvical characteristics of the trees, and accurate estimates of annual growth and yield. This is a tall order. In fact, some professional foresters do not have the skill needed for successful selection cutting. Also, many have a bias against selection cutting because of its complexity and problems.

Through study, high quality professional advice, and long-term ownership, selection cutting can work in many woodlots. For owners devoted to the Dauerwald concept of the forest as a single, continuous organism, further study of this method could result in a satisfying experience.

Selection Cutting Advantages...

1. Maximum protection of site and least alteration of ecological conditions.
2. Most aesthetically pleasing.
3. Excellent wind protection.
4. Reduces likelihood of devastating insect or disease outbreaks and wildfire.
5. Excellent conditions for many types of wildlife.
6. Allows shade tolerant species to be favored over intolerant ones, where desired.
7. Yields regular income and the simultaneous production of a variety of products ranging from firewood to lumber or veneer-quality logs.
8. By including high-value trees, may attract loggers who would not otherwise do improvement cuttings.

Disadvantages...

1. Logging costs are high because the operation is spread out and extra care must be taken to prevent damage. More skill needed.
2. Technically complex. Extreme care needed to keep volume of harvest in balance with annual growth and yield; restraint needed to prevent removal of trees too early or only those of best quality (leading to high-grading and genetic degradation of the stand).
3. Income at any one time may be low to moderate.
4. Trees may have too much room, developing too much taper and too many limbs (knotty lumber).
5. Not well suited for shade intolerant species.
6. The risk of damage from logging to remaining trees is high.
7. A well-planned, permanent road system is necessary.

Diameter Limit Cutting

This method of cutting is mentioned because it is both common and unwise. Often called the D-limit method, it is simply the cutting of all trees that are equal to or above a certain merchantable diameter. This is done regardless of age, species, vigor, form, or the regeneration needs of the stand.

The result of D-limit cutting is a residual stand with a high percentage of poor trees and a species mixture governed by chance, not design. D-limit cutting almost always high-grades the stand, bringing in quick cash but reducing its future value. This is *not* selection cutting, although many people think it is.

The only advantage of cutting based solely on diameters—and this is the reason for its unfortunate wide-spread use—is that it is so easy to use. Little advance planning is needed. The logger is simply turned loose in the woods to cut all trees over the specified size. For anyone with a real interest in his woods, diameter-limit cutting should be shunned like a plague.

Coppicing

There are many other variations on the major harvesting systems, but coppice cutting deserves a special mention here. It is a technique that has been used for centuries in Japan, Europe, and other countries where small-wood products have been important. Early settlers in North America used coppicing in the hardwood forests for producing fuel wood and charcoal. Later this method fell from favor as coal and oil displaced wood as fuel. With today's return to the forests as a source of fuel, coppice cutting is a method worth thinking about.

Many species—especially northern hardwoods—have dormant buds hidden in the lowest parts of their trunks. This is survival insurance that allows trees to develop "vegetatively" rather than through seeds. When wind snaps off a tree or fire sweeps through a stand, the dormant buds close to the ground are triggered to life. Sprouts result from the stumps of the old trees, which in turn grow into new trees.

In coppice cutting, the stand is clearcut and sprouts are relied upon to provide the new forest. In some species, such as aspens, root suckers provide the same effect. For best results, the harvest cut should be made during the late fall or winter when the whole tree is dormant. Food stored in the roots is then at its maximum and can be concentrated in the sprouts when spring arrives. The resulting rate of growth can be quite spectacular, and the new sprouts are well established prior to the fall frosts.

COPPICING

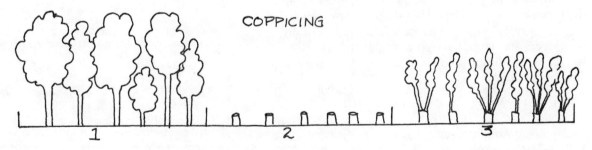

HOW TO CUT FOR COPPICE REPRODUCTION

A LOW, SMOOTH, SLANTING CUT MADE DURING DORMANCY

MOST VIGOROUS SPROUTS

SLANT SHEDS WATER

ROOT COLLAR ZONE

AVOID: HIGH STUMPS AND CUTS THAT COLLECT SNOW OR RAIN

This vigorous growth, combined with multiple stems developing from a single stump, can produce large quantities of trees of firewood or pulpwood proportions in 10 to 20 years. In fact, the main characteristic of this method is its short rotation period. Usually, trees grown from seedlings have much slower initial growth. For rotations over approximately 40 years, the advantages of sprouts give way to those of seedlings. Not only does sprout growth slow at an age when seedling growth gains, rot more easily enters coppice sprouts, resulting in spotty or inadequate distribution of mature trees. Also, the straighter trunks of seedlings may add to the quality of trees destined for lumber or veneer. In fact, when planting is intended as the source of the future forest, stump sprouting becomes a curse. Herbicides, summer logging, or mechanical methods must be used to control the sprouts that would otherwise quickly overtop the seedlings.

Coppicing is best suited for the production of firewood, charcoal, pulp, or small products such as mine props, posts, garden stakes and willow rods. It works particularly well with poplars, oaks, black locust, red maple and redwoods. Most hardwoods will sprout, although some, like beech, cannot be depended upon to reach tree-size. In some cases, such as in red maple or willow swamps, coppicing may be the only logical way to regenerate the stand.

The ability of a tree to produce vigorous sprouts after being cut diminishes with age and diameter. Stands being considered for coppice cutting should be relatively young and growing rapidly.

The biggest argument against the use of coppicing is that there are usually more economic advantages in allowing rapidly growing trees to grow than in cutting them. Usually enough firewood, posts and other small products can be obtained from thinnings or improvement cuttings to justify leaving the best and most rapidly growing trees for later harvest at higher prices. Still, under some conditions, coppice cutting is a harvest method to consider.

Coppicing Advantages...
1 . Relatively short rotations.
2 . Produces trees rapidly.
3 . Relatively high-net income because of the above. Low or no cost for site preparation or planting.
4 . Can retain good genetic features.
5 . Management is relatively simple; less care needed in logging.
6 . Excellent for deer and some other wildlife species.

Disadvantages...
1 . Same as clearcutting except for faster regeneration.
2 . Must have good market for large quantity of small-diameter products.
3 . Thinning is often required.
4 . Not recommended in frost pockets, at high altitudes, or in very cold climates. (Sprouts continue growth over the whole summer and the entire season's growth can be lost due to early frosts.)
5 . Not suitable for growing quality timber trees because of rot potential, crooked butt logs, and other problems.

Best Guides to Silviculture

Silvicultural Systems for the Major Forest Types of the United States. (Agriculture Handbook No. 445). U.S. Forest Service, Washington DC 20250.

For the cost, this concise, 114-page booklet is the best guide to silvicultural treatments of forest stands. For each of the types there is a brief description of its composition; the major insect, disease or other problems to expect; advice on improvement or other intermediate cuttings; and recommendations on harvest cuttings.

Regional Silviculture of the United States edited by John W. Barrett. John Wiley & Sons, New York.

This book is hefty not only in its 551-page size, but also in its price. However, eleven experts describe the forests of 10 regions and go into great (and useful) detail on the same subjects covered only briefly in the Forest Service booklet listed above. It is written for professional foresters, but there is nothing too difficult for the non-professional to understand.

The Practice of Silviculture by Ralph C. Hawley and David M. Smith. John Wiley & Sons, New York.

Another tome for professionals, but equally useful to the serious student of forests. This one goes into the mechanics of each silvicultural treatment. It is definitely not light reading, but if a section of it is applicable to your management objectives, it will provide a valuable source of detailed information.

Choices in Silviculture for American Forests. Society of American Foresters, 5400 Grosvenor Lane, Washington, DC 20014.

This one is written for the non-professional. It is a slim 80-pager with nice art work and general treatment of nine widely distributed forest types. Its greatest and a heavy virtues are its low cost and a heavy emphasis on multiple use of woodlands. In fact, it was written in cooperation with The Wildlife Society and offers advice on caring for wildlife habitat as well as forest growth.

See appendix for abbreviated *"Guide to Regeneration Cuttings By Regions and Major Forest Types"*

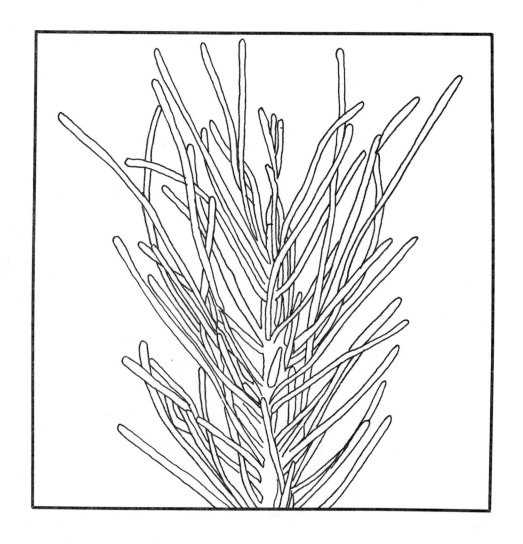

6 Planting
and
Improving the Woodlot

It is almost a marvel that trees should live to become the oldest of living things. Fastened in one place, their struggle is incessant and severe.

—Enos A. Mills

Planting and Seeding

Consider yourself lucky if the condition of your woodlot allows regeneration through the combination of an appropriate harvesting system and sprouts, root suckers or a natural seed source. This is natural regeneration, and it means little or no investment on your part.

Unfortunately, the seed source is often not there, or the species is not suited to coppicing. It is also increasingly common to own a woodlot that has become genetically debilitated. This results from decades of highgrading— taking the best and leaving the worst. Also, it is often considered desirable to speed up the process of getting a stand established, either to shorten the time to the next harvest, or to give the young trees a better chance of competing against brush, grass, drought, birds, mice or the myriad other things lurking at soil level. In any of these situations, artificial regeneration becomes a must.

The choice in artificial regeneration is between direct seeding and planting. Seeding has the advantage of lower costs, but the major disadvantage of spacing problems. Even if seeds are planted individually or in groups at desired intervals, their ability to survive is much more precarious than it is with seedlings. Coatings of animal repellents on the seeds have helped improve their chances in recent years, and if seeding is your choice, be sure to pay the extra price for properly treated seeds. The other disadvantage in seeding is the extra years it takes for the seeds to sprout and grow.

Preparing the Site

If ever there were a babe in the wilderness it has to be the young seedling at soil level. There it stands under the constant threat of being gnawed upon by rodents or rabbits, trampled by grazers or people passing by, heaved from the soil by frost action, burned, drowned, shaded or starved. Seedlings need all the help they can get.

Growing Your Own Seedlings from Seed

For the forest owner with time, patience, a green thumb and a love of watching things grow, home grown seedlings may be a way to both reduce costs and have the advantages of seedlings. The technicalities are beyond the scope of this book, but some inexpensive publications that can get you started are:

"Collecting Forest Tree Seeds and Growing Your Own Seedlings"
USDA Forest Service
Pacific Northwest Region
319 SW Pine Street
P.O. Box 3623
Portland, OR 97208

"Raising Forest Tree Seedlings at Home"
A Pacific Northwest Cooperative Extension publication available from the land grant colleges in Washington, Oregon and Idaho (see appendix).

"Hardwood Nurseryman's Guide"
USDA Forest Service Agricultural Handbook No. 473
U.S. Government Printing Office
Washington, DC 20402

"How to Root Tree Cuttings"
USDA Forest Service
Southern Forest Experiment Station
701 Loyola Avenue
New Orleans, LA 70113

Every threat to a new plantation should be considered and minimized. Posting the area, fencing out cattle, and reducing piles of brush that harbor rabbits and rodents may be necessary. Avoiding heavy clay soil or other unsuitable planting sites will also help. But of all the challenges, the greatest one is to maximize the chances that the seedlings get their full share of moisture and nutrients from the soil.

In most cases, planting is done on recently logged areas or old fields, so the job is to reduce competition for the seedlings by removing as much brush, grass and weeds as possible. Properly preparing the site is an essential first step or your entire investment of time and money may be for naught. Here are some common ways of beating the competition.

Fire

Used with care, controlled fire is a good way to clean up logging debris (called slash). Using it for other site preparation is controversial and will depend largely on local conditions. Its biggest drawback — besides air pollution — is the uncertainty of its effects upon the soil. When a fire burns too hot, it may destroy the moisture-holding humus. Also, it usually does not kill the roots of brush and grass, so the relief from competition is brief, if at all. Another problem is that fire depletes the available nitrogen supply, sending it up in smoke. On some sites this may have the offsetting benefit of neutralizing acidic soils and making inorganic nutrients available as soluble salts. The effect, however, may at best be temporary because the nutrients are rapidly leached so deeply into the soil that they are beyond the reach of seedlings or are washed away entirely before they even enter the soil. For advice on using fire, contact your local service forester.

Machines

Bulldozers or farm tractors, usually in combination with rootrakes, plows, heavy disc harrows, choppers or other specially-designed devices are included in this method. In recently used areas with only light ground cover, discing may be all that is necessary. On dry, grass-covered sites, scraping off the sod may be required. Often, simply bulldozing logging slash into piles or windrows to burn or rot away is enough to scarify the soil and clear light brush cover in advance of planting. Whatever is used, it is usually necessary to delay planting until the disturbed soil has settled, reducing chances of air pockets and damaging movements of soil. Because this work is usually done on contract, it is expensive, but it is often the best alternative.

Chemicals

Herbicides are controversial and can be dangerous, not only to the user, but to the environment. However, extensive acreage can be covered quickly from the air, or more slowly but under closer control from the ground either by mechanical sprayers or hand applicators. Either way, herbicides are often the most cost-effective method. Applications are usually made following the first flush of plant growth. At this point food reserves in the roots are low, and the new leaves have just started to manufacture and pump back replenishment. Weeds and brush are most vulnerable at this time, and chances are good that even their roots can be killed. An applicator's license may be required to use herbicides on all but a small area. Extension agents can provide details and recommend the safest brands that have proven effective in your area.

"Safest" usually means the one with the shortest residual life.

Other Alternatives

For both economical and ecological reasons, it is worth looking for other ways to prepare a site for planting. These include clearing by hand using machetes, pulaskis or similar cutting and grubbing tools. This is sometimes possible on small areas when the only thing needed is for the sod to be scraped off at the spots where seedlings will be planted. In some areas of the East, grazing cattle have been used successfully to discourage jungle-like invasions of honeysuckle. Goats are virtual brush-clearing machines and might also be considered.

Sources of Seedlings

Seedlings can be obtained through a variety of commercial and government-operated nurseries. Sometimes state or provincial stock has strings attached requiring that it must be used only for pulp, pole, lumber production, windbreaks, or watershed protection. However, these seedlings are sold at quite modest prices, thanks to the largess of the federal government who helps pay the bills. In the U.S., it is a feature of the Clarke-McNary Act of 1924 which, like the tax incentives described on page 33, were designed to encourage private landowners to plant and maintain trees. Prohibited uses of the subsidized seedlings include ornamental or shade tree plantings, wildlife food or cover, and in some states, Christmas tree production. Application forms are available from state forestry offices, Cooperative Extension or the Soil Conservation Service.

Many states are engaged in tree improvement programs to develop planting stock with faster growth, better form, greater resistance to insects and diseases, and other desirable characteristics. A number of nurseries now offer genetically improved stock for sale, and when it's available, the use of improved strains to match your planting site is one of the best decisions you can make.

There are over 300 forest tree nurseries in the United States and nearly as many in Canada. A state by state listing of private and government sources of seedlings is compiled periodically and may be obtained for the asking from:

"Directory of Forest Tree Nurseries in the United States"
USDA Forest Service — State and Private Forestry
P.O. Box 2417
Washington, D.C. 20013

Canadians may obtain this information from:
Forestry Service
Environment Canada
Ottawa, Ontario K1A 1G5

HAND TOOLS FOR TREE PLANTING

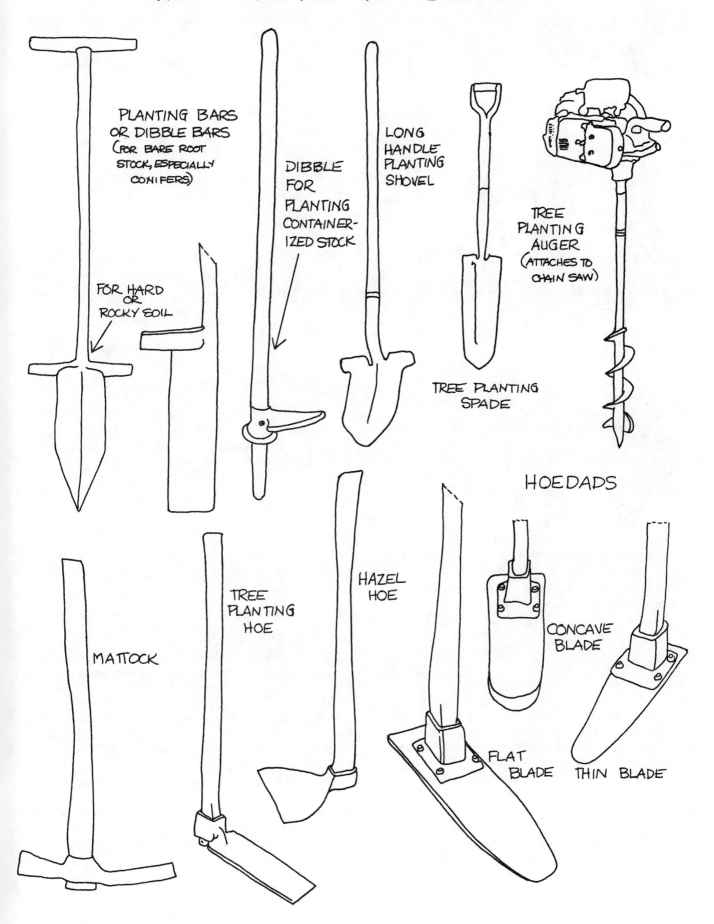

PLANTING BARS OR DIBBLE BARS (FOR BARE ROOT STOCK, ESPECIALLY CONIFERS)

FOR HARD OR ROCKY SOIL

DIBBLE FOR PLANTING CONTAINER-IZED STOCK

LONG HANDLE PLANTING SHOVEL

TREE PLANTING AUGER (ATTACHES TO CHAIN SAW)

TREE PLANTING SPADE

HOEDADS

MATTOCK

TREE PLANTING HOE

HAZEL HOE

CONCAVE BLADE

FLAT BLADE

THIN BLADE

SEEDLING TERMS

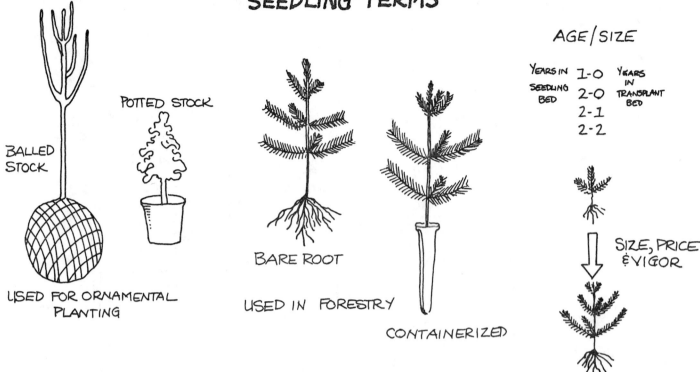

BALLED STOCK

POTTED STOCK

USED FOR ORNAMENTAL PLANTING

BARE ROOT

USED IN FORESTRY

CONTAINERIZED

AGE/SIZE

Years in Seedling Bed 1-0 Years in Transplant Bed
2-0
2-1
2-2

SIZE, PRICE & VIGOR

Spacing

Proper spacing is important because it determines the total cost of your seedlings. Eventually it will also affect the amount of light reaching the ground. This, in turn, helps determine what understory will come in and how much of it there will be, and whether the stand will be stunted from crowding, limby from the freedom of too much space, or disciplined by well-spaced neighbors into the straight growth that yields good poles, lumber and fine veneer. Close spacing, such as 4 x 4 or 5 x 5, is suitable for erosion control or Christmas trees, but 6 x 6 or 8 x 8 is often recommended for timber purposes.

If all seedlings survived, any plantation, except Christmas trees, would quickly become overcrowded. A certain amount of mortality is not only acceptable but beneficial. For example, if trees for timber are planted at 8 x 8 spacing and mortality is a rather common 25 percent, there are still 500 trees per acre. Even at this number, thinnings will be needed and pre-harvest products such as posts or firewood can be obtained. The danger in starting out with wider spacing, such as 12 x 12, is that when normal mortality occurs, large gaps will result and brush can invade more easily.

Too much initial mortality, even with close spacing, will have the same effect as normal mortality at wide spacing. This often means replanting will be needed in the openings—an essential but expensive proposition at best. The keys to keeping down mortality are care for the planting stock and careful planting. One study showed that owner-planted trees had nearly double the survival rate as those that were contract-planted; cultivated areas had over twice the survival as areas not cultivated; and 33 percent more seedlings survived when hand-planted instead of machine-planted.

The best guides to spacing your seedlings are local experience and the intended use of your trees. This chart will show how many to order, depending on what spacing you decide to use.

Spacing (in feet)	Trees Per Acre
4 x 4	2722
5 x 5	1742
6 x 6	1210
6 x 10	726
8 x 8	680
10 x 10	430

Planting Seedlings

In the South, the Midwest and on the gentler slopes of the East, most large-scale tree planting is done by machine. Usually one or more people sit on a tractor-pulled device and insert seedlings into a slit opened by a plow-like blade. A pair of closely-spaced wheels then pass over the slit, closing it on the roots. Up to 10,000 trees per day can be planted this way under favorable conditions. This machinery, however, is a poor investment for the small landowner unless it is also used to supplement income through rentals or contracting. For most landowners, rental or contracting is the most efficient method of large scale planting.

There is one inexpensive, semi-mechanized method of planting available to anyone with a farm tractor. It consists of a home-made planting bar mounted on the outside rim of the wheel. With each revolution of the wheel a slit is punched into the soil. If the wheel is 12 feet in circumference, protruding blades on both ends of the bar would place holes every 6 feet. Workers walking

Each year millions of Americans turn their thoughts to trees at least *once* each year. And that day, usually set by the state forester, is a good guide to the best time for planting. Arbor Day, celebrated by school children and community groups since 1872, is most often scheduled in late April. Exceptions are:

January — Florida, Louisiana, Texas
February — Alabama, Arizona, Georgia, Mississippi, Nevada (southern), Oklahoma
March — Arkansas, California, Kansas, New Mexico, North Carolina, Virginia
Early April — Oregon
May — Alaska, Maine, North Dakota, Vermont
November — Hawaii, Guam
December — South Carolina

Of course, local site conditions may dictate earlier or later dates. The goal is to plant just as the growing season begins. This usually coincides with the rainy season. In the West, containerized stock allows planting to be extended well into the drier months of summer if necessary.

Arbor Day was founded by J. Sterling Morton, a Nebraska pioneer and then secretary of the Nebraska Territory. Like many plains settlers, Morton longed for more trees. After successfully landscaping his own farm near Nebraska City, he proposed to the State Board of Agriculture that an annual planting day be established. To gain public attention, he suggested a prize of $100 to the county that properly planted the largest number of trees, and a farm library valued at $25 to the individual who did the same. The result was that on April 10, 1872, Nebraskans planted more than one million trees.

Other states followed Nebraska's lead and a national Arbor Day is often proclaimed for the last Friday in April. Information and ideas for Arbor Day may be obtained from an organization devoted to keeping alive this wonderful celebration of life: National Arbor Day Foundation, Arbor Lodge 100, Nebraska City, NE 68410.

"Other holidays repose upon the past, Arbor Day proposes for the future."

— J. Sterling Morton

along behind then insert seedlings and close the slit with a shovel or boot. Plans for this clever device are available from Cornell University (see appendix).

A HOME MADE, WHEEL MOUNTED PLANTING BAR

Most owners of small acreages, especially on hilly land, will find hand-planting to be the best method. A variety of special tools are available for this purpose, but a regular old shovel is usually best for the job. The basics of using these tools are easier to illustrate than to describe and can be seen on the accompanying pages. Depending

on the soil and your physical condition, you should be able to plant up to 700 seedlings a day with a dibble or planting bar. Hoes and hole-digging may take twice as long, and the average for most woodland owners is about 300-400. The thing to be more concerned about is how well you plant, not how many you plant, and the survival of your seedlings. For this reason, a little extra time spent with each seedling is one of the best investments you can make.

One of the biggest causes of seedling deaths is that roots become dry during planting. In conifers, even a few seconds of dryness will kill their smallest roots, called root hairs. From the moment you receive your planting stock, keep the roots moist and well protected from direct sunshine and air flows. Plant immediately, if possible. Otherwise, for short term storage of dormant seedlings:

- Use an old refrigerator if available, keeping the bundled seedlings at 30° to 45° F
- If refrigeration is not available, leave the trees in their shipping packages. Check to make sure the protective material around the roots is moist, and re-dampen if necessary. Then store in a shaded place out of the wind. Cover the bundles with snow, if available.

When ready to plant, carry seedlings in a bucket or other container. Keep the roots wet at *all* times, but don't use pure water. A mud, moss or sawdust mixture is best. Remove one seedling at a time for planting.

Another danger point related to drying is in the

planting hole itself. Great care should be taken that no air pockets are left. This includes making sure you fill in the "second" hole when using a planting bar (see illustration).

Many of the hazards of planting bare root stock can be avoided by using containerized seedlings. In some cases the container is biodegradable and can be placed directly in the hole. Otherwise, the seedling is gently pulled from its tapered growth chamber and placed in the hole. To save on shipping costs, some nursery operators remove the containers for you, then carefully bundle the seedlings. In any case, the roots should remain coated and undisturbed in their own blocks of soil. One poke with a dibble bar makes the hole, providing a rapid and easy planting process. Even a shovel hole is easier to dig and fill using this stock, and will usually result in a better growing environment. Containerized stock may cost a little more and be a little bulkier to handle, but the advantages may well outweigh the drawbacks.

Will Planting Pay?

The answer depends on your purpose. Certainly for the enjoyment of watching trees grow, or for windbreaks, wildlife, soil stabilizaiton or visual enhancement, there is no way to measure the results of planting in terms of dollars. However, if financial returns are important, then it is essential to carefully consider the costs and expected income resulting from planting.

Before anything else, the soil and other site conditions should be checked by a service forester or the Soil Conservation Service. Next, the species should be carefully selected to match the site and your planting objectives. Finally, a financial projection should be made using the best estimates possible. Extension foresters may have formulas to help, and even computer programs in some cases. Or you can do it yourself using a more simplistic method presented in the cost/income chart offered on page 145 for Christmas tree production. A few modifications will be necessary based on the use you plan to make of your trees.

Time Before First Harvest

Product	Number of Years Before Useable (Average Site)
Christmas Trees	5-12
Firewood	6-15
Posts, Poles	15-25
Pulpwood	15-20⅓
Sawlogs, Veneer	25-40⅓

Fertilizing

As dangerous as it is to make general statements, the conclusion on fertilizing plantations and woodlots is that it just doesn't pay off. If the site is so nutrient-deficient that fertilizing is absolutely necessary, then that site

should probably not have priority for planting or growing trees for harvest. Better that it be used for wildlife cover or something else.

Financial considerations aside, there are positive things to say about fertilizing plantations. Adequate nutrition can stimulate better growth, increase the density and desired color of foliage, and sometimes provide a higher degree of disease and drought resistance. In Christmas tree or holly plantations, the benefits of fertilizing often outweigh the costs. Another time fertilization usually pays is when the site is deficient in one or more trace elements that would increase productivity significantly.

The active ingredients of most inorganic, commercial fertilizers are expressed in a three-part number indicating the three chemicals needed in largest quantities for plant growth. These chemicals are always listed in the same order—nitrogen (N), phosphorus (P), and potassium (K). For example, a general-purpose fertilizer often recommended for ornamental evergreens and windbreak trees is:

10-8-6, which means   10% N (Nitrogen)
                        8% P (Phosphorus)
                        6% K (Potassium)

Most of the remaining percent consists of neutral bulk materials. However, since there are a total of 13 nutrients essential for plant life, many fertilizers will also contain all or some of these. Because only minute amounts are needed, they are called "trace elements."

Trace Elements
Calcium
Magnesium
Sulfur
Chlorine
Iron
Manganese
Copper
Boron
Zinc
Molybdenum

In the U.S., if you decide to fertilize, soil samples may be sent to the land grant institution in your state for analysis. Your local Cooperative Extension Service Office can provide more details, including how to collect your samples. With an analysis, a commercial fertilizer can be mixed to the exact proportions needed to supply any missing or inadequate elements. This prevents buying components of fertilizer already well supplied in the soil. The result is that you don't waste money on what you don't need.

Organic fertilizers, such as manure, green vegetable wastes or compost, provide mostly nitrogen. This is usually quite beneficial since nitrogen is most often the nutrient in short supply. Sawdust, wood chips and peat moss have little nutrient value, and can even have the detrimental effect of tying up nitrogen or other elements already in the soil, making them unavailable to the tree roots.

HOW TO PLANT SEEDLINGS

SHOVEL
(THE METHOD MOST RECOMMENDED FOR BEST QUALITY)

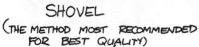

1.

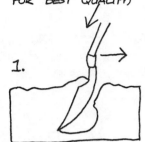

2.

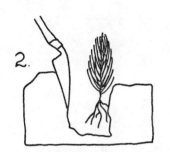

3.

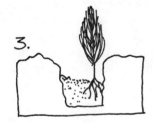

4.

5.

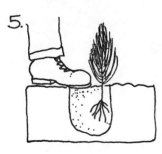

PLANTING BAR

1.
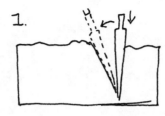

2.

3.
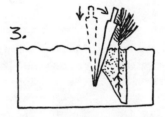

THIS STEP CLOSES THE SLIT AND HOLDS THE SEEDLING IN PLACE PRIOR TO MAIN STEP OF FIRMLY PACKING THE SOIL)

4.
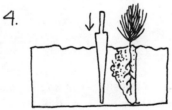

5.

THE PACKING STEP

6.

BE SURE TO FILL THE SECOND HOLE

MATTOCK OR HOE

1.
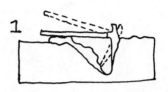

2.

3.
4.
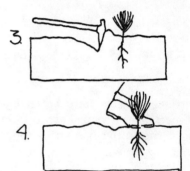

CAUTION: WITH ANY METHOD, TAMP THE SOIL FIRMLY AFTER PLANTING TO REMOVE AIR POCKETS AND ASSURE ROOT CONTACT WITH THE SOIL.

61

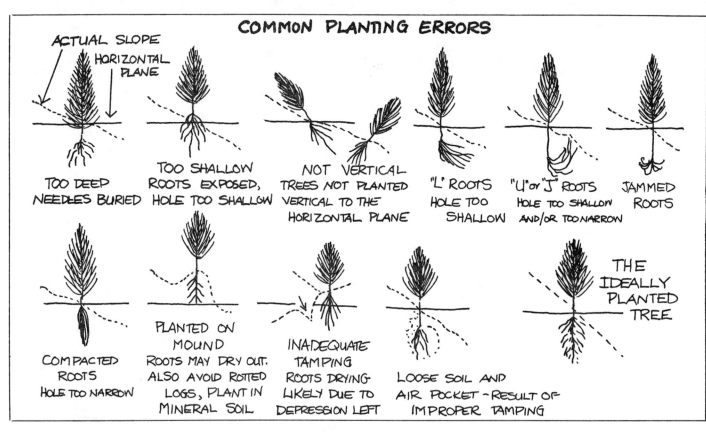

COMMON PLANTING ERRORS

ACTUAL SLOPE
HORIZONTAL PLANE

TOO DEEP
NEEDLES BURIED

TOO SHALLOW
ROOTS EXPOSED,
HOLE TOO SHALLOW

NOT VERTICAL
TREES NOT PLANTED
VERTICAL TO THE
HORIZONTAL PLANE

"L" ROOTS
HOLE TOO
SHALLOW

"U"or"J" ROOTS
HOLE TOO SHALLOW
AND/OR TOO NARROW

JAMMED
ROOTS

COMPACTED
ROOTS
HOLE TOO NARROW

PLANTED ON
MOUND
ROOTS MAY DRY OUT.
ALSO AVOID ROTTED
LOGS, PLANT IN
MINERAL SOIL

INADEQUATE
TAMPING
ROOTS DRYING
LIKELY DUE TO
DEPRESSION LEFT

LOOSE SOIL AND
AIR POCKET – RESULT OF
IMPROPER TAMPING

THE
IDEALLY
PLANTED
TREE

Fertilizer tablets have become popular in recent years, especially with small acreage planters. One tablet is placed in the bottom of each planting hole and is said to feed seedlings for up to two years. Some have been known to "burn" the trees' roots, but safer versions are available that advertisers claim have corrected this problem. The tablets are not expensive and they prevent inadvertent fertilization of weeds and brush between tree rows. As illustrated, they can also be used to give large trees an added boost.

Improving the Stand

There is much to be done in the woodlot between planting and maturity. How much is done depends on the type and condition of the forest, but even more on why you own it. If your **reasons are** strictly financial, it may be important to do as little as possible, carefully seeking a balance where further investment of time or labor no longer pays a return in increased wood production. To most people, however, the joy of working the woodlot and producing a fine stand of trees is reward of its own. For these aficionados, timber stand improvement, known as TSI, is a continuous process. And TSI means exercise, health and satisfaction just as much as it means straight, taller, and more vigorous trees.

Weeding and Cleaning

Of the many joys of TSI, *weeding* is not one of them. This is tedious, back-breaking work that meets hardly anyone's standards of pleasure. Weeding, as its name implies, means pulling or otherwise removing the weeds and unwanted tree species from the immediate vicinity of newly planted seedlings. This drudgery is best avoided by scarifying the site prior to planting, giving planted trees a year or two head start over their competition. Otherwise, if the grass and brush are thick, you have no

TIME RELEASE
FERTILIZER TABLETS

THE PLACEMENT OF TIME
RELEASE FERTILIZER TABLETS
FOR...

SEEDLINGS &
TRANSPLANTS

3-4 YEAR
OLD TREES

MATURE
TREES

choice but to hoe, mow, cultivate, pull or carefully spray with an appropriate herbicide. Competition for moisture, and in the case of some species, light, is costly in terms of rate of growth or even survival. This may make weeding necessary. If so, the cost must be borne over a period of time second only to the cost of the planting operation itself. Prevent it when you can.

Cleaning is sometimes considered the same as weeding, but I think of it as a similar operation later in the life of the stand when the trees are saplings (usually considered under 4 inches DBH). It, too, is the removal of unwanted species, but now the problem is not grass, but other woody vegetation. Thus, the term "brush control."

In many areas of the U.S. and Canada, brush control is a major problem. In the South, for example, the war on hardwoods in pine plantations is legend. In the Pacific Northwest, massive brushfields on federal lands have become the object of public controversies. Civil disobedience has even invaded the woodlands as citizens seek to prevent the widespead spraying of herbicides on these brushy areas. Unfortunately, the application of herbicides that kill hardwood competition without harming conifers is usually the most efficient method of brush control. When hardwoods are the favored species, brush cutting usually becomes the only alternative.

Guidelines for 'Cleaning' a Young Stand

- Clean before unwanted growth begins to suppress the trees to be favored. However, cleaning too soon will allow resprouting to catch up to the trees and make cleaning necessary again.
- To minimize resprouting, clean in mid-summer when food reserves in the roots are at their low point.
- Tolerant species and rapidly growing species need cleaning less than intolerants and slow growers.
- When cleaning by mechanical means, also take out the favored species if it will improve the stand. For example, thin out crowded patches and remove crooked or damaged stems.
- In a mixed stand, first prepare a list of preferred species so, when possible, the least preferred are first to be cut or poisoned.

Thinning

Of the many things that can be done to improve woodlots, *thinning* is often the treatment needed most. In New York, for example, it has been estimated that over 90 percent of all plantations on private land need to be thinned. The need is equally as great in many other parts of the United States and Canada.

Thinning is a treatment that can pay off handsomely in both immediate income and in greater yields in the years ahead. It can also help keep your woodlot healthy, since faster growing trees are less vulnerable to the attacks of insects and diseases.

The objective of thinning is to concentrate the increase of wood volume in a smaller number of trees. Scientists are still arguing about it, but it appears that

tree height and total volume of wood produced is fairly constant in a given stand. When some trees are removed, the volume that would have been added to their diameter is instead added to the diameters of the uncut trees. The result is increased diameter growth, and this faster growth is on trees selected as future crop trees because of their species, straightness, soundness and other desirable features.

Thinning makes especially good sense on high quality sites and in young, even-aged stands when growth is vigorous. Under such conditions, diameter growth can be increased by one inch or more per decade. This may not seem like much until multiplied over the length of each log and the number of trees in a stand. The added dollar value can be highly profitable for either hardwoods or conifers on all but the poorest of sites.

From the financial point of view, there are two kinds of thinnings—precommercial and commercial. Precommercial means the stand is thinned when the removed trees are still too young to be sold for anything. This was once a big deterrent to thinning. However, as our country urbanizes and wood products become more valuable, it is increasingly easy to find a market even for the smallest trees. Healthy markets for small trees have been the rule in Europe for centuries, and the time will come here when "precommercial" thinning is a term of the past. The demand for posts, stakes, charcoal and especially firewood are hastening that day. Incentive payments from the government for thinning and TSI make thinnings even more attractive.

When to Thin

Failure to thin leads to slow growth and stagnation. Once stagnated, many trees will not respond to the release of thinning. They are beyond help. It is important, therefore, to thin before competition drastically slows growth. This can be monitored by checking growth rings with an increment borer, or by simply watching the crowns. As the crowns get closer together, shade causes the lower branches to die. When the living crown is less than half the height of a tree, the tree is getting too crowded. If it is less than one third, it is probably too late. In plantations, the first thinnings are usually needed at about age 10-20.

The time of year usually doesn't matter in thinning, but there are exceptions. Freshly cut pine trees often attract insects such as *Ips* bark beetles that can harm the uncut trees, a disaster if their numbers are large enough. Fall and winter cutting can reduce this problem in areas where the threat exists.

How to Thin

Thinning scientifically can be very complex, requiring the services of a skilled forester. His tasks would be to determine the existing basal area of the stand, to find out what research or past experience has shown to be the ideal basal area for trees of the given species and size growing under similar conditions, then to devise a method of removing the number of trees whose basal area

THINNING PAYS

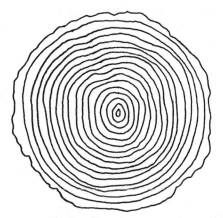

THE TREE ON THE LEFT WAS GROWN UNDER IDEAL SPACING CONDITIONS. ON THE RIGHT, A TREE OF THE SAME AGE GROWN IN A STAND THAT SHOULD HAVE BEEN THINNED.

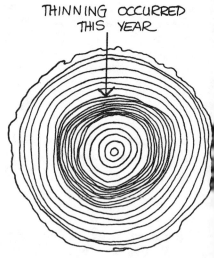

THINNING OCCURRED THIS YEAR

THE RESULTS OF THINNING SHOW CLEARLY. THESE ANNUAL RINGS TELL THE STORY OF A TREE THAT RESPONDED NICELY TO THE REMOVAL OF SURROUNDING COMPETITION

Rules of Thumb for Thinning

1. **D + X Rule**

   D + X = Desired average distance between trees, in feet

   D = Average DBH in inches of pre-thinned stand

   X = Factor between 2 and 6

   For X, use: 2 for conservative thinning of slow-growing tolerant species such as spruce or balsam, and for redwood and Douglas-fir on the West coast.

   3 for mixed western stands of white pine, tamarack, Douglas-fir and ponderosa pine.

   4 for northern pines such as white or red pine up to 8 inches DBH; and for ponderosa pine stands in the West.

   6 for pole-size, second growth southern pines.

   For other species, check with a local forester.

2. **D × X Rule**

   The X factor approximates basal area and is more consistent regardless of diameter. For example, an X factor 1.75 = a basal area of approximately 80 sq. ft. Thus, if the desired stocking is 80 sq. ft. per acre, 1.75 is a useable factor. 1.75 is recommended in Appalachian and southern regions. Check with a forester for other areas or specific species.

3.

   Tree Height Divided by X Rule

   This rule has been used successfully in Lake State conifers.

   For X, use: 6 or 7 for tolerant species (closer spacing)

   5 or 6 for intermediate tolerants

   4 or 5 for intolerants (wider spacing)

is equal to the difference.

At the other extreme is a series of easy-to-use rules of thumb. Every forester has his favorite, and none are very satisfactory. Several that are listed by the Society of American Foresters are shown in the accompanying box.

So much for the ideal and for rules of thumb. Here is a suggested method that is easy to use and provides most of the benefits of proper thinning. The first step is to realize that in an even-aged stand grown for sawlogs or veneer, the number of trees remaining at harvest time should be:

| Hardwoods | 110-115 per acre |
| Conifers | 150-225 per acre |

Most planted stands contain 400 to 1,000 stems when young, or 2,000 or more when naturally reproduced. Therefore, even when taking natural mortality into account, it is plain to see that a drastic reduction by thinning is needed.

The second step can be taken in one of two ways. The simplest is to go periodically through the stand opening up the canopy so that all well-formed trees have approximately 3-5 feet around their crowns. Some people also clear out smaller trees below the crown line, but the time and cost is probably not worth the effort. The smaller trees are usually not serious competitors and will die or stagnate on their own in many kinds of stands.

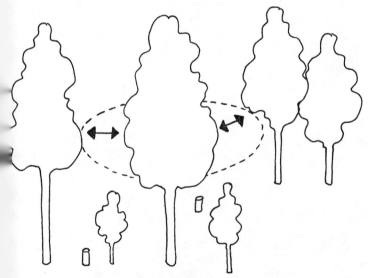

3-5 FEET AROUND CROWN OF FUTURE CROP TREE

Repeated thinnings, coordinated when possible with the demand for firewood or other products will eventually bring the number of stems down to the optimum for maximum growth and harvest.

Another way to thin is to select and mark the final crop trees early in the life of the stand. These, of course, should be the best formed, most vigorous, and of the preferred mix of species desired in the final harvest. On the average, they will be spaced about 19 feet apart, or as close as 10 feet in the case of some conifers. After marking by visual inspection and estimation of space, the actual number-per-acre can be checked by a plot or strip cruise over a small, but randomly selected, portion of the stand. Once the future crop trees are selected and marked with tree paint, tags, or plastic ribbon, all other trees can be removed at 5 to 10 year intervals. To reduce your workload, or if there is a market for "cut-your-own" firewood, divide the woodlot into sections so that some thinning is done each year. By dividing it systematically, the first section will be ready for thinning again the year after the last section is cut.

Since the goal of thinning is to concentrate growth on the best trees, spacing can not be the only consideration. All rules of thumb aside, good judgment must be used in deciding which trees to cut out and which to leave. In an area with a high number of defects, spacing may be wider than the ideal. On an excellent site with a high number of vigorous co-dominant trees, you may want to leave a few more. It is also a good idea to leave more at the edge of openings. Do not remove more than one-third of the trees at once, except in cases of serious overcrowding. Too much sunlight will cause the crowns of the crop trees to become too large with limbs that reduce the value of clear lumber or veneer. Under ideal conditions there will be enough room for maximum growth, but enough competition to force this growth to go straight up, and to shade lower limbs so they die and fall off (natural pruning).

Thinning a bit on the conservative side also helps prevent drying of the soil and the invasion of brush or weed species, as well as assuring future interim crops and providing insurance in case the intended crop trees are prematurely damaged or destroyed.

Thinning by careful selection, especially early in the life of a stand, is time consuming and expensive, since the investment in added growth must be carried over such a long period of time. Logging individually selected trees adds to the difficulties, particularly when it is done within the rows of a neatly planted plantation. These problems can be overcome with small logging equipment or horses, and the costs can often be defrayed through government cost-sharing or the sale of firewood and other small diameter products. Still, a thinning well done must be a labor of love, especially if it is precommercial. If not viewed as an investment in future quality, you will be better off staying indoors and watching television.

For those with an eye to efficiency, *strip thinning* is an alternative method that should be investigated. It is suitable in conifer plantations where the trees are in straight, evenly-spaced rows. It simply requires following a set pattern, such as removing certain rows, or every other tree. The removal of every third row, then every other tree, is a good pattern and is illustrated here.

An advantage of strip thinning, besides being simple and inexpensive, is that the thinned rows become access roads. Logging becomes more efficient, especially by felling all the trees in the same direction. Be sure, of course, to cut the stumps as low as possible so vehicles can pass easily. The biggest disadvantage of this method is that since all trees are *not* created equal, even if planted at the same time, strip thinning does not allow you to favor the most vigorous or best formed individuals.

PROVIDING GROWING ROOM

WEEDING—AT SEEDLING STAGE

CLEANING— AT SAPLING STAGE
(UNDER 4" DBH)

THINNING #1—AT AGE 20-30

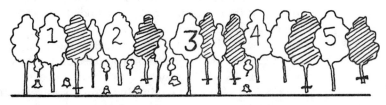

THINNING #2—AT AGE 40

THINNING #3—AT AGE 50

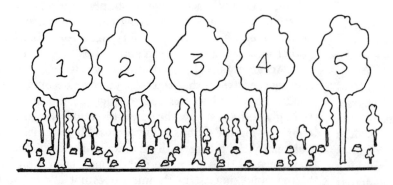

THE STAND AT HARVEST

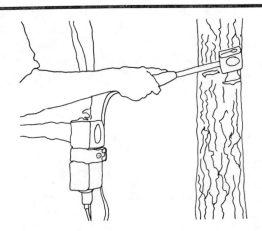
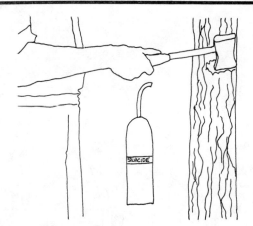

Precommercial Thinning with Silvicides

When trees to be thinned are small or when no market exists, the injection of tree-killing chemicals called silvicides offers an efficient and safe method of thinning. Left, "Hypo-Hatchet" + is used to inject a measured amount of silvicide. Up to 500 trees per hour can be treated by one person. Right, a squirt bottle is used to apply the chemical into a cup or frill chopped with a regular hatchet. This method is slower but requires no extra investment in equipment. Hypo-Hatchet + is manufactured by TSI Company (see appendix). Silvicides are available through forestry suppliers and local farm stores. Consult local foresters for brands that will work best for you.

STRIP METHOD THINNING

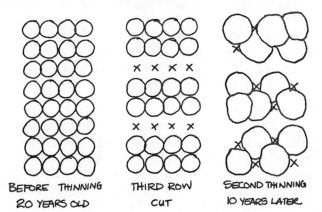

BEFORE THINNING 20 YEARS OLD   THIRD ROW CUT   SECOND THINNING 10 YEARS LATER

Improvement Cutting

Improvement cutting, as its name implies, is an excellent method of improving the quality of a stand. By definition, it is a technique used in stands past the sapling stage and it means removing immature trees of poor form, defective trees, or undesirable species. Certainly, spacing is considered, but since it is usually a technique used in uneven-aged stands, it may be appropriate to leave shade tolerant trees under the crowns of larger ones. The main concerns are *form* and vigor of the remaining trees.

Improvement cutting should be viewed as a sorting over of your trees. Often trees should be left temporarily that are not suitable as final crop trees. As with thinning in even-aged stands, not all the excess trees can be taken out at one time or the woods will be opened too severely. This would invite brush and vines, and make the stand vulnerable to drying, ice or snow damage, and windfall.

Do improvement cutting gradually, like an artist slowly sculpting the final shape of his creation.

This method of timber stand improvement is particularly well suited to valuable hardwood forests. As with other methods of improving the stand, financial assistance may be available.

Pruning

For a young stand of trees destined to produce lumber, veneer, or poles, *pruning* may be a reasonable investment. Little equipment is needed, so the investment is one of time only. The dividends, both aesthetically and monetarily, can be worthwhile.

Pruning of forest trees, as opposed to fruit or shade trees, is simply the removal of lower branches. When branches are cut flush with the bark, subsequent diameter growth engulfs the stub and produces clear, knot-free wood outward from that point. This, of course, doesn't happen overnight. At least 10 years are required for the growth to be sufficient for clear boards to be cut from the log. In the case of poles, pruning should be done about 5 years before harvest.

Besides providing clearer, stronger lumber or veneer, pruned trees are delightfully easy and quick to log. All together this may mean prices to the landowner four times or more higher than for unpruned trees. Another benefit is fire prevention. There are few sadder sights than to watch half a generation of work and love go up in flames. By pruning an entire plantation, a ground fire can pass harmlessly through a middle-aged stand. Bark protects the cambium of the lower trunk, and without limbs from ground level to canopy, there is no "wick" to carry the flames to the more vulnerable crown.

Pruning is best suited to young conifers and those hardwoods capable of producing high quality wood. Eastern pine, walnut and black cherry are good examples. Preferably, the trees should be 3 to 6 inches

67

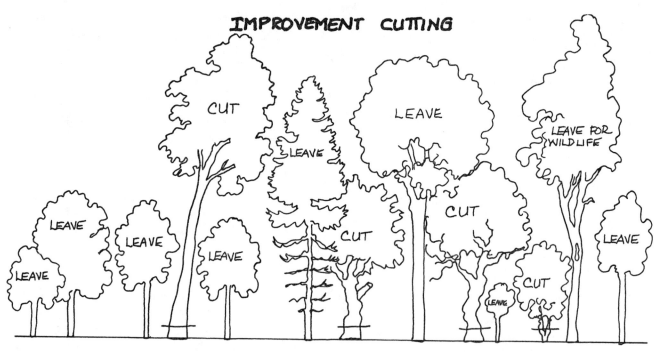

DBH (about 12 to 20 feet tall) when first pruned, so there is plenty of time to produce clear wood.

For the benefit of fire protection in areas where the danger is high, all the trees in a plantation should be pruned. Trees around the edges are an exception unless the fire potential is so extreme as to make this necessary. Otherwise, protection against the drying effects of wind and sun is a good tradeoff for the lower grade wood produced on those trees. This row of cover is also appealing to wildlife and may make the stand appear more natural.

In areas where fire is usually no problem, a better alternative is to select and prune only future crop trees. On large areas this is the only practical thing to do.

A small bow saw or specially designed pruning saw works best for this job. A lightweight pole handle or ladder with wide base can be used to help get at the higher branches. All cuts should be made flush with the trunk, even to the point of scraping the bark slightly in the process. Pruning shears, hatchets and axes leave protruding or jagged stubs that waste valuable years in the healing and overgrowth process. However, there may be an exception to this rule of tidiness. Recent research suggests that when pruning *dead* hardwood branches, a short stub should be left. The belief is that there is a protective layer inside the collar at the branch base that compartmentalizes heartwood rot and will therefore keep rot from entering the trunk.

By the time a pruned tree matures, it should have clear trunk of at least 17 feet (16-foot log plus stump). This means that pruning will be necessary in successive steps over several years. The first step is when the tree is between 3 and 5 inches DBH. Although no more than half the living crown should ever be removed, it is fairly safe to generalize and say that all branches to a height of 6 or 7 feet should be removed during the first pruning. This is as high as most of us can comfortably reach from the ground. Depending on how fast the tree grows, return to prune two more times, with the years spaced so

that not more than the lower ⅓ of the living crown is removed in either step.

In plantations, a good pruning guide for trees beyond 3 inches DBH is:

When the trees are closer than 8 feet apart, prune the dead branches plus the lowest whorl or two of live branches. When they are 8 feet apart or wider, live branches may be removed from up to 50 percent of the total tree height

These guidelines, plus the principles illustrated on page 69, should make pruning one of the easiest ways to improve your woodlot.

Is it Worth It?

For those who want an answer to this question in dollars and cents, there is no easy solution. In the case of pruning, one might try comparing prices offered for clear vs. limby logs at a sample of lumber or veneer mills in the area. For thinning and improvement cutting, there are various formulas and computer programs available. Most extension or service foresters have access to these. However, all such assessments are complex, and are only as good as the current and projected volume and growth figures obtained through cruising and professional opinions. If you are willing to pursue this scientifically, here is a free publication that can provide some reasonable formulas and graphs to help:

The Economics of Timber Stand Improvement by W.L. Mills, Jr. and Burnell C. Fischer. Purdue University, Cooperative Extension Service, West Lafayette, Indiana 47907

Economics aside, pruning is what we might call a high satisfaction activity because the results are in one sense immediate and easily seen. Likewise, improvement cuts and thinning provide a feeling of accomplishment. To the woodland steward, these things often outweigh the cold facts of cash.

SOME PRUNING PRINCIPLES

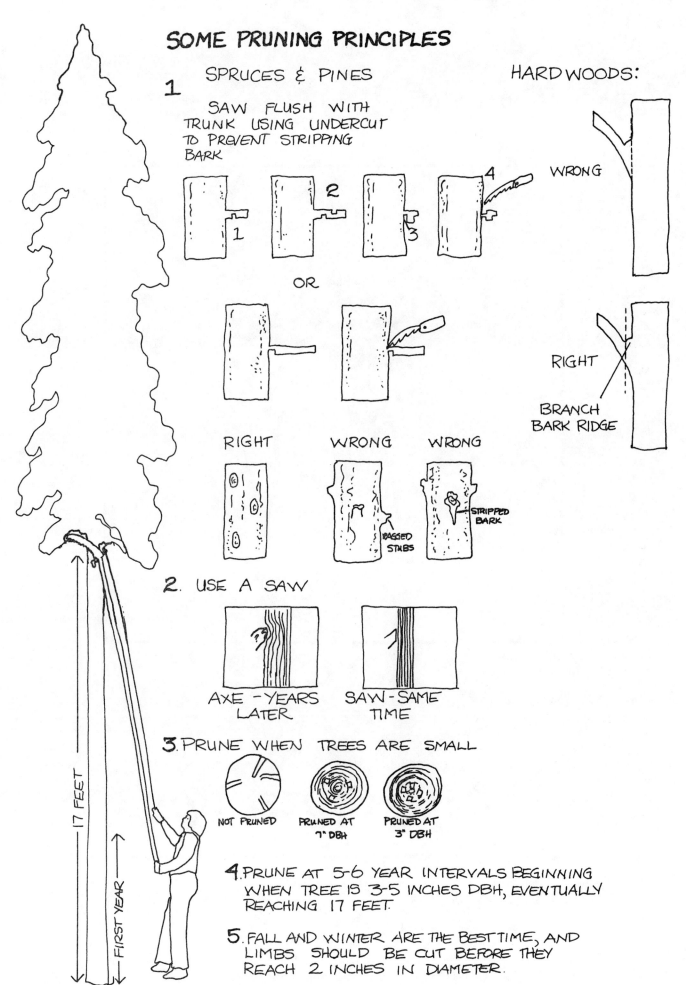

1 SPRUCES & PINES

SAW FLUSH WITH TRUNK USING UNDERCUT TO PREVENT STRIPPING BARK

1   2   3   4

OR

RIGHT   WRONG   WRONG

RAGGED STUBS

STRIPPED BARK

HARDWOODS:

WRONG

RIGHT

BRANCH BARK RIDGE

2. USE A SAW

AXE – YEARS LATER

SAW – SAME TIME

3. PRUNE WHEN TREES ARE SMALL

NOT PRUNED

PRUNED AT 7" DBH

PRUNED AT 3" DBH

4. PRUNE AT 5-6 YEAR INTERVALS BEGINNING WHEN TREE IS 3-5 INCHES DBH, EVENTUALLY REACHING 17 FEET.

5. FALL AND WINTER ARE THE BEST TIME, AND LIMBS SHOULD BE CUT BEFORE THEY REACH 2 INCHES IN DIAMETER.

17 FEET

FIRST YEAR

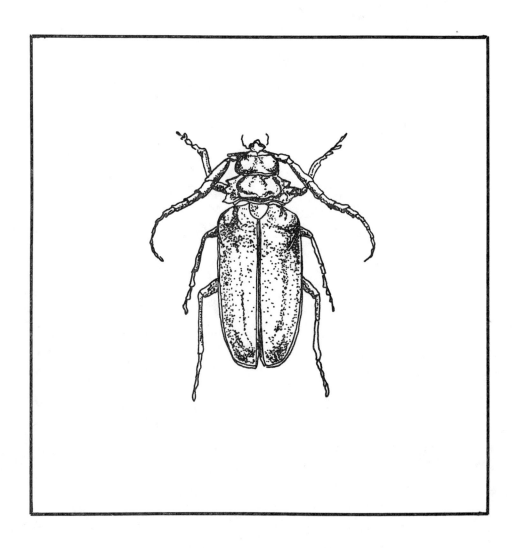

7   Protection

All things in moderation.

I recall many years ago a forestry professor asking his new crop of freshmen, "What destroys the most timber each year?"

I bit and gave him what he expected, "Forest fires."

"Wrong!" he shot back with obvious delight as I suffered my first twinge of collegiate embarrassment.

Today my guess might be a bit more sophisticated. From what I see when traveling through North America I would now suspect the spread of urbanization to be the culprit. According to the National Wildlife Federation, over one million acres of prime wildlife habitat ends up under concrete and houses each year. Undoubtedly, much of that is forest land.

But the correct answer is that insects and diseases cause greater annual losses than fire, sometimes by twice as much. When fire is added to the toll, the annual destruction reaches some 13 million board feet in the United States alone, an amount equal to one-fourth the timber growth.

Wind, erosion, floods and grazing are only a few of the other things that destroy trees. But wildfire is a universal problem and the one major threat over which we have the greatest control.

Wildfire

One of my earliest memories is hearing about how my great uncle set the woods afire in Idaho when his campfire spread. The blaze ran quickly up a hill, but he and his fellow campers helped bring it under control before a great deal of damage had been done. Because of their help, the deed went unpunished. No such good fortune awaits the careless today. In most states and provinces, campers and landowners alike are liable for the cost of controlling any fire they start, and for damages to the land that is not their own. This can be financially ruinous, since the costs frequently run into the tens or hundreds of thousands of dollars.

As a teenager, I recall one fall day in Pennsylvania when I looked across our field just as a gust of wind carried off a piece of burning rubbish from a fire being tended by my grandfather. He was the brother of the Idaho firebug and one might suspect some deficiency that ran in the family. But the statistics show that up to 50 percent of the wildfires on private land begin exactly like this one—using fire in a harmless way and ignoring the signs of nature that virtually cry out against burning anything that day. In our case, friends were on hand, and shovels and swatters were stored in the garage. Within minutes we controlled the burning grass before it reached our woods.

Fire is a threat facing everyone who owns woodland. It is an awesome force capable of immense destruction. The great Tillamook Fire in Oregon in 1933 destroyed more timber than was harvested in the rest of the country that year. Wisconsin's Peshtigo fire in 1871 burned 1,280,000 acres and claimed 1,500 lives. In Maine, one fire in 1947 blackened 233,000 acres, killed sixteen people and destroyed over 800 homes in Bar Harbor. In 1963, 110,000 acres of the pinelands in New Jersey were lost, along with seven people. And in the South and California, the devastation is almost an annual event

Although nearly all fires caused by debris burning can easily be prevented, incendiary fires are a different matter. These are arson—the willful and malicious starting of fires on someone else's land. Frequently these acts are brought on through jealousy or a desire for revenge, and there is no easy way to prevent them. The best solution is to make every effort to stay on friendly terms with neighbors and the community. Allowing hunting or picnicking on your land is one way to achieve this. "Positively" worded boundary signs such as HUNTING WITH PERMISSION instead of POSTED or KEEP OUT may also help. Simply practicing good public relations is the best deterrent to incendiary fires.

A Night in Fiery Battle

I think the best prevention of carelessly caused wildfire would be for every person to experience the terrible might of a forest fire. There is such a feeling of helplessness. There is also the feeling of disgust for the waste of our natural resources. Witness the vanished promise of a living tree as it crackles then explodes with a roar when flames sweep up the lower limbs and into the crown. Witness the fear as heat becomes unbearable and flames on a dry hillside spread faster than you could ever have imagined. One fire near Newcastle, New Brunswick travelled 80 miles in only nine hours, burning a swath 25 miles wide. The intensity of fire is also awesome. Even in the relatively low and sparse cover of Southern California's chaparral forest, it is estimated that each two-and-one-half acres on fire produces the heat equivalent of the atomic bomb that leveled Nagasaki.

I stood in the path of such a fire one hot summer night in California. It was just above Pasadena where the forest consists of head-high manzanitas, creosote bushes and mountain mahoganies. The sea of lights below in Los Angeles made the scene as beautiful as it was terrifying.

We were a crew of firefighters working like infantry alongside the heavy armor of a bulldozer. Our dozer had cleared a firebreak along the ridge, and just before sundown low flying bombers made pass after pass dropping their loads of sticky retardants down slope from our line. Now it was our turn.

The job was threefold. At the command of our crew boss, backfires would be lit to burn slowly down the slope, clearing out brush before running headlong into the advancing front of the main inferno. Next, we were to watch for spot fires that might start from embers carried skyward by powerful updrafts and dropped behind our line. These fires at our back would need to be controlled or the entire effort to stop the fire would be lost, and our lives threatened as well. There was a third task, most onerous yet crucial. It is one reason I say that an experience like mine would help make people more careful with fire. The assignment was to stop any burning animals from crossing our line.

I had heard of wildlife fleeing from forest fires, and it was my understanding that few animals are ever caught by the flames. But this night the trees and shrubs were explosively dry. The fire, generating its own wind from the intense heat, rushed toward us with a speed so great that no human and few animals could escape. I wasn't prepared for what I saw.

As the head of the fire neared our position and the puny backfires crept down the slope to meet it, the forest became alive with animals. A deer ran by, oblivious to the row of men. Then came rabbits and wood rats. Like a pathetic mob of refugees, they streamed out of the brush and started their dash across the bare earth of our fireline. I had never seen a sight like this, nor had I ever seen an animal on fire. As they ran, many had smoke streaming from their fur. Our job was to intercept them and bash out their lives with our shovels. Otherwise, they would spread the fire behind us. It was an eerie, deadly game. A crew of men, their own lives in danger, running about in the fire-lit night trying to hit terrified rabbits and rats with shovels.

The climax came quickly. A wall of flames and blowing embers made us forget the animals as we, too, wished to flee for our lives. Some cried and panicked and

had to be held in place by older, wiser firemen. Soon there was little to do but crouch behind the dozer, using it as a shield from the heat. The line was lost. Spot fires, too numerous to stop, quickly carried the blaze on its way beyond us. We had been passed over by the fire, impotent to even slow its advance and alive only because the dozed line was wide enough and our backfires had deprived the wildfire of some of its fuel. This fire burned on for two more days, charring thousands of acres. In my memory, it will go on forever, having left in its passing a new respect and dread of fire that serves me well.

Prevention

Most wildfires on private land can be prevented. Here is a simple checklist with suggestions that could save your woodlands:

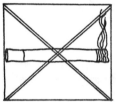

During dry periods of the year, ask visitors not to smoke while on your property. Follow this rule yourself. For work crews provide smoking spots for use during breaks. Keep 3-foot circles clear to mineral soil. Enforce your rules.

Mow access roads and the edges of your roads regularly. Burning materials thrown from car windows will be less likely to ignite in closely cropped grass.

Provide gravel, dirt or mowed parking spots. Any place where hot mufflers or catalytic converters come in contact with grass can be considered an invitation to disaster.

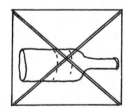

Pick up old bottles and glass. Under the right conditions they have been known to act as magnifying glasses in igniting wildfires.

Carry a fire extinguisher (in good working order!) and a shovel in your rig at all times. In dry weather, have them within reach anytime a chain saw is in use.

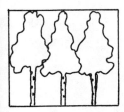

When possible, prune all trees in a plantation to at least 9 feet. This breaks the "ladder" that a ground fire might otherwise use to climb into crowns. The exception are those trees around the edge. They provide more of a service keeping out the drying effects of wind and sunlight.

Reduce potential fuels. Scatter pruned branches, and place them in contact with the ground to hasten rotting

Pile and safely burn logging slash or accumulations of blown down limbs during damp weather. Pay special attention to areas within 100 feet of roads. This is where most fires begin. The cleaner you keep them, the less likely it is that a fire will start, and the easier it will be to control a fire there or to start backfires.

When burning debris, whether it is household trash or logging slash, landowners could prevent thousands of acres of wildfires each year simply by being sensitive to environmental conditions. Remember—*some of these conditions can change within hours.* What begins in the morning as an excellent day for safe burning can turn into a day when the use of fire is pure madness. When this happens, change your plans—no matter what—and wait for safer conditions.

Here are the signs to look for:

Wind The danger sign easiest to see. Wind over 20 mph is extremely dangerous. Direction may also be important depending your circumstances. When planning larger burns, be sure to know the weather forecast.

Humidity Relative humidity below 30 percent dries out forest litter and other potential fuel rapidly. It makes a spreading fire difficult to control.

Fuel Moisture Professionals keep a close eye on this. A wood stick of standardized size is used as the measure. When its moisture content drops below 8 percent, the fire danger is high. Wind, low humidity and the time since last rainfall all contribute to low fuel moisture.

Site Characteristics These are pretty much fixed, but should always be taken into consideration. They include slope (remember that fires spread fastest uphill and on drier south and west slopes); natural breaks (such as roads and creeks) or lack thereof; and type of potential fuel (grass, leaves, young conifers, pruned branches, and slash).

Fire Readiness

The smart woodlot owner assumes that someday, regardless of the best prevention, there *will* be a fire on his land. The objective must be to control it quickly and hold losses to a minimum. There are several important ways to be ready:

— Join with others. If a volunteer fire department or landowners' cooperative association is available, join or support it. In cooperatives, the amount for membership is usually based on the number of acres owned.
— Discuss fire potentials with neighbors and agree to mutual aid.
— Find out what agency or organization has fire control responsibilities in your area.
— label and put phone numbers of the above by your telephone.
— Include firebreaks in your management plan for all new plantations. Then build and maintain them.
— Build and maintain 18- to 25-foot access roads to all parts of your property.
— Keep a fire tool cache in a handy place and keep the tools in good condition.
— Check the weight of local fire trucks, including water tankers, and be sure any bridges on your property are constructed to carry those loads. Post weight limits.
— Have places available for drawing water into fire trucks. Mark these on your map(s).

A 'Must' Booklet for Landowners

Wildfire Safety Guidelines for Rural Homeowners by J. Bruce Coulter. Colorado State Forest Service, Colorado State University, Fort Collins, CO 80521.

This 23-page booklet is free but could be worth its weight in gold if only one of its many suggestions saved your house or other buildings from wildfire. Drawings and text offer excellent tips on house design, property layout, safety zones, water systems and fire prevention.

FOR SAFE BURNING

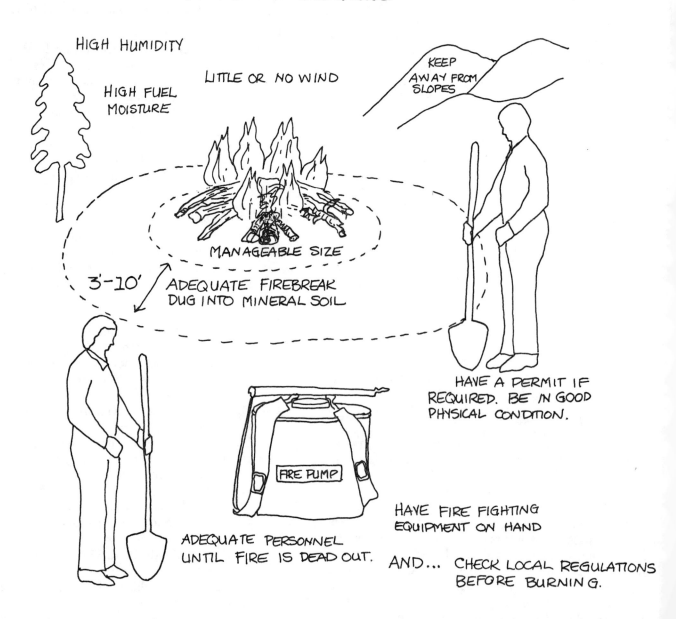

HIGH HUMIDITY

HIGH FUEL MOISTURE

LITTLE OR NO WIND

KEEP AWAY FROM SLOPES

MANAGEABLE SIZE

3'-10' ADEQUATE FIREBREAK DUG INTO MINERAL SOIL

HAVE A PERMIT IF REQUIRED. BE IN GOOD PHYSICAL CONDITION.

FIRE PUMP

ADEQUATE PERSONNEL UNTIL FIRE IS DEAD OUT.

HAVE FIRE FIGHTING EQUIPMENT ON HAND

AND... CHECK LOCAL REGULATIONS BEFORE BURNING.

Fighting a Fire

If wildfire strikes, the thing *not* to do is panic. The first thing *to* do is call those numbers you've posted by the phone. Then follow these procedures suggested by the California Department of Forestry, an organization with plenty of experience:

Step 1. Size up the fire and decide on the best attack. Note the fire's speed and intensity and weather conditions. What direction is it moving and are there natural or man-made barriers ahead of it?

Step 2. A. If possible, stop the main spread of fire at its head by digging or raking a firebreak, or fighting it directly with dirt and/or water if it's small enough. Then work on the flanks and the rear, completely encircling it with a fireline dug to mineral soil. Recognize that direct attack is very dangerous! Or...

B. If the fire head is too hot or dangerous to handle directly, attack the flanks from the rear and work rapidly toward the head. Extinguish spot fires away from the main fire.

Step 3. When the fire is surrounded by lines or otherwise contained, widen and improve the lines at the critical points, taking necessary steps to prevent burning material from rolling across the line. This can be done by making it into a ditch. Extinguish or fall burning snags.

Step 4. Take mop-up action. This means going through the burned over area putting out smouldering stumps, roots and logs, particularly near the lines. Many fires have come back to life when ashes later blew across the line or burned *under* the line in roots.

Step 5. Patrol the fire until it is dead out.

TOOLS FOR A FIRE CACHE

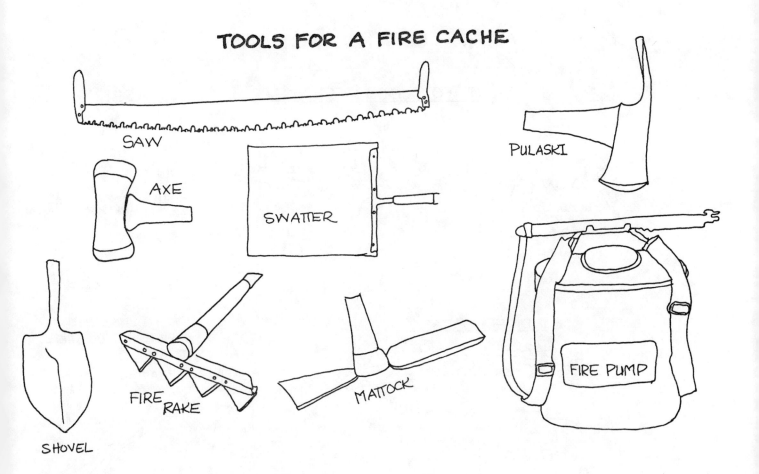

SAW

AXE

SWATTER

PULASKI

FIRE PUMP

SHOVEL

FIRE RAKE

MATTOCK

FIRE BREAKS AROUND AND THROUGH THE PLANTATION SHOULD BE BUILT AND THEN MAINTAINED. PLOWING OR DISCING IN SPRING, THEN IN MID SUMMER, KEEPS THEM FREE OF GRASS

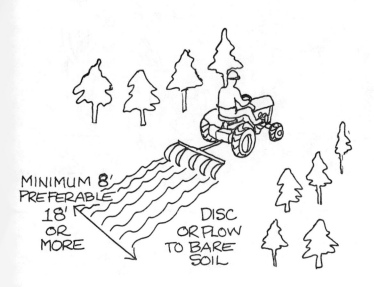

MINIMUM 8'
PREFERABLE
18'
OR
MORE

DISC
OR PLOW
TO BARE
SOIL

Not All Fires are Evil

Not all fires are destructive monsters. In fact, fire in the woods is little different than fire in the home. When controlled, it is highly useful and often indispensible. A term that reflects this concept is *fire management.*

Fire as a mangement tool can be used to dispose of logging slash, pockets of dense brush, and some other fire hazards. Periodic controlled burning often reduces the buildup of fuels so that if wildfire does strike, its effects on the standing trees will be minor. Fire can help prepare seedbeds or planting sites, and in the South it is even used to control brown spot needle blight, a disease in longleaf ' pine. Fire is helpful in changing or maintaining forest types. For example, it is an inexpensive way to prevent the takeover of hardwoods in pine plantations of the South. When the hardwoods are under four inches DBH, their thin bark is more susceptible to the killing action of fire than are the pines which have a more corky, fire resistant bark. Great care must be exercised so the flames burn hot but low, staying below the crowns of the pines.

The constructive use of fire is a very delicate matter. The risks are great. Under no circumstances should it be used without the advice of a competent forester, adequate control measures, sufficient help, and required permits.

In nature, fire has always been as much of the environment as water, wind or snow. It was not a question of *if* a forest would burn, but *when.* Depending on the frequency of fire in a forest environment, the face of the land was determined. At the turn of the century,

FIRE CONTROL ACTIONS

METHODS OF DIRECT CONTROL

BACK FIRING

HEAD OF FIRE

DIRECTION OF FIRE

INDIRECT ATTACK

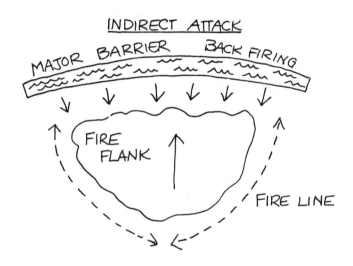

MAJOR BARRIER   BACK FIRING

FIRE FLANK

FIRE LINE

DIRECT WATER, DIRT, OR FIRE EXTINGUISHER AT BASE OF FLAMES

THE SHOVEL - MOST VERSATILE FIRE FIGHTING TOOL

CUTTING TOOL FOR BRUSH OR SMALL TREES

THROWING DIRT HIGH ON A BURNING SNAG

THROWING DIRT DIRECTLY ON APPROACHING FLAMES

CUTTING SOD AND ROOTS

DIGGING FIRELINE

CAUTION: FIREFIGHTING IS DANGEROUS, ESPECIALLY TO THE ELDERLY. BURNS AND HEART ATTACKS RESULT FROM POOR JUDGEMENT, EXCITEMENT AND NOT BEING IN GOOD PHYSICAL CONDITION

we began to change all that. Because of the new economic value of forests, romantic perceptions of beauty in parks, and the increase in farms and buildings across the landscape, government policy has been directed against fire. Today, fire is allowed to assume its natural role only in a few wilderness areas and national parks. There, in pre-determined zones, lightning fires are allowed to run their course. This change in policy is not only saving the government millions of dollars in fire fighting costs, it is preventing the abnormal buildup of fuels in these remote areas. It guarantees that we will always have ecological benchmarks where the effects of naturally occurring fires can be compared with our other forests where fire is excluded or carefully used.

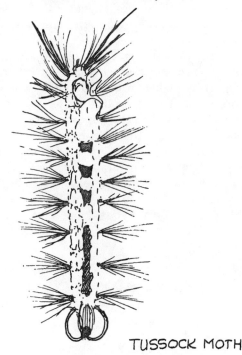

TUSSOCK MOTH

Insects

"For three weeks the destruction wore on, and the incessant munching almost led me to insanity." So wrote an irate citizen to the Pennsylvania Department of Environmental Resources. The comment, along with hundreds of others, helped lead to the state's $6.5 million aerial spray attack on gypsy moths in 1982.

Insects are a more destructive force in the woods than wildfire. Unlike the spectacular destruction of fire, however, insects usually take a tree here and a tree there and few people notice the damage. That is until the little creatures one day become so numerous that we have on our hands what the ancients called plague and we know as epidemic. The gypsy moth is a good example.

Gypsy moths, like so many epidemic-prone insects, were introduced from overseas. In 1869 an inept Harvard astronomer turned loose some of the moths in Medford, Massachusetts. The problem was very apparent by 1890 when the state legislature hired three people to spread arsenical Paris green in an attempt to control the defoliator.

Like an army on a campaign of destruction, the moths have steadily spread in concentric rings outward from Medford. As the 1980s began, over 5 million acres of oaks and other species of its preferred diet had been stripped as the march reached Maryland, Ohio, and scattered points in hopscotch fashion throughout North America.

The thing about an epidemic is the hopelessness of most human control methods. Although some chemicals such as DDT or its safer relative, Sevin, can reduce populations by as much as 95 percent, the potential side effects are well known. Also, the benefits are short-lived. In the case of gypsy moths, the reduced population just means more food (leaves) for the 10 percent that escape. In turn, they breed readily, quickly building a new and healthy population that some people speculate may even be genetically improved— a super race, so to speak. That may be stretching things a bit, although it has happened in some other insect control programs. What we know for certain is bad enough: by artificially reducing the population with chemicals, the escapees are spared nature's method of epidemic control. Population booms usually crash when food supplies run short, the young are physically stressed, and diseases are easily transmitted among the dense number of creatures. Reducing an insect population only puts this day further off.

If the crash comes soon enough, defoliated trees can spring back and put on their normal growth each year. In cases of bark beetles or other deadly attackers, forest succession moves forward, and the insects fade away for lack of suitable hosts. This is little consolation for the forest owner in the path of an epidemic, but it is the natural alternative to chemicals.

Coping With Insects

Besides trying to retain your sanity while insects munch their way to oblivion, there are some steps you can take to protect your trees. As with fire, the best methods are preventive; in most cases they are simply the result of good forest management. Good silviculture means healthy, vigorous trees—and this is the best defense against most insect problems.

Some Preventive Methods
- During improvement cutting, remove low vigor trees, infested trees and those that are especially susceptible to local insect problems.
- Maintain the vigor of your woodlot through regular thinnings.
- Promptly clean up fresh windfall areas, logging slash and fire-damaged areas.
- Leave old snags for cavity-nesting birds. Tree

killing insects are rarely found in old, dead trees and the birds attracted by snags will help control insect pests.

- When thinning or logging, prevent damage to residual trees.
- Do not prune branches over 2-3 inches in diameter.
- In the spring and summer, do not leave piles of pulpwood or saw logs in the woodlot for any extended period of time.
- Find out what insects are traditionally or potentially a serious problem in your area, and either avoid planting the affected species or follow silvicultural procedures for minimizing the risk.
- Some believe pure stands should be avoided (one species, or "monoculture"). In some cases this may be prudent. But it is more important to be sure that the species planted or favored in selection cutting are carefully matched to the growing site.
- When possible, plant genetically improved strains of species that are insect or disease resistant.

When Prevention Fails

One of the advantages of knowing your woodlot thoroughly is that you will notice if trees are attacked or start dying. A tree here and there is not important. But when trees die at what seems like more than the usual natural mortality rate, or when whole groups or all of one species start showing signs of distress, early detection can pay off. In California and some other areas, landowners are required to report suspected insect outbreaks to state foresters. Even where not required, this is a good first step. It will give you the services of a professional in helping to identify the cause of the problem and suggesting control if necessary.

Control Measures

Direct control includes burning active tent caterpillar webs, cutting and removing trees containing the broods of bark beetles, and hand-spraying chemicals on individual trees. Direct control requires a high investment of time and has limited effectiveness over large areas, but it is the least ecologically damaging method.

Once considered a panacea, the widespread application of *chemicals* is now seen as a measure of last resort. It is expensive, and landowners are required to share the costs with the responsible government agency when it is used. Nevertheless it is the most effective means short of letting nature run its course. Its lack of selectivity and its potential for harm to all living creatures, including people, make it a cure that may be worse than the ailment.

Biological controls are being actively studied by scientists and in some cases are actually in use. Introduction of sterilized insects into the breeding population or the use of sex attractants to trap the hapless creatures are two of these means. Other controls include encouraging large populations of birds such as swallows or woodpeckers to help keep insects in balance, or introducing laboratory-raised predators that feed on species we consider pests, for example, ladybugs eating aphids in a pine plantation, or a predatory beetle controlling mealybugs in citrus orchards. All of the above have been used with limited success, birds being the least expensive method and the one available to all of us.

In recent years, much hope has been placed on the use of bacteria or viruses that kill problem insects, such as a bacterium called Bt (short for its scientific name *Bacillus thuringiensis*) that is beginning to be used against the gypsy moth. Unfortunately Bt, like other chemical or biological methods, is not so refined that it only goes after the gypsy moths. It kills the larvae of *all* moths and butterflies, reducing the wonderful diversity in nature and depriving other animals of an important food source.

So much for biological controls as the panacea. All methods have their drawbacks, including biological approaches which are often touted by environmentalists as *the* answer. In controlling forest insects, there is no single answer. The real hope is what the professionals are calling integrated pest management (IPM): a combination of prevention through good silviculture and a variety of other carefully considered control methods.

Specific insect and disease control recommendations change rapidly and vary widely depending on local conditions. Contact your Cooperative Extension Agent or local government forester for specifics in your area.

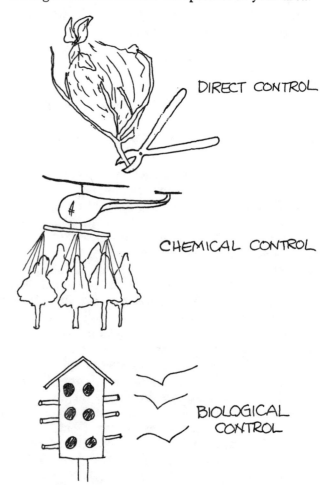

DIRECT CONTROL

CHEMICAL CONTROL

BIOLOGICAL CONTROL

Common Forest Insects

Defoliators

Defoliators eat the leaves of trees, their infestation sometimes reaching epidemic proportions. Presence of these insects can easily be detected by the loss of needles on conifers or the loss of leaves out of season on hardwoods. Resulting loss of the tree's food manufacturing ability causes a slowing of timber growth, and in the case of sugar maples, seriously affects sap production. Conifers can be quickly killed, or lose their beauty if intended as Christmas trees. Hardwoods, however, can usually withstand several years of defoliation without death. Fortunately, epidemics are usually cyclic and the insect boom will collapse through starvation or other natural checks and balances before the forest is irreversibly damaged.

Trees Affected

Conifers

Jack pine budworm	Jack pine in Lake States
Sawflies	A widespread group of at least 22 species that affect spruces, firs, western larch, cedars, loblolly, shortleaf, jack, red, Scotch, pitch and lodgepole pines.
Spruce budworm	True firs (Abies), Douglas-fir, spruces
Tussock moth	True firs, Douglas-fir, Blue spruce.
Texas leafcutting ant	Young planted pines, especially in Texas and Louisiana.
Western hemlock looper	The "inch worms," this one a killer of older western hemlocks.

Hardwoods

Elm spanworm	Nearly all hardwoods, but ash, hickory and walnut are preferred.
Forest tent caterpillar	Most broadleaved trees, especially aspens and the northern hardwoods.
Gypsy moth	Oaks, birches and aspen are most susceptible. White pines and eastern hemlocks also attacked.
Leafminers	Numerous hardwood species; lodgepole and white pines.

Bark Beetles and Other Bark Borers

This group of over 100 insect species is the most destructive in North America. It is estimated that approximately 60 percent of all tree growth loss is due to these burrowing pests. Bark beetles excavate egg galleries in fresh phloem, the inner bark which carries food from leaves to the roots of a tree. When the eggs hatch, hundreds of larvae eat their way from the main gallery, mining the inner bark in all directions. The pattern of their work is like a fingerprint for the species, and their collective eating nearly always spells doom for the tree. The first easily noticed sign of this is a reddening or fading appearance in the top of the tree, followed by complete browning. Less noticeable are patches of pitch seeping out where the insects first entered the trunk. These insects are usually only a problem in mature or maturing trees beyond the sapling stage, but some species plague young plantations.

Trees Affected

Conifers

California flathead borer	Overmature ponderosa pine on West Coast
Douglas-fir beetle	Douglas-fir and western larch
Mountain pine beetle	Lodgepole and most other western pines; Engelmann spruce.
Red turpentine beetle	Pines; sometime spruces, larches and firs.
Southern pine beetle	Shortleaf, loblolly and other pines and spruces in the Southeast.
Spruce beetle	Mature black spruce, Engelmann spruce
Western pine beetle	Ponderosa, coulter, sometimes lodgepole.
Engraver beetles	Pines throughout North America; true firs (Abies) and Douglas-fir in West
Hemlock borer	Hemlocks
Northern pine weevil	Southeast Canada to North Carolina in large areas of fresh stumps, including Christmas tree plantations.
Pacific flatheaded borer	Wide variety of trees on West Coast, including those newly planted.
Pine root collar weevil	Many species of pines, especially red pine on poorer sites and introduced pines.

THE DESTRUCTIVE EGG GALLERIES OF BARK BEETLES ALSO PROVIDE CLUES TO THEIR IDENTITY.

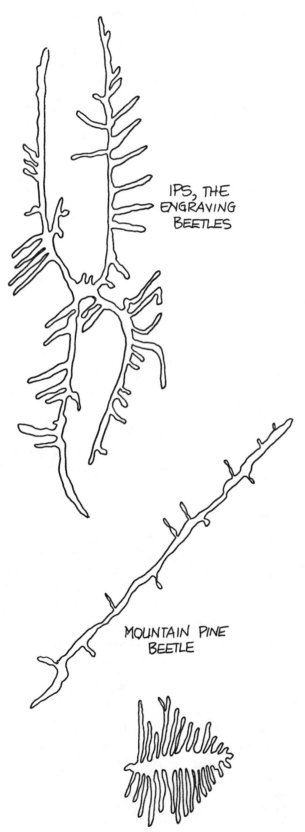

IPS, THE ENGRAVING BEETLES

MOUNTAIN PINE BEETLE

NATIVE ELM BARK BEETLE

| Zimmerman pine moth | Causes damage and sometimes death in pine plantations, S. Canada and N. United States. |

Hardwoods

Bronze birch borer	Birches
Flatheaded appletree borer	Wide variey of deciduous trees in North America, including those newly planted.
Sugar maple borer	Sugar maple
Twolined chestnut borer	Once, chestnuts; now, oaks and sometimes beeches.

Wood Borers

Wood borers go deeper than bark beetles, doing their damage in the sapwood and even the heartwood of a tree. But while some wood borers attack living trees, others drill into recently cut longs, lowering their value for lumber or pulp. Some even attack finished lumber. Often the tunnels have a secondary effect of providing an entry point and channels of spread for fungus (rot).

Although not true of all species of wood borers, a telltale sign is often the sawdust and other wastes (frass) that accumulate outside holes in the trunk or limbs.

The best defenses against many members of this group are to keep trees healthy, vigorous and undamaged, and to sell or use cut trees quickly rather than letting them lie around. This is especially important in the South and in the summer.

Trees Affected

Confiers

Firtree borer	Dead or dying true firs, Douglas-fir, spruces, hemlocks and larches in Western United States and Canada.
Horntails	Logs in western coniferous forests.
Southern pine sawyer	Damaged or freshly cut coniferous logs in Northeast.
Western larch borer	Living western larch and hemlock, Rocky Mountains and Pacific Coast.

Hardwoods

| Ambrosia beetles | Ruinous primarily of green lumber |

Carpenterworm	Living locusts, oaks, elms and poplars in the United States and Southern Canada.
Flatheaded appletree borer	Also a phloem insect, but may drill deeper. Walnut, hickory, poplar, willow, beech, oak, elm, hackberry and others in a weakened condition.
Locust borer	Living black locust at all stages.
Oak borer	One of the most damaging in high grade Southern hardwoods. (Woodpeckers are a major control!)
Pitted ambrosia beetle	Various living hardwoods, especially young maples.
Poplar and willow borers	Living poplars and willows throughout the U.S. and Canada; often causes wind breakage.

Terminal Feeders

Terminal feeders eat buds or roots. Some in this class also do their damage by girdling twigs. Their attacks are fatal only if repeated year after year, so their real damage is in the deformities caused as a tree overgrows its injured buds. This often slows growth as well. Root insects, mostly white grubs, some borers and root weevils, are problems only in seedlings and ornamental shrubs.

Entomologists suggest that many terminal insect problems could be avoided by more carefully matching planted species with the site conditions of their natural range.

Trees Affected

Conifers

Douglas-fir twig weevil	Douglas-fir seedlings in Northwest, and in Christmas tree plantations.
European pine shoot moth	Prefers red pine, but attacks other pines. Serious in plantations in southern New England, New York, and the Central states. Introduced, has spread to other moderate climate areas in the South and Northwest Coast.
Nantucket pine tip moth	Pines, especially loblolly, shortleaf and Virginia pine.

Pales weevil	May be most important insect pest in young pine plantations in South. Fatal to seedlings in harvested areas.
Pine reproduction weevil	Ponderosa pine seedlings, especially in California plantations.
Pitch pine tip moths	Pitch, shortleaf, loblolly and slash pines throughout East coast and west to Texas.
Western tip moths	Primarily ponderosa pine
White pine weevil	Eastern white pine, Norway spruce, Sitka spruce, mostly in sapling stage. Scotch pine and Douglas-fir in Christmas tree plantation.

Hardwoods

Twig borers	Deciduous trees throughout North America, but important mostly in ornamentals.

Sucking Insects

This group is named because its insects have sucking mouth parts and feed on plant fluids. A huge number of species are included, but few cause actual death to trees. Their main offense is robbing the tree of its food and water. This, of course, will eventually affect growth and health. They are also known to spread tree diseases, and sometimes the slits they make in branches weaken the branch enough that it dies or snaps off.

Trees Affected

Conifers

Aphids	Species of aphids, or plant lice, are everywhere. In large numbers, they can kill spruce, Douglas-fir and others. Also transmit diseases.
Balsam woolly adelgid	Serious introduced problem in true firs; New England, Maritime Provinces, Northwest coastal ranges.
Pine spittlebug	All pines in East, especially injurious to Scotch
Saratoga spittlebug	Conifers throughout the United States, especially red and jack pine plantations in Lake States.
Scales	Red pines, various Christmas tree species; junipers.

Spruce gall adelgids	Spruces, firs, Douglas-fir, larch, pines
Hardwoods	
Cicadas	Periodically cause mechanical damage to twigs of young hardwoods.
Lacebugs	Hardwoods, especially yellow birch, basswood, maples, ironwoods, oaks, sycamores and willows.
Scales	Ash, maple, beech and others.

Other Insects

The importance of other insect pests depends on the degree to which they interfere or help with the landowner's objectives. For example, galls are made by a variety of wasps, flies, aphids and mites when they "sting" a twig. The swollen, cancer-like reaction provides shelter and food for the insect's young. Galls are usually not a serious problem unless they deform the main stem, or unless you happen to be a Christmas tree grower.

Then, of course, there are the beneficial insects. Bees and many others provide pollination service; lady beetles control aphids and scales; checkered beetles prey on bark beetles; butterflies entertain and inspire—and all help to stave off that awful year of the silent spring. Insects are an integral part of the woodlot and most of the time live out their lives unnoticed and unoffending. Getting to know them, to learn their ways and to keep them in balance with human goals, can be one of the more interesting challenges of owning a woodland.

GALL

Disease

Most diseases in forest trees are actually tiny organisms, usually fellow members of the plant kingdom, living out their lives at the expense of the tree. They derive their nourishment by robbing the host tree of its water and nutrients. We label them parasites.

Parasitic diseases are far less spectacular than wildfire and even less dramatic than an insect. Yet they claim more good lumber each year than fire, and certainly compete with insects for top honors in destruction. Like insects, diseases are a constant part of the woodlot. In a virgin forest of the West, over half the standing volume of wood is infected by fungi or other disease. That is nature's way. But commodity-conscious humans can't stand such waste, so we look for ways to keep tree diseases to a minimum.

The five groups of forest diseases may be seen at a glance in the illustration. Fortunately, of the myriad diseases, very few have caused widespread mortality. But the few that have must be recorded among the most significant events in the history of North American forests. Here are some examples.

The American chestnut was once one of the most prized trees in the extensive forests of the East. It was a dominant tree, grew rapidly, gave its fruits to wildlife, settlers, and merchants, and yielded a strong, rot-resistant wood that was useful in countless ways. What sugar maple is to many of us today, chestnut was to generations of Americans.

The end of chestnut as a viable forest species began in 1904. In that year a strange new disease was discovered in New York City. It was a fungus, a native of Japan, and was assumed to have been introduced on oriental nursery stock. American chestnuts were vulnerable to the exotic fungus, and the disease began spreading at a rate of about 24 miles per year. Within 50 years, nearly every mature American chestnut was dead or dying.

Today, sprouts from the old root systems still make attempts at regaining a place in the woods. But all are struck down by the fungus before they can reach maturity. Scientists and landowners continue to search for just one with the right genetic key to form a resistance to the disease. To date, however, any large chestnut to be found is of the Asiatic species and is not our magnificent native chestnut.

Chestnut blight is caused by a fungus that grows in a tree's inner bark and sapwood, eventually depriving the tree of food. A similar fungus sends its thread-like fingers (hyphae) into a tree's water-conducting tissues, causing the tree to wilt or turn brown. One such fungus causes oak wilt, a disease that affects at least 50 species and varieties of oaks, posing a serious threat in the eastern forests. For some time experts thought this fungus attack might do to oaks what chestnut blight did to chestnuts. Fortunately, however, infections of the oak wilt fungus spread slowly, allowing time for landowners or service foresters to spot the trouble and clear out a circle of oaks around the infection center. Deprived of susceptible species, the spread of the disease can be controlled.

We are less fortunate with another type of wilt fungus, the one that caused Dutch elm disease. Like chestnut blight, and despite its misleading name, this was also a disease from Asia. However, it came to us by way of Europe, being imported on elm burls intended for veneer in 1930. The fungal spores are spread by bark beetles, which has led to relatively rapid distribution of the disease and death of as many as 400,000 elms each year.

Control measures have generally not been effective. In urban areas, chemical sprays and internal injections have had limited success. In the forest, however, the future of this species looks grim. The only practical prevention of the disease is to maintain elms in a vigorous state of growth and avoid any activity that will break the bark of the trees.

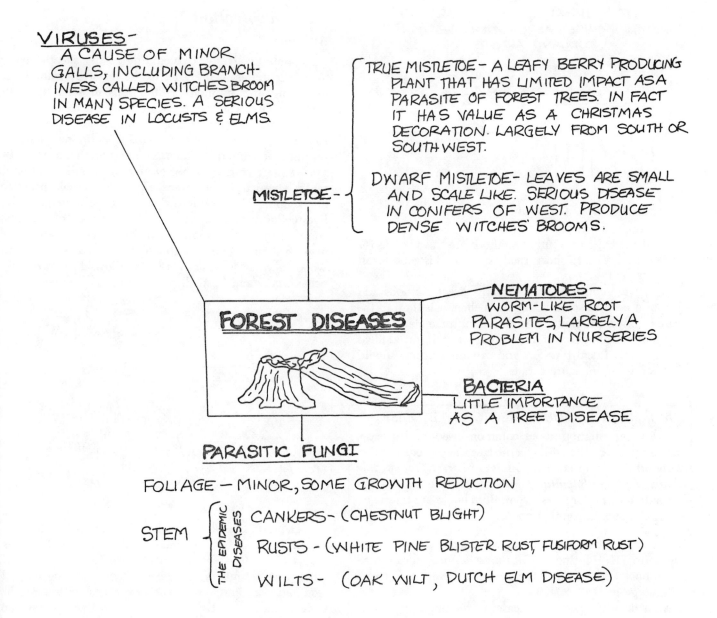

VIRUSES –
A CAUSE OF MINOR GALLS, INCLUDING BRANCH-INESS CALLED WITCHES BROOM IN MANY SPECIES. A SERIOUS DISEASE IN LOCUSTS & ELMS.

MISTLETOE –
TRUE MISTLETOE – A LEAFY BERRY PRODUCING PLANT THAT HAS LIMITED IMPACT AS A PARASITE OF FOREST TREES. IN FACT IT HAS VALUE AS A CHRISTMAS DECORATION. LARGELY FROM SOUTH OR SOUTHWEST.

DWARF MISTLETOE – LEAVES ARE SMALL AND SCALE LIKE. SERIOUS DISEASE IN CONIFERS OF WEST. PRODUCE DENSE WITCHES' BROOMS.

FOREST DISEASES

NEMATODES –
WORM-LIKE ROOT PARASITES, LARGELY A PROBLEM IN NURSERIES

BACTERIA
LITTLE IMPORTANCE AS A TREE DISEASE

PARASITIC FUNGI

FOLIAGE – MINOR, SOME GROWTH REDUCTION

STEM { THE EPIDEMIC DISEASES

CANKERS – (CHESTNUT BLIGHT)

RUSTS – (WHITE PINE BLISTER RUST, FUSIFORM RUST)

WILTS – (OAK WILT, DUTCH ELM DISEASE)

Fungi called "rusts" are particularly destructive worldwide as they attack rice and other cereal crops. In the forest they also take their toll on many species of trees. A curious feature of most rusts is that each species is specific to only one or a few host species. In addition, the rust needs to live on *two* different plant species at different times during its cycle. From the human standpoint, the less important of the two hosts is called the alternate host.

Our best-known example is white pine blister rust introduced to North America in 1906 on the East Coast, and in 1921 at Vancouver, British Columbia. It posed such a threat to eastern and western white pines and sugar pine in California and Oregon that armies of young men were hired each summer to scour the woods in search of wild currants and gooseberries (the alternate hosts, all in the genus *Ribes*), attempting to eradicate them by pulling them out by the roots. These efforts were largely futile, and today genetic strains of white pine that are resistant to the disease have been nursery grown and

are available for planting. In areas with high, persistent densities of *Ribes*, the planting of white pine is avoided.

Heart rots, or wood decay fungi, do not cause epidemics. Their spores must come in contact with exposed heartwood to gain a foothold, so to speak. Wounds from logging, fire, and wind breakage provide such openings. Stringy hyphae then grow through the woody cell walls causing what we see as "rot" when the tree is cut open. Sometimes the rot extends long distances inside the tree, giving few external clues to the progressive weakening of the trunk or branch. One sure clue, however, is the fruiting body—we call them cankers, "punk," or shelf fungus.

The best defense against rot is good silviculture with careful thinnings, improvement cuts, and harvest cuts. Interestingly, close relatives of the heart rots are saprophytic fungi that do us the service of decaying dead wood. They hold down the fire hazard, recycle nutrients, and allow us to walk through the woods without being head high in old branches and fallen logs.

THE FRUITING BODY OF HEART ROT OFTEN PROVIDES AN UNUSUAL MEDIUM FOR WOODLAND ARTISTS

Prevention and Control

Most of the prevention methods are the same as for insects (page77). In short, the best method is good forest management.

Disease controls include many direct methods and less of a need to spread dangerous chemicals than in the case of insect problems. A summary of these methods for the more common forest diseases can provide initial ideas for control. Local foresters and extension agents should be consulted for more details.

INFORMATION ABOUT INSECTS AND DISEASE

For information about common insect and disease problems associated with specific tree species, consult the wonderfully comprehensive *Silvics of Forest Trees of the United States. Silvicultural Systems* provides similar information by major forest types. Both books are referenced in Chapter 5. Another one is:

Diseases of Forest and Shade Trees of the United States by George H. Hepting. USDA Forest Service, Agriculture Handbook 386, U.S. Government Printing Office, Washington, D.C. 20402
Like a doctor's guide to diseases of human body parts, this inexpensive volume lists 200 trees and the diseases known to affect each. It is incredibly detailed, with a gargantuan bibliography.

Also, every state Extension Service has leaflets on the common forest pests and diseases in their region. These brochures contain control information and are well worth obtaining. Books to identify insects are available at most bookstores, but be careful to not buy one that is so general and simple that is proves useless.

For the kind of depth only a textbook can provide, we recommend the following:
Principles of Forest Entomology by Fred B. Knight and Herman J. Heikkenen. McGraw-Hill Book Co. This is a classic, up-dated regularly through new editions. Comprehensive yet understandable.
Tree Pathology: A Short Introduction by William H. Smith. Academic Press, New York. Reasonably comprehesive and academic, but understandable enough for the layman; nicely illustrated. Not for the mildly interested.

Other Protection Needs
Animals

Domestic livestock, including cattle, sheep, goats, hogs, and horses bring grief to the forest by trampling, uprooting and nipping off the tops of seedlings and saplings. They also compact soil, depriving roots of water and air, and in some cases strip the bark off older trees. In hardwood forests, they can virtually eliminate natural reproduction and deform any young trees that are left. In some cases a small number of animals in a large area of mature trees poses no threat. However, the old practice of "keeping the woodlot clean" by turning loose the livestock is considered by many foresters one of the most counterproductive practices a landowner could allow. As a general rule, livestock should be fenced out of small woodlots, and on larger acreages, allowed to graze only occasionally and in small numbers.

Deer, elk, and moose have a dramatic effect on natural reproduction in hardwood forests. The tender shoots of young trees are their main food supply, and when their numbers are great, they can wipe out all seedlings, saplings, and lower branches within reach. Unfortunately, in the eastern forests, deer prefer the same species of trees that are most prized for their timber value. Like domestic livestock, wild grazers can be especially damaging in plantations. When their preferred supply of deciduous trees and shrubs runs low, conifers are eaten, and they sometimes cause damage by rubbing their antlers on saplings. (See page 86 for a way to determine their impact on your woods.) Big game animals cannot be fenced out except at the great expense of erecting high, wire fences. Repellents are available but are also expensive, so the best approach is to allow or even encourage hunting. Hunting by permission only (preferably in writing) or through leasing hunting rights on your land to a sportsmen's club are good ways to control who hunts and how. But check with your attorney first about the liability you assume under such arrangements.

Mice take their toll by gnawing on stems, especially those of seedlings and saplings, girdling them in the process. Trapping or poisoning only reduces the mouse population temporarily. Nature's law is that if the living conditions are right, animals (mice in this case) will move

SOME FOREST DISEASES

Disease and Hosts	Main Symptoms	Control
Anthracnose (Hardwoods, especially sycamores and oaks)	Leaves and twigs die in the spring. Repeated attacks are fatal	Chemicals; none practical in woodlot management
Brown Spot Needle Blight (Longleaf pine seedlings; sometimes other pines)	Light spots on needles, then a brown band encircling the needle; tips die. Dwarfs and causes mortality	Precription burning in winter, assuring a low intensity fire. At 3-year intervals until seedlings grow above 18" height
Dieback (Ash, maple and other hardwoods)	A catchall term; a dying back of branches in the crown. May be from a virus drought, nutrient deficiency (especially copper) or some combination.	None practical in woodlot situation. Remove affected trees and utilize.
Dutch Elm Disease (All species of native elms)	Leaves may dwarf; yellowing and dropping of leaves or branches or entire crown; usually fatal if untreated.	Injections available for shade trees, but impractical in woodlots. Prompt removal and burning.
Dwarf Mistletoe (Conifers of West, especially in North)	Thickening of affected branches within 2 years; mistletoe plant shows within 4, witches' brooms within 6. Reduces growth rate, increases chance of mortality.	Prune affected limbs when practical. Otherwise, remove infected trees.
Eutypella Canker (Sugar & red maples)	Lesions, or tree sores, on trunk or branches; a slow buildup of concentric callus-like growth.	Removal of infected trees
Fomes Annosus (Conifers)	A root rot that eventually kills tree. Entry is through fresh stumps from thinnings, etc., then spreads from root contact with live trees.	Treat fresh stumps with borax or cresote. Commercial root dips available for seedlings at time of planting
Fusiform Rust (Slash & loblolly pine; sometimes longleaf)	Swellings on trunk and branches, sometimes with breakage; orange spores in spring from "blisters."	Prune affected branches; encourage natural pruning by maintaining a dense canopy.
Heart Rots (All species of mature trees)	Swellings, cankers or "conks", open "sores" with soft wood inside	Control is through good forest management; usually will not affect vigorous trees. Remove, or leave for wildlife.
Hypoxylon Canker (Aspen)	Yellow or brownish indentations around a wound; eventually oblong cankers, vertical cracks in bark; breakage.	Removal of infected trees.
Littleleaf (Shortleaf & loblolly pines)	Over 3-10 years, progressive decrease in terminal growth; yellowing and size reduction in needles.	Removal of infected trees.
Nectria Canker (All hardwoods, especially red & sugar maple, walnut, birches, beech and largetooth aspen)	Open or "target-like" cankers on trunk	Removal of infected trees.
Oak wilt (All native oaks, especially red & black	Leaves dry, turn brown and drop beginning at top of crown	Killing or removing oaks within 100 foot radius of infected tree(s)
White Pine Blister Rust (Eastern and western white pines and sugar pine)	Within 2 years, yellow or orange lesions, later becoming cankers. In spring and summer, cankers bear blisters containing orange spores. Cankers eventually girdle and kill.	Plant genetically resistant seedlings or avoid white pine in problem areas. Eradicate species of Ribes (currants, gooseberries) within at least 900 feet of pines.

in from surrounding areas and will breed rapidly to fill in the vacuum. So, a more effective method of control is to plow, cultivate or otherwise plant on a "clean" area, keep down weeds and brush, and burn piles of slash or other good nesting spots. Protecting hawks and owls, the natural predators of mice, can also aid your efforts.

Pocket gophers present a problem that can grow serious enough to require drastic action. There are over 100 different species in the United States, but they have one nasty habit in common. They eat the roots of plants, including seedlings and other small trees, reaching them through a network of carefully constructed tunnels. They give away their presence with small mounds of excavated dirt outside tunnel entrances, and sometimes by long tubes of soil where they've worked close to the surface

under snow. Controlling grass with herbicides is one way to keep gopher numbers down, but traps and poisons inserted into the holes out of the reach of other animals are the usual methods of control when their numbers become a problem. Extension agents can recommend the best bait or poison for your area.

Rabbits bite off seedlings and gnaw on the bark of young trees, often girdling them. Hunting usually keeps numbers under control. Repellents are available from nurseries and garden stores under a variety of brand names. Clean plantations free of brush piles will also help, especially where these semi-open areas border older and denser stands.

Porcupines thrive on the bark of older trees (mostly conifers) and usually feed high up on the trunk in the branches. Around buildings they are notorious for chewing on canoe paddles, outhouse seats, cabin steps and other strange things. Usually their numbers are few and the most effective control is shooting them. Since they are quite slow, it is also possible to capture them in a wooden apple crate or other sturdy box. The problem then becomes: to whose land do you transport them?!

On the ledger sheet of nature, birds clearly come out on the plus side. One rare exception is when they sit on top of valuable Christmas trees, breaking off the buds and causing deformation. See page 143 for the one solution we know.

DEER EXCLOSURE

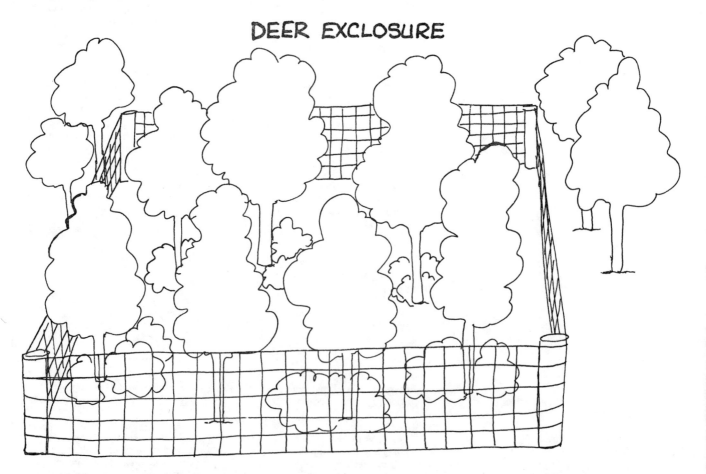

A 7 TO 8 FOOT WIRE ENCLOSURE CAN BE USED TO COMPARE AND MEASURE THE EFFECTS OF DEER AND OTHER GRAZING ANIMALS IN YOUR FOREST.

Air Pollution

Slow and insidious it has been called. Air pollution can affect many species of trees, but is a special threat to conifers which "breathe" through the same needles for several years. It seems also to be an increasing threat, even great distances from the source of pollution. Sulphur dioxide from nearby smelters has been a long-standing culprit, but the smogs of Los Angeles have been known to affect ponderosa pines 100 miles away on the far side of the San Gabriel Mountains. Peroxyacyl nitrates, ozone, fluoride and ethylene are among the agents causing today's problems. As more is learned about acid rain, it is likely this source of pollution will be found to be as harmful to trees as it has been to fish. This threat points up the need for forest owners to be as concerned with environmental problems on the grand scale as they are with planning their own woodland management. Meanwhile, find out which local species are less vulnerable to local pollutants and favor those over the more susceptible in your silvicultural plans.

Erosion and Logging Damage

Careless logging breaks young trees and causes scrapes and gouges which in larger trees often open the way for insects and disease. Protection comes through good contracts and matching the size and type of equipment with the size and condition of the woodlot (see next chapter).

Logging in muddy weather, on poorly placed roads, and on denuded hillsides are the main causes of erosion. Common sense provides most of the answers here. What may not be apparent, however, is that soil erosion is one of our most serious natural resource problems. Deep, rich soil, relatively undisturbed, is a real treasure. Consider any loss of it the same way you would view tree theft. Check local soil maps to determine what limiting factors may be associated with the characteristics of your soil types.

Flooding

A few species such as bald cypress have evolved to withstand excessive water on their roots. Most other species essentially drown in standing water. Roots need oxygen, so flooding for more than a few days poses a serious threat. Flooding also brings ice or debris that can scour the bark off a tree, or bury its lower trunk in suffocating mud. It is sometimes better to devote regularly flooded areas to shrubs and grass for wildlife than to try growing trees. Where possible, prevent flooding by keeping creek channels and culverts clear of debris and provide proper drainage around seeps and springs.

Wind and Drying

Little can be done to protect against the occasional catastrophic wind storm that results in large scale blow-down. Otherwise, maintaining proper spacing for optimum vigor and growth is the best prevention. Keeping the edges of woodlands "closed" with lower growing shrubs and dense areas of shorter trees can help

direct windflow over the canopy. This helps prevent both windthrow and drying of the soil. Keeping roads off slopes whenever possible also prevents drying (see next chapter).

Loving 'Em to Death

Forests are for people. But too many people, or people uncontrolled in their recreational pursuits, can mean destruction of the very resource all outdoor folks love. People, including hunters, in very young plantations inadvertently trample seedlings. A favorite picnic site used too often will compact soil which in turn starves tree roots for oxygen or starts erosion from the rapid runoff of rain on sloping land. And dirt bikes! There is one place for them—on roads and trails, and then only when the tread is dry or solid. Snowmobiles, too, should stay in travel lanes at least until snow depths are adequate to prevent breakage of young trees or wildlife shrubs. In open areas, excessive snowmobiling can affect local populations of birds of prey. The problem is that snow compaction makes life tough for small rodents that live at the interface of soil and snow. A reduction of their numbers (usually a blessing to tree growers) means a reduction in local hawks and owls (a curse to tree growers when these aerial patrolmen disappear).

The answer to human use problems is strict control of who does what and when. In general, the old proverb can be well applied—all things in moderation.

WOODLAND INSURANCE

At the present time, insurance against woodland losses is difficult to obtain. Intensive uses such as Christmas tree production or large scale sugar maple production can be covered under ordinary business insurance. But for protection against other woodland losses it is a different story.

Two encouraging developments are underway. One may be woodlot insurance made available to tree farmers through the American Tree Farm System. The other is the extension of federal crop insurance to include forest crops. Both future possibilities are worth watching.

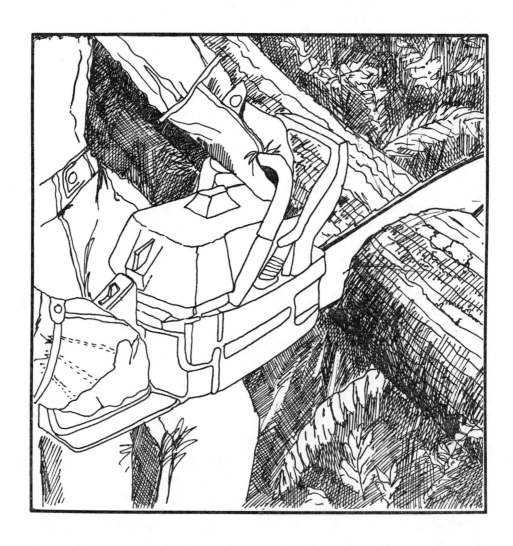

8 Harvesting

...draw from the forest, while protecting it, the best returns which it is capable of giving.

—Gifford Pinchot
Father of American Forestry

Harvest time is often viewed as a necessary evil to be put off as long as possible. Stories of the devastation caused by logging abound, and we all know of woodland owners who were cheated, deceived or otherwise disappointed by the performance of loggers or mill operators. On the other hand, a good harvest can be the payoff for years of good management. At intermediate stages in the life of a stand it can be the way to improve woodlot quality. For both financial and biological reasons, the cutting of trees is usually essential; when done properly, it can be a rewarding part of the overall management of your forest.

When to Harvest

The time for thinning and improvement cutting can easily be judged from visual signs such as when the tree crowns interlock or deterioriate, when defects appear, or when inferior species begin to become dominant. Judging the time for a final harvest is not so easy.

Biological maturity is one guide to harvesting. This is the time when a tree reaches its maximum merchantable volume. Beyond this point signs of deterioration begin to appear. Another biological guide is the slowing of growth or loss of vigor. Despite adequate growing room, if tree rings begin to get closer, the point of diminishing returns has been passed and the tree or stand should be cropped.

Most people make their decision on final harvests based on a combination of factors, including the size of their trees and the need for cash. While this may not be the best way, it is reality for most of us.

For those determined to obtain maximum financial returns on their investment in trees, "financial maturity" must be the guide to harvesting. It can be applied to individual trees removed through selection cutting or to an entire stand harvested through clearcutting or some other even-aged method.

Financial maturity is that point beyond which the expected value increase no longer equals or exceeds the net return which would be obtained if the tree or trees were sold and the cash were invested elsewhere. This point can be determined with a fairly high degree of accuracy if present growth rates and both present and future tree values can be reasonably estimated. One must also decide what alternative investments are available and acceptable from the standpoint of risk and yield. Beyond that, formulas and tables help you pinpoint the time to harvest if your goal is to maximize income. Guidelines to this method can be obtained in:

Financial Maturity: A Guide to When Trees Should Be Harvested by W. L. Mills, Jr. and John C. Callahan, Cooperative Extension Service, Purdue University, West Lafayette, Indiana 47907.

Roads

Whether you decide to have your land logged by a contractor or to do it yourself, a first step is to provide adequate roads. If none exist, use aerial photos or a topographic map to help plan. Think in terms of all the uses of your property, then sketch out the main road or roads to provide permanent access to those places you would like to reach regularly (plantation sites, picnic areas, overlooks, building sites, etc.). When possible, the main road—a "haul road" in logging terms—should connect the public road with the highest usable area of your property. But the grade should be kept to between 3 percent and 10 percent, and both the length and width should be kept to a minimum. A single-track road, 10 to 12 feet wide, wider at curves, with turnouts provided as necessary, is adequate. "Spur roads" are branches off the main road that provide loading areas (landings) in convenient locations. Skid trails can then extend off in either direction to reach the side valleys and slopes.

Here are some other design considerations:
- When possible, locate major haul roads on south and west slopes to hasten drying.
- Keep all roads out of and away from streams or creeks.
- Cross creeks and streams at right angles.

- Avoid flat areas when possible, because of drainage problems in wet weather, and exposed sidehills where the scars of road building are visible from afar.

Erosion Control

A serious problem with woodland roads is erosion. If poorly designed, they result in loss of valuable soil, ruts and gullies that make travel difficult, and reduction of water purity in creeks, ponds, and lakes. Most of these problems can be avoided by anyone who cares about the land.

The keys to good drainage and erosion control are careful placement, good design, and stabilization during and after logging. It is also important to use roads only when they are frozen or dry. During spring snowmelt or periods of prolonged rain, logging and traffic (including trail bikes and four-wheel drive vehicles) should be stopped.

Illustrated are some of the easiest and most important ways to provide water drainage without erosion. Water bars are used on skid trails, whereas bulldozed dips (sometimes called "thank-you-ma'ams") are placed in roads during or after construction. Dips work best on low grades and when little water drainage is expected. Open-topped culverts may be needed on steep grades or where more water is common, although constant maintenance is needed to keep them open. Closed steel or concrete culverts will be needed where the road crosses small creeks or where drainage ditches must be emptied from an insloping section to the downslope side of the road. A 3 to 4 percent grade in culverts will help keep them free of sediment or debris. Their size and spacing should be geared to handle drainage at the wettest time of the year.

Culverts and bridges add considerable expense to roads, so plan the route to avoid wet areas and reduce the number of creek crossings. Use outsloping to minimize ditches and culverts. Ford the creeks when possible. Fords should be solid with gravel added to both sides. Bridge crossings and other approaches should be at right angles to the creek to minimize disturbance of the banks.

When bridges are necessary, a local civil engineer, experienced forester, or logging contractor should be consulted about the size and strength needed for the expected weight load. Banks around bridge abutments and outflow areas from culverts should be stabilized with banks of rock known as riprap.

When the logging job is complete, it is a good idea to seed landing sites, skid trails and even the road bed if it is not to be used until the next cutting. Local Extension or Soil Conservation Service foresters can recommend a grass or other cover crop that grows well in your area and serves both as soil stabilizer and wildlife food.

| Booklets on Woodland Roads |

Permanent Logging Roads for Better Woodlot Management by Richard F. Haussman and Emerson W. Pruett. USDA Forest Service, Upper Darby, PA 19082.

Woodlands of the Northeast: Erosion and Sediment Control Guides by Robert E. Hartung and James M. Kress. USDA Forest Service, Upper Darby, PA 19082.

Selling Your Timber

Of all the horror stories surrounding well-intentioned management of woodlots, tales of timber sales and contract logging head the list. In Oregon there is a family who was offered $10,000 for their timber; with the aid of a forester, they found out it was really worth $60,000. In Georgia, a clever farmer sought bids on his timber, and he received three that ranged from $7,000 to $10,000. He felt this was a good indication of the crop's true value. Fortunately, a county extension agent convinced him to hire a consulting forester to handle the sale. The forester secured a high bid of $33,000 for the timber, which after his 10 percent fee meant a net of almost $30,000 for the farmer.

These examples point out the essential first step in selling your trees—know their volume and value. Cruise it yourself or have it cruised, but by all means don't fall into the common trap of selling something from your woodland without obtaining a careful and reliable measurement of it first.

Lump Sum Sales

Selling on the basis of a lump sum value is the easiest, but often poorest, method of sale. It is usually to the seller's disadvantage because he is paid an agreed-upon price before it is determined exactly how much volume will come off the land. The logger will say, "I'll give you $10,000 for all your trees over 12 inches DBH." Not only is this falling prey to diameter limit cutting (see page 51), but there is usually more volume removed than the landowner realizes. It is neither good stewardship nor good business.

A better way to conduct a lump sum sale is to tally and mark all trees to be cut. Figure a fair asking price based on your estimated volume and try to get that price. To maximize the value and attract buyers, it may pay to advertise the size distribution of the trees and potential of uses instead of simply the volumes of each species. For example, if 5 percent of the volume is suitable for poles, or 10 percent is of veneer quality, this should be stated.

Selling by Lump Sum

Advantages
- Easy to understand and manage.
- Disputes about actual volume are eliminated.

CONTROLLING WATER ON WOODLAND ROADS

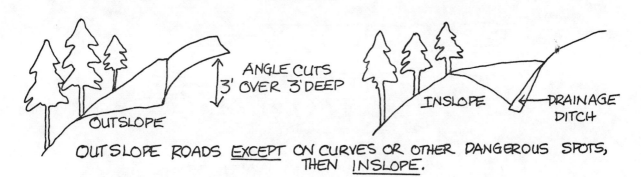

ANGLE CUTS 3' OVER 3' DEEP

OUTSLOPE   INSLOPE   DRAINAGE DITCH

OUTSLOPE ROADS EXCEPT ON CURVES OR OTHER DANGEROUS SPOTS, THEN INSLOPE.

TO INSTALL WATER BARS ON SKID TRAILS WHEN LOGGING HAS BEEN COMPLETED

1.  DIG TRENCH AT 30° ANGLE

2.  CUT 6"-8' SNAG OR INFERIOR TREE

3. PLACE IN DITCH WITH LOG EXTENDING BEYOND TRAIL IN BOTH DIRECTIONS

4.  PLACE ROCKS AND/OR STAKES ON DOWNHILL SIDE (UNLESS TRAIL TO BE USED BY MOTOR BIKES)

5. 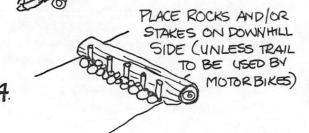 FILL IN ANY SPACE IN DITCH SO FINISHED CROSS SECTION APPEARS LIKE THIS

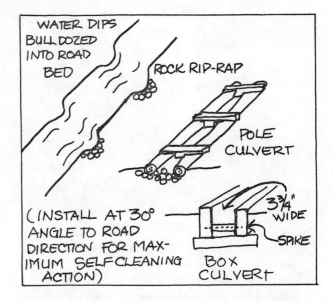

WATER DIPS BULLDOZED INTO ROAD BED

ROCK RIP-RAP

POLE CULVERT

(INSTALL AT 30° ANGLE TO ROAD DIRECTION FOR MAXIMUM SELF CLEANING ACTION)

3¾" WIDE   SPIKE

BOX CULVERT

SPACING GUIDE FOR WATER BREAKS DISTANCES IN FEET		
ROAD OR TRAIL GRADE %	FOR WATER BARS OR OPEN TOPPED CULVERTS	ROAD WATER DIPS
1	400	500
2	245	300
5	125	180
10	78	140
15	58	
20	47	
25	40	
30	35	
35	32	
40	29	

6. BRUSH SCATTERED ON THE TRAIL BETWEEN WATER BARS WILL ALSO HELP SLOW WATER FLOW AND CONTROL EROSION.

A SIMPLE ROAD BRIDGE

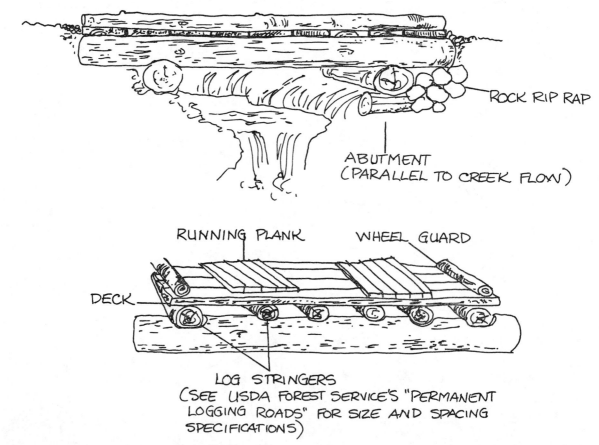

ROCK RIP RAP

ABUTMENT
(PARALLEL TO CREEK FLOW)

RUNNING PLANK   WHEEL GUARD

DECK

LOG STRINGERS
(SEE USDA FOREST SERVICE'S "PERMANENT
LOGGING ROADS" FOR SIZE AND SPACING
SPECIFICATIONS)

- There are fewer delays and coordination problems between seller and buyer.
- The buyer takes care to utilize more wood, taking poorer trees and poorer parts of trees.
- There is less likelihood for the seller to be cheated.

Disadvantages
- Either a diameter-limit cut must be made or cruising and marking are necessary.
- There may be income tax disadvantages for the seller, especially if lump sum sales occur too frequently.
- This method usually entails having the buyer do the logging, which may or may not be a disadvantage.
- A lower price will be paid when the buyer buys "on the stump" than if you deliver to the mill, roadside or railroad siding.

Selling By Unit Price of Logs

Using this method, seller and buyer agree to a price of so much per board foot of timber. This is referred to as the "stumpage price." Then at some point between the woods and the mill, the cut timber is measured ("scaled"), defects are deducted according to established scaling rules, and the seller is paid according to net volume. Using this method, the seller or his representative should scale the logs before they are hauled from the loading site and sell them on that basis. More often, however, the buyer does the scaling at the mill and pays accordingly. Sometimes the loads are weighed and bought on that basis.

Selling by Unit Price

Advantages
- The pre-sale estimate need not be as carefully conducted.
- A more accurate estimate of wood volume can be determined, which is an advantage especially in high quality timber.
- There may be income tax advantages if the sale agreements are worded correctly.

Disadvantages
- The seller or his representative must be present to measure logs before they are hauled, or the seller is at the mercy of the buyer's scaling figures
- There is considerable room for disagreement on volume and opportunity for cheating.
- The buyer may take only the better portions of trees, wasting the rest, and refuse to take lower grade logs.

LOG SCALING

The purpose of log scaling is to estimate how many board feet of useable lumber can be sawed from a log. Theoretically, this should be the same amount predicted during a good cruise when the tree was still on the stump. In practice, it is a more refined estimate, and it is based on the actual length of the log (s) cut from the tree. However, like volume estimates during a cruise, any one of a number of log rules (Doyle, International, etc., see page 201) can be used to convert the cyclindrical shape of the log to the predicted volume of a rectangular finished product. In addition, scalers use a complicated system to estimate how many board feet should be deducted for various defects.

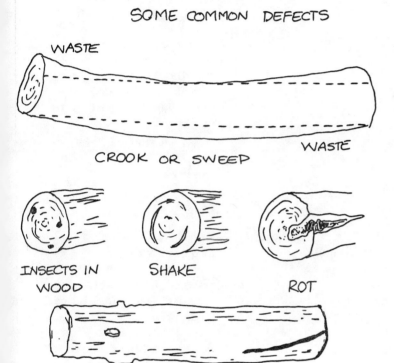

SOME COMMON DEFECTS

WASTE

CROOK OR SWEEP

WASTE

INSECTS IN WOOD

SHAKE

ROT

KNOTS

SEAM

GROSS VOLUME IS DETERMINED BY MEASURING DIAMETER, INSIDE BARK, AT THE SMALL END OF THE LOG AND THE LOGS LENGTH.

VOLUME OF DEFECTS IS THEN DEDUCTED ACCORDING TO STANDARD RULES FOR LOG GRADING.

OTHER DEFECTS

- SPLIT LOGS
- CROTCHES
- FUNGII STAIN
- FENCING OR SIGNS NAILED TO TREE

- SPLINTER PULL (FROM POOR FALLING)
- TAP HOLES (MAPLE)

Logging—Do It Yourself or Contract It?

When a landowner sells a timber crop, especially stumpage, the buyer usually does the cutting and hauling. The price offered reflects the work that has to be done. In fact, the seller can often receive two or three times as much for his logs if he cuts and skids them to a roadside landing, and even more if he delivers them to the mill or a railroad siding. Another advantage for the do-it-yourselfer is that most damage to a woodlot is done during the falling and skidding process. Despite the skill a professional logger may have, no one in the world cares as much about your land as you do.

Contracts

Sometimes there is no choice. Many landowners simply do not have suitable equipment or the physical ability to do a logging job. Others see it as no fun at all. If so, the cardinal rules for a happy contractual arrangement are to: (1) mark and/or measure what is being sold and advertise to get the best prices, (2) check on the reputation of the prospective logger by talking with foresters and other landowners who have employed him, and (3) use a good, *written* contract—even if the logger is your own brother-in-law.

Many people entrust the welfare of their woodlot to a logger on the basis of a handshake. This is as absurd as selling a crop without measuring it. Even with a solid contract there is rarely a perfect marriage between logger and landowner. Throughout my travels in writing this book, people complained to me about the insensitivities of loggers. What happened to my father-in-law, Walter "Chappy" Chapman, is a good example. At one time, he had overall responsibility for 12,000 forested acres of his company's land. The land was peripheral to the company's business (open pit mining), but Chappy is a prudent guy and favorably disposed to forestry. So they hired a forester and began management, selling trees periodically on a contract basis. As Chappy put it, "It turned out to be more headaches than the added income was worth." Even with a forester available to enforce points of contractual agreement, the woods were unduly damaged, trees were taken that were not marked, time schedules were forgotten, and the logging personnel had to be constantly nagged into living up to their agreement.

The result of Chappy's experience, like those of many other disappointed landowners, closed the forest to future harvests. The land is now held for hunting, as a buffer zone for the mine, and for the aesthetic enjoyment of company officials. Management for wood products has come to a halt.

Contracts do *not* offer a panacea. However, one that is well written and entered into with a reputable logger is the best protection you can get. And some loggers do an excellent job.

No contract can include all possible conditions, but it should be tailored to your needs and environmental situation as much as possible. Some sample contracts are included in the appendix, but a woods-wise lawyer should be consulted to draft your version. Most logging contracts should include:

Contracting Parties	It is wise to include a statement prohibiting the buyer from subcontracting or conveying the contract to anyone else without your permission.
Land Description	This should be a legal description of the parcel to be logged and how the boundaries are marked. A sketch map might also be attached.
Product	Include species, the agreed upon price for each, who will do the scaling, where and what scale is to be used (Scribner, International, etc.), if not sold on a lump sum basis. Duplicates of all scaler's sheets should be required. Other things might include, if appropriate: • how trees are marked • maximum stump height, minimum log length above

which logs are to be taken if sound
• minimum top diameter
• percent cull (defects) a log/tree may have and still be considered merchantable.

Land Protection	Here is where you can be as creative as you want in protecting your woodlot. In addition to specifications for roads, culverts, bridges, etc., you can include: • post-sale erosion control measures • type of logging equipment allowed • avoidance of springs or creeks • repair of damage to existing structures and roads • protection of residual trees • litter clean-up.
Permits and Slash Disposal	Know state or local requirements and specify who is responsible for obtaining permits and compliance with various regulations. Protect yourself from any damages arising from fires started by the buyer and be sure to clearly specify in what condition slash will be left or who is responsible for disposal.
Payment	How, when and to whom payments are to be made. Include penalty rates for damaged residual trees or saleable trees left in the woods if it is not a lump sum sale. A severe penalty rate, such as triple the stumpage price, should be set for trees taken that are not part of the agreement.
Time Limits	Set definite but reasonable beginning and ending dates, with a statement that all timber rights revert to you after the closing date. Provide for your right to suspend operations in case of very wet or dangerously dry weather.
Sale Performance	Many loggers don't like this, but if you can, insist on a

surety bond to guarantee performance. This can be some percent of the total expected sale price, and it is placed in escrow until all conditions are met. Other methods include advance payment for lump sum sales and payments made currently as timber is cut. It is also a good idea to specify how three arbitrators will be selected in case of disputes.

They Logged a Girl Scout Camp!

"There ought to be more warning to people like us. Like maybe Smokey Bear signs against loggers."

It was a humid summer evening in Buffalo, New York and the sun was losing itself west of the gray mire of city air. A welcome breeze parted the lace curtains but did little to chase the musty smell of the living room. From outside came the steady din of traffic noise and children playing on the sidewalk. And inside the lady blasted logging operators in terms that would make a sailor blush.

"You've really got to be careful," she concluded. "We have some real butchers come pounding on our door!" Her husband nodded agreement.

I was interviewing absentee landowners and the door she was referring to was at the family's second home property in the hills of southern New York. What she was telling me I had heard before and it seemed to be one of the main reasons these people eschewed forest management on their land. They seemed to reflect an image of loggers I saw quoted in Stewart Holbrook's book, *The American Lumberjack*—"public ogres who fairly sweated destruction from every pore and who ate up everything but the sawdust, which they left in unsightly piles."

I know some Girl Scouts who disagree. Like Girls Scouts everywhere, they own a camp, Camp Hoover, in upstate New York. Appropriately enough, it has a lakeshore, a nature trail, a large rustic building and many tent platforms. They have a large clearing for council fires and they also have sugar maples, basswood, ash, elm and black cherry. To hundreds of girls, mostly from cities, their 40 acres are hallowed ground. Then the loggers came.

For years, some members of the camp committee had realized that some kind of forestry was needed in their woods. Many of the trees were small, slow-growing and mixed with large, overaged 'wolf trees.' Hundreds of dead or twisted saplings marked events in a losing struggle for survival. Then, too, rotting tops were an increasing hazard to safety. Perhaps the committee had heard of a California study which revealed that in one 7-year period, falling trees or tree limbs in federal recreation areas killed six people and injured eight others. At any rate, some of the members were convinced that some drastic cutting was needed. Others, however, were not, and the latter were quite vociferous in their opposition to *any* cutting.

Some of the trees were deteriorating so badly that even the dissidents finally agreed to the removal of two oaks overhanging one of the buildings. A tree surgeon was called on to do the job and his bill came to a sweet $800—an awful lot of Girl Scout cookies!

The stark facts of economy did what silvicultural arguments had failed to achieve, for the cost of removing each hazardous tree on the compound individually would be bankruptcy. In addition, the job would never end, for the cause of the condition—overcrowding—would not be treated.

A forester was called, and eventually the land was logged. Seventy thousand board feet went to a local mill, thousands of dollars went to the Girl Scout coffers, and to the surprise of many, the land did *not* go to hell! In fact, the camp has become a showcase of careful logging. This "logging with a difference" is what is widely becoming known as "aesthetic logging."

When I heard of this logging job, I visited the Kettle Lakes area of New York to see for myself what was meant by this relatively new term. I did not find a park-like stand of trees clear of its underbrush like a college campus. Nor was it a jungle of impenetrable tops and branches. Here and there was a small scrape on a tree, but the stumps were low, and the slash was low, too. I could see deep into the stand and walk easily in any part of the woods. The road was not a rut. Near the tent platforms were some stumps, but at those places I found absolutely no trace of debris from the trees I knew had been felled there. The clearing where council fires lit the summer nights had been the log landing. I had to be told that, for there were few signs of the event. Finally, there were no oil cans, no lunch bags, and no lengths of jagged cables littering the woods. It had indeed been a beautiful job of logging!

A local service forester convinced me that such a logging job is possible on any piece of land if the landowner desires it. In his opinion, most landowners who want to sell trees don't care enough about the results of logging to take the extra measures necessary to assure a good job. If they don't care, why should the logger? After all, he is in business to make a profit, and this means doing the job as rapidly and economically as possible. His comments made me wonder if the finger of guilt, which is always pointing at loggers, should be pointing, in many cases, at the landowners.

This thought bothered me. Is the public crucifying the wrong party? More than one forester feels that it is. I wanted the logger's viewpoint, so the forester directed me to the company that harvested the Girl Scout camp.

Gutchess Lumber Company of Cortland is one of the larger mills in the southern tier of New York counties. It produces about 5 million board feet per year, mostly hardwoods. It competes well and is a picture of prosperity.

I arrived early for my appointment and had a chance to look over the magazines in the mill office waiting room. Trade journals are common in such places, but the colorful pages of *National Wildlife* and *The New York Conservationist* seemed a little out of place. Actually, they were my first indication of the philosophy that seemed to pervade the thinking of the Gutchess logging enterprise.

Maynard Spencer, the company's log buyer and a graduate of the College of Forestry at Syracuse, explained his view of aesthetic logging. He said, "Our primary motive is to make money, but conditions in this business are changing, and the ranks of loggers are continually thinning. Those of us who survive have to adapt, and part of it means going along with the landowner." Practically all their advertising, he added, is through word of mouth from one landowner to another. Care of their properties and residual stands, and prompt attention to any complaints, seem to be paying high dividends.

In his opinion, doing the job the way a landowner wants it done actually makes money for a company. This shoots a hole in the cherished belief of many loggers that cutting corners and doing things the "old way" is the only way to make a profit. To the contrary, Gutchess, like Macy's Department Store, sees the profit in "Give the lady what she wants."

This brings up the most important point of all, and the one which led to the successful job at Camp Hoover. The landowner must clearly state his or her objectives and select a reputable logging operator who will comply with the conditions necessary to meet them. If money is the only objective, forget aesthetic logging. You must be prepared to compromise a portion of the stumpage price to compensate the logger for the extra time and effort needed to leave the woods with an "untouched look." Next, put it in a contract.

Gutchess insists on a contract so that there is no question about what is expected of them. Should any landowner do less? In the Gutchess-Girl Scout contract, here are some of the special provisions which added up to an outstanding example of aesthetic logging:

Directional felling was required (using wedges and cables) to protect buildings, tent platforms, and trees in the residual stand.

Stump height was clearly specified (18 inches or less in the immediate camp area and not to exceed the diameter at DBH elsewhere).

Winter logging was done for at least four reasons: (1) bark is tighter on the trees, so there is less chance of objectionable scars left in the residual stand, (2) frozen roads mean less damage, (3) there are no leaves on the tops and limbs, and (4) there are few people around.

Culls and dead trees were marked and were required to be cut and tops lopped to specification.

Top lopping was clearly specified. All slash had to be cut to lie not more than 4 feet off the ground. In addition, tops had to be moved to a minimum distance of 75 feet from buildings, trails and lakeshore.

Aesthetics was unmistakably emphasized by the provision which read, "The buyer recognizes that the seller wishes to preserve the natural beauty of the site and agrees to conduct his operations to protect these values."

Depending on the property and the landowner, other stipulations might include "no-cut" areas, road layout that blends into scenery, road seeding, no littering, fence protection, and size or type of equipment. At the Girl Scout camp, hemlocks were left untouched because of their visual appeal.

Thanks to an awareness of aesthetic logging, the Girl Scouts of central New York still have what means most to them—a beautiful, "natural" woodland. They also have a safer camp, a vigorous forest for the future, and a much thicker bankroll.

Do It Yourself Logging

For the intrepid landowner who wants to do his own logging, there is the promise of higher prices, better care of the land, and serious injury! When cutting and hauling—be it firewood, pulpwood, or lumber—the spare time logger has many obstacles to overcome in order to do the job and do it safely. For most, the purchase of professional equipment is impractical, so the discussion here focuses on methods any rural landowner can use. For large-size timber or vast acreages, logging should be left to the pros.

Felling

Felling a tree holds a certain fascination for most of us. It is the exciting part of logging and is considered more play than work by many. It is also one of the most dangerous activities in which most of us will ever participate. The principal tool of felling, the chainsaw, is involved in 30 percent of all woods accidents, two-thirds of which take place during felling.

Safe and efficient tree felling (some call it falling and both spellings are correct) begins by recognizing the dangers and acting accordingly.

Before the Cutting

Read your owner's manual! The chainsaw is a machine that puts 1,000 pounds of deadly thrust in your ten fingers. Know it well and remind yourself constantly of its potential for injury.

Go prepared for business. Goggles or safety glasses, hearing protectors, leather gloves (cloth is slippery), hard hat, sturdy boots and saw-resistant safety pads that can be strapped around your legs or sewn into your trousers may be the best investments you ever made. Most chainsaw stores and forestry suppliers have these items. Also, chain guards come with most saws. Use them during transport and when the saw is sitting around home. Finally, be certain that your saw is maintained regularly for peak operating efficiency, and the chain is sharp, tightened according to specifications. Getting mad at a saw that won't start is the first step toward an accident!

Around the Tree

The first step in felling is to size up the tree. Look for which way and how much it is leaning, loose or attached dead limbs that may break off while sawing, and an

CHAINSAW USE

START ON THE GROUND OR ON A STUMP, <u>NEVER</u> WHILE HOLDING IT IN THE AIR

WHEN SAWING KEEP A FIRM GRIP AT ALL TIMES WITH YOUR THUMB UNDER THE HANDLE BAR.

LIMBING WITH A CHAINSAW IS DANGEROUS. KEEP THE TRUNK BETWEEN YOU AND THE SAW. BEWARE OF "KICK BACK" IF THE END OF THE BAR STRIKES A LIMB OR OTHER OBJECT.

WHEN BUCKING, BEWARE OF ROLLING LOGS AS THEY ARE CUT FREE.

SELECTING A CHAIN SAW

The most common saw bar lengths are 12, 14, 16 and 20 inches. Below 12 the saw is barely practical, and sizes above 20 or 25 inches are best left to the muscular pros. For most non-professional woodlot jobs, a 16 inch bar is the size to own if you can only own one. Otherwise, a lightweight saw with a 14 or 16 inch bar is good to have around for limbing and bucking firewood or pulpwood, with a 20 or 25 incher for felling. Much depends on the size of the trees you'll be working with and the amount of work.

For maximum power and minimum strain on the saw, it is a good idea to buy a saw engine capable of handling one bar size larger than you plan to use. For example, for a 16 inch bar, buy a saw capable of also using a 20 inch bar.

	Mini-Saws	Light Weight	Medium Duty	Production
Weight (Without fuel or cutting attachments)	6-9 lbs.	9-13.5 lbs.	12.5-20 lbs.	18-28 + lbs.
Engine Displacement	2-2.5 cu. in.	2.5-3.7 cu. in.	3.5-4.8 cu. in.	4.5-8.5 cu. in.
Bar Lengths	8"-14" 12" aver.	14"-18" 16" aver.	15"-20" 18" aver.	16"-60" 21" aver.

AROUND THE TREE

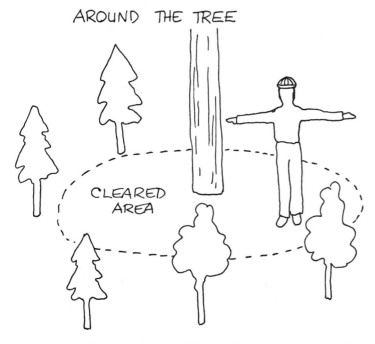

CLEARED AREA

escape path to use when it falls, and one or more to use if it falls the wrong way.

After studying the tree and its surroundings, clear out all brush, stumps, chunks of wood, logs and other obstacles in an area approximately two arm lengths around the tree. This gives you a safe working area free of things you might strike with the saw or trip over. Plan your cut and post a second person to watch for falling limbs that are appropriately called "widow makers." On windy days, stay home.

Direction Felling

There is skill in felling trees that enables professionals to drive stakes into the ground where the trunk will land. By following the basics as illustrated, you too can gain a level of skill that is most useful in logging. However, factors such as rot, wind, trunk irregularities and unusually large diameters may alter the normal mechanics of a cut.

In selecting the direction of the desired fall, consider five things:

- Fell with the lean or side of heavy branching when possible.
- Fell the tree in a way to make pulling it out of the woods (skidding) easiest. Usually this is at an angle of 45° to the direction of skidding.
- Fell onto a smooth surface free of perpendicular logs, stumps, snags, deep gullies or anything else that may break or damage the falling tree.
- Avoid hitting desired regeneration or trees that are to be left.
- Fell uphill when possible. It helps in skidding the log out.

Avoiding Two Common Bugaboos

When the tree begins to fall, the old cry of "Timber!" still serves the useful purpose of warning others who may be in the area. When you complete the cut, turn off the saw, set it aside, and make your retreat

at a 45 degree angle from a line extended back from the direction of fall. This will reduce the chances of your being struck if the log kicks back as it strikes the ground.

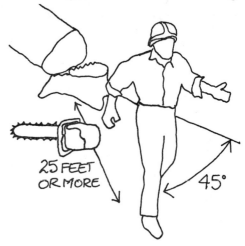

25 FEET OR MORE   45°

Another of the most common and dangerous problems in felling is the "hung up" tree. This occurs when branches become entangled, preventing the tree from falling. It happens sometimes, especially in dense woodlots, despite directional felling. The easiest, safest way to solve this problem is to pull the tree off the stump with a tractor or other skidder and a long, sturdy chain or cable. The other safe method is to use a "come-along." This handy tool can also get your truck un-stuck, lift logs, move rocks and do a variety of other Herculean chores for you.

Limbing and Bucking

Smaller limbs can be removed almost as quickly with an axe as with a chain saw, and usually an axe is safer. With practice, limbing with an axe can be done with a single stroke, leaving no trace of a stub. For limbs that are too large for efficient removal by this method, a lightweight chainsaw is the tool to use. For safety and the smoothest cut by an axe or chainsaw, stand on the opposite side of the trunk from the limb and swing or saw with the direction of growth. For efficiency, begin limbing at the butt end of the tree and work toward the top.

Limbing can either be done in the woods or at the loading area; both have their pros and cons. Limbing on site scatters the slash (which is desirable unless you prefer to pile and burn it), makes skidding easier, and does less damage to residual trees. Limbing at the landing may be more efficient if you are logging small trees or if you have a lot of helpers. If chipping equipment is available for reducing waste wood to pulp chips, livestock bedding or some other product, then roadside limbing has one more advantage.

Bucking, or sawing the trunk into log lengths, is best done at the landing. This reduces the number of skidding trips needed and makes sorting more efficient. For example, small ends of tree-length logs might be stacked for a pulp shipment and especially good logs might be rolled aside for separate sale as veneer. Odd pieces may be piled for firewood. The exception to this procedure is

FELLING WITH CONTROL

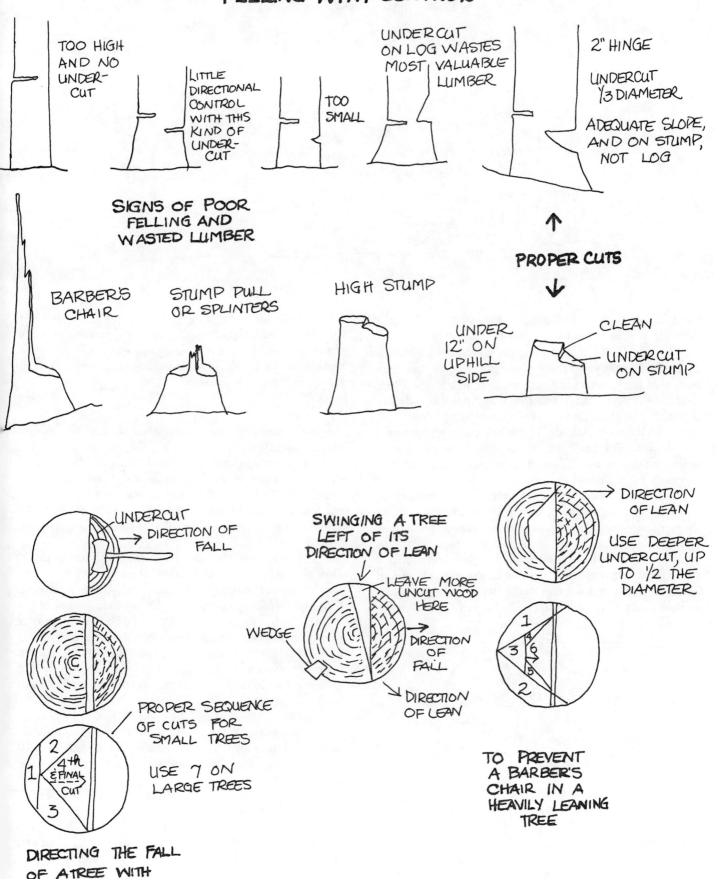

TOO HIGH AND NO UNDER-CUT

LITTLE DIRECTIONAL CONTROL WITH THIS KIND OF UNDER-CUT

TOO SMALL

UNDERCUT ON LOG WASTES MOST VALUABLE LUMBER

2" HINGE

UNDERCUT 1/3 DIAMETER

ADEQUATE SLOPE, AND ON STUMP, NOT LOG

SIGNS OF POOR FELLING AND WASTED LUMBER

BARBER'S CHAIR

STUMP PULL OR SPLINTERS

HIGH STUMP

PROPER CUTS

UNDER 12" ON UPHILL SIDE

CLEAN

UNDERCUT ON STUMP

UNDERCUT → DIRECTION OF FALL

SWINGING A TREE LEFT OF ITS DIRECTION OF LEAN

LEAVE MORE UNCUT WOOD HERE

WEDGE

DIRECTION OF FALL

DIRECTION OF LEAN

DIRECTION OF LEAN

USE DEEPER UNDERCUT, UP TO 1/2 THE DIAMETER

PROPER SEQUENCE OF CUTS FOR SMALL TREES

USE 7 ON LARGE TREES

2   4th & FINAL CUT
1
3

DIRECTING THE FALL OF A TREE WITH NO LEAN

1 4
3 6
5
2

TO PREVENT A BARBER'S CHAIR IN A HEAVILY LEANING TREE

99

THE 'COME ALONG'

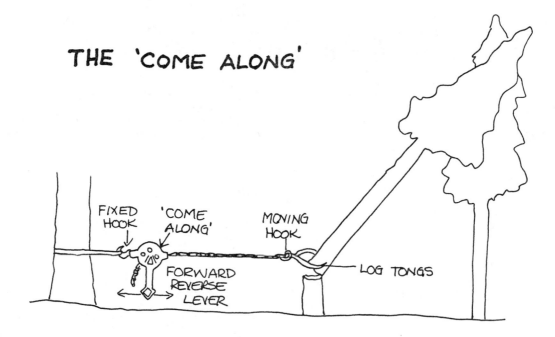

FIXED HOOK 'COME ALONG' MOVING HOOK LOG TONGS

FORWARD REVERSE LEVER

the stand that is very dense. In that case, tree-length skidding will increase bark injuries.

Proper bucking is an important way to increase profits. By studying the tree-length log, it becomes apparent that there are many ways to cut it up. First, find out the preferred or required lengths at the mills you are selling to. Also find out how much "trim allowance" you must leave on each log. Usually this is an additional 3 to 6 inches. For example, to sell a 16-foot log, it may actually need to be 16 feet, 6 inches, or the buyer may pay only for a 14-foot log.

Mark the best cuts on the entire tree trunk before you start. A long, crooked log can sometimes be cut into shorter pieces that will scale with less defect deduction. Rotten sections can be cut out and left in the woods, or a crotch can be cut out and used for firewood, with a subsequent improvement in grade of the logs above and below it. Bucking is not diamond cutting, but it is as close to it as many of us will come!

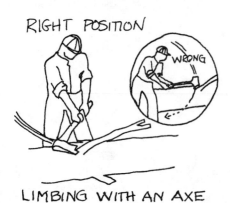

RIGHT POSITION   WRONG

LIMBING WITH AN AXE

Skidding

Do-it-yourself logging becomes more difficult with the skidding process, the moving of logs from the woods to a loading area. Few can afford rubber-tired skidders or other equipment built specially for logging. However,

most woodland owners have other kinds of equipment that can be adapted to logging small properties. There is also lightweight, inexpensive equipment coming on the market, and some folks are even joining a revolutionary return to the use of horses.

Tractors

Farm tractors are the most commonly used machine on non-industrial private woodlands. When carefully operated and kept off steep slopes, a tractor fitted with a winch and cable can meet most logging needs. Safety canopies, winches and other skidding equipment are available from many tractor sales outlets in forest country. By catalog, TSI Company (see appendix) offers kits for tractors ranging from 18 H.P. to 120 H.P.

Efficiency and minimum disturbance of the land and trees are the twin objectives in skidding. The key to success is reduction of friction, hauling reasonably large loads each trip, and careful route selection. Illustrated are some of the ways to cut friction and maximize loads. The rest is a matter of common sense such as staying out of boggy areas, felling and skidding progressively away from the landing to open up pathways to the landing, staying clear of valuable growing stock left for future years, and designing skid roads with gentle curves only.

Skidding has inspired the imaginations of loggers for centuries—horses, hot air balloons and helicopters have all been used to move trees. Recently, operators of small woodlots, stimulated by the growing demand for firewood and other small-diameter products, have devised ingenious ways of moving logs. One New Englander welded parts of an old pickup to parts of a Toyota Corolla. The result is the Woodchuck (see appendix), with a low, 10- x 4-foot cargo bed, the ability to handle 30 percent slopes, and front and rear wheels that steer independently so it can maneuver between trees planted as close as 6 x 6 feet. The Woodchuck can carry as much as a cord of firewood each trip.

BUCKING WITHOUT PINCHING

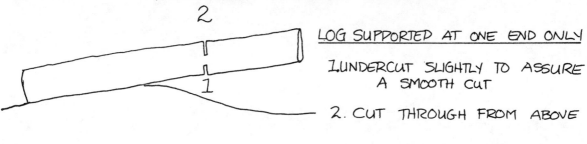

LOG SUPPORTED AT ONE END ONLY

1. UNDERCUT SLIGHTLY TO ASSURE A SMOOTH CUT

2. CUT THROUGH FROM ABOVE

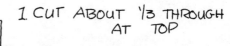

LOG SUPPORTED AT TWO ENDS

1. CUT ABOUT ⅓ THROUGH AT TOP

2. CUT THROUGH FROM BELOW. WATCH OUT FOR YOUR FEET AND FOR LOG ROLL!

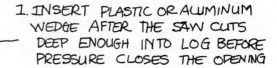

LARGE LOG LYING FLAT ON GROUND

1. INSERT PLASTIC OR ALUMINUM WEDGE AFTER THE SAW CUTS DEEP ENOUGH INTO LOG BEFORE PRESSURE CLOSES THE OPENING

2. CONTINUE DOWNWARD CUT CAREFULLY. DO NOT CUT INTO THE GROUND

A new kind of lightweight skidder (also called "forwarder") that is inexpensive enough for most woodlot owners is typified by William Spence's Quadractor. Built in a remodeled Vermont veneer mill, it looks a bit like a large suburban riding mower on high wheels. Its high clearance allows the leading edge of long, small diameter logs to be winched under the vehicle almost to its center. This increases traction and cuts down on friction and skidding damage. A highly maneuverable invention, its wheels pivot vertically 15 degrees to follow rough terrain and can be locked on either side to give it a turning radius no longer than its 7-foot length. Its 900-pound weight, 8 H.P. Briggs and Stratton engine and 12-volt battery-powered winch make it look like the weakling of the woodlot, but really it is a mechanical Samson in disguise. See Woodlot Suppliers in the appendix for a mailing address.

There is no single method of forwarding logs to the landing. It depends on the size of the job, size of the trees, terrain, objectives, available time and equipment and, most of all, imagination.

Loading and Hauling

It is usually best to end the do-it-yourself part of forestry at roadside. From there the log buyer can load and haul your product, saving you time, the dangers of highway transport, and the need to have an expensive truck large enough to do the job efficiently. Of course, you will receive less for your logs at the landing than if you deliver them yourself, but far more than if you sold them on the stump. In some cases, the happy medium might be to sell directly to the mill and simply contract the hauling.

If you sell logs at roadside or contract the hauling, be sure to get bids from several outfits and complete your agreement before you log. The hauler may require that the logs be piled in a way that facilitates his mechanical loader. It also keeps logs from sitting around vulnerable to log thieves, firewood cutters and insects.

If you have access to a truck with the springs, bed size and wheel base sufficient for hauling logs yourself, there are several ways to make the loading inexpensive, if not easy. Loading pulpwood and firewood by hand is still the cheapest way to go if time is not important. Various cable systems and conveyor belts have been cleverly devised to save some of the lifting or a front end loader on a farm tractor can aid in the task. In hauling, remember that wood is an extremely heavy cargo. A cord of green wood can easily weigh up to two tons! Overloading can cause accidents by breaking springs or axles. Be sure to check the highway laws on hauling loads in your state.

Loading full size logs is trickier, and their hauling is definitely not for amateurs. Yet, some landowners want

HAND TOOLS FOR HANDLING LOGS

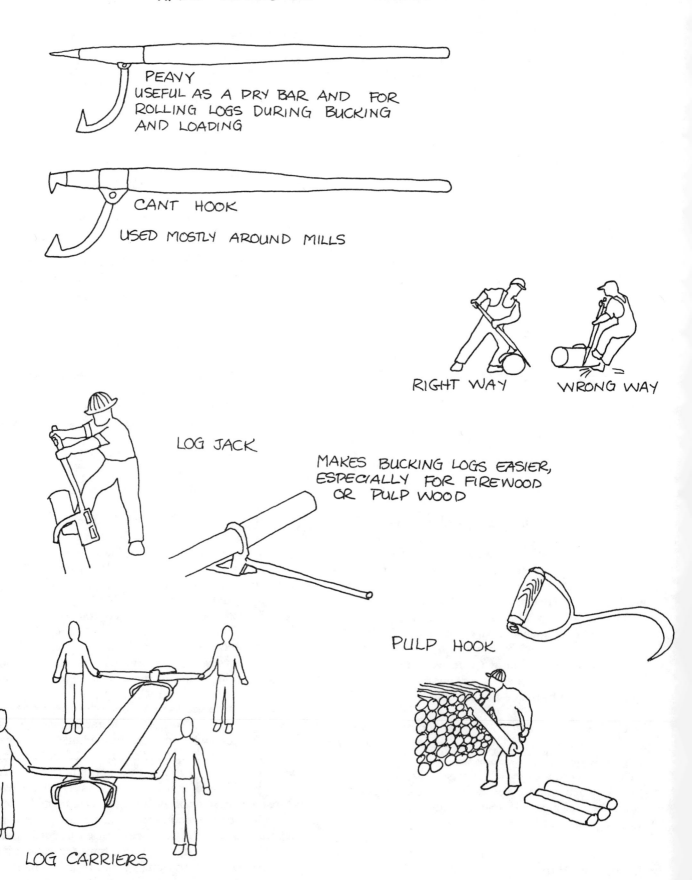

PEAVY
USEFUL AS A PRY BAR AND FOR ROLLING LOGS DURING BUCKING AND LOADING

CANT HOOK
USED MOSTLY AROUND MILLS

RIGHT WAY   WRONG WAY

LOG JACK

MAKES BUCKING LOGS EASIER, ESPECIALLY FOR FIREWOOD OR PULP WOOD

PULP HOOK

LOG CARRIERS

DO-IT-YOURSELF SKIDDING EQUIPMENT

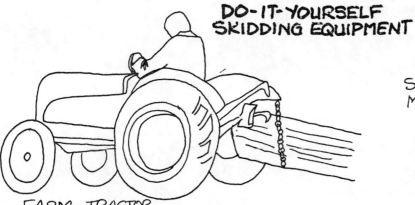

FARM TRACTOR WITH HYDRAULIC LIFT

SKIDDING GRAPPLE SKIDS WHEN FORWARD MOTION BEGINS. HELPS RAISE AND STEER LOGS AROUND OBSTACLES WHEN YOU HAVE NO WAY OF RAISING LEADING END OF LOG CLEAR OFF THE GROUND

CABLE OR WIRE ROPE

LOGGING OR SKIDDING CHAIN

SKIDDING TONGS

AN OLDER AND CHEAPER METHOD— WHEN GROUND SKIDDING (NO HYDRAULIC LIFT) PRODUCES LESS FRICTION THAN LOOPING A CHAIN AROUND THE LOG

KEY HOLE SLIDER

USED TO CONNECT LOGGING CHAINS TO CABLE FOR SKIDDING SEVERAL LOGS AT A TIME.

CHOKER

USED TO LOOP CABLE AROUND A LOG

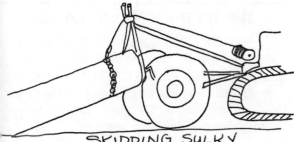

SKIDDING SULKY

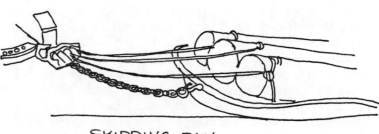

SKIDDING PAN

VARIOUS COMMERCIAL AND HOMEMADE DEVICES CAN BE USED TO KEEP LOGS OFF THE GROUND TO REDUCE FRICTION.

WINCHES

A GOOD WINCH IS INVALUABLE. USES INCLUDE PULLING OUT EQUIPMENT STUCK IN MUD, OR GETTING IT UP OR DOWN STEEP AREAS; PULLING LOGS FROM STEEP OR WET AREAS INACCESSIBLE TO SKIDDERS; OR OPERATING HOMEMADE SUSPENDED CABLE SYSTEMS TO HAUL LOGS FROM THE WOODS WITHOUT ENTRY BY MOBILE SKIDDERS.

SOME HOMEMADE LOGGING METHODS

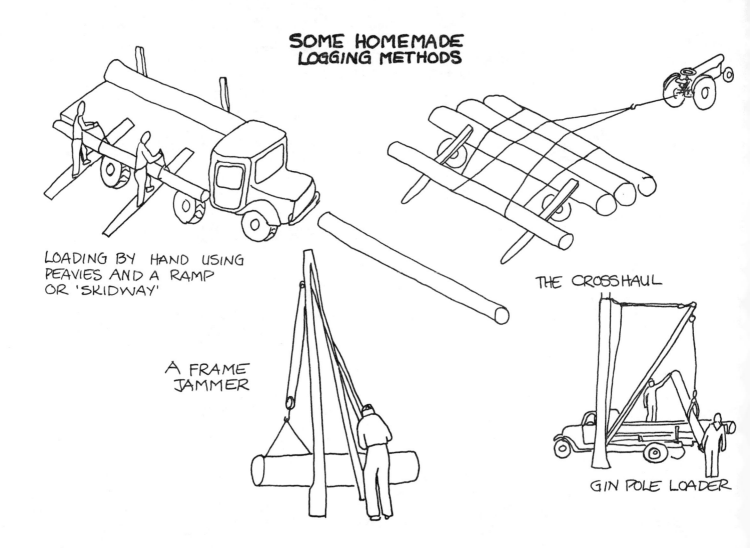

LOADING BY HAND USING PEAVIES AND A RAMP OR 'SKIDWAY'

A FRAME JAMMER

THE CROSSHAUL

GIN POLE LOADER

to haul a few logs for custom sawing and personal use. Or, perhaps a small quantity of high value veneer logs can make it worth hauling them to a mill yourself. House logs for your own use, if transported in small quantities, is another example of when it may not pay to hire a log hauler.

A hydraulic lift on a farm tractor can be used for loading full sized logs, as can a variety of homemade lifts, such as the ones pictured. The skidder can be used to pull the logs via a cross haul onto the truck as shown. For a small amount of loading, the time-honored method of rolling logs on-board with peavies is probably the easiest of all. A high bank next to the road helps. Otherwise, several ramp logs and a lot of muscle power can do the job.

Horse Logging

There is a revolution going on in the woods today, with the charge being led by none other than a horse brigade. The return to horse logging is belittled by manufacturers of skidders and even by some foresters, but by others it is being hailed as the only hope for winning thousands of private landowners to the side of forest management.

To get at the roots of the issue, Dawn and I visited a horse logger by the name of Scott Barbour. He is one of

BEST BOOKS FOR THE WOODLOT LOGGER

Barnacle Parp's Chain Saw Guide by Walter Hall. Rodale Press, Emmaus, PA. 18049

This paperback is the book to buy when considering the purchase of a chain saw or acquainting yourself with its use and maintenance. Its 257 pages are comprehensive, well-illustrated and easy to understand.

Professional Timber Falling — A Procedural Approach D. Douglas Dent. P.O. Box 905 Beaverton, Oregon 97005

As its title implies, this book is intended for the men who make their living falling timber. However, it is richly illustrated and written by an authority. It goes into more depth than you'll ever need, but it is the best book I have seen on this subject.

about a half dozen operating within an afternoon's drive of our home in Moscow, Idaho. But he is the only one who is trying to make a go of it full time and he is also a graduate from the University of Idaho's College of Forestry.

It was a bright winter day when we visited Scott. The sun was melting snow in the trees, making it sound like rain as the drops came down all around us. Winter is the slow period for horse loggers in mountain country. This is not because the horses can't make it, but because it is difficult to get trucks over the woods roads to pick up the logs for transport to the mill. Getting to Scott's house is in itself pleasantly difficult. We had to park about a mile down the mountain and walk through the melting snow to the log cabin Scott and his wife, Karen, and their horse named Duke call home. Scott and Karen manage the daily trip by skis or 4-wheel drive and feel it's a bargain in exchange for the peace and isolation of their little clearing high on the west Twin of Moscow Mountain.

I think 'peace and solitude' may be the key to Scott's motivation, and from what I can tell, it is the same for other horse loggers. Horse logging is not easy, but it also is not as complex, noisy or expensive as mechanical skidding operations. It is available to people who cannot afford the investment required for logging by machine, and it is ideal for the rare man or woman who wants to work alone. Scott is such a person, having no appetite to work for the Forest Service, industry or any other bureaucracy. Instead, he is working toward the goal of forming a consulting partnership with another forester with the intent of advising owners of small, private woodlands and doing their logging by horse. Scott says his partner can do the talking and he and the horses will tend to the logging. By his estimation, they will eventually reach peak efficiency by having Karen drive the horses while Scott fells and bucks the trees.

Scott admits he'll never get rich, but the figures he showed me are convincing that he'll be able to live quite comfortably. It also appears he will soon have all the work he can handle.

So how is it that Scott Barbour can compete successfully in this era of high tech logging and forestry? There are two reasons, both simple but important.

First, you can horse log where the production or volume per acre is too small to interest mechanized loggers. Thinning, improvement cutting and selection cutting often fall in this category. With low investment and no need to move large volumes of wood to make his equipment pay, a horse logger can afford a smaller yield per acre. Scott, for example, is happy skidding twenty 16-foot logs in a day's work with Duke alone. If someone else does the felling, limbing and bucking, he can triple that. But no mechanized logger could feed his gas hog on that amount of board feet per day and stay in business very long.

The second reason is that landowners who would never allow a mechanized logger to harvest their land will open their lands to horse loggers. The fear of damage to a beloved woodland reflects values that dollars alone cannot alter. These same people see horses as a way to practice forestry without ruts, erosion, crushed regeneration and scarred tree trunks.

Scott agrees that both reasons portend a bright future for horse loggers, but he is not a romantic. As he explained, 'People should not contract for horse logging if they think there will be no mess. There is still logging slash, some skid trails and some residual trees that get damaged during felling. There will be marks on the land, but it's a matter of degree." He also uses two chainsaws and has a small D-4 Cat. In fact, he won't accept a job unless the landowner allows the Cat as well as his horse. "This isn't uncommon," he explained. "Many or most horse loggers also have some mechanical equipment. Some haulers won't even come into a job unless a tractor of some kind is available in case they get stuck. I use mine for road building. After all, there is a limit on the time you can spend using animals. It may take me 15 minutes to do some work with the Cat that would take all day with my horse."

Limits play other important roles in horse logging. One of these is slope. The experts say that slopes over 45 percent are too tough to horse log, but Scott says he has gone as high as 60 percent by leaving limb stubs on the logs as brakes for the downhill trip. Just about all horse skidding must be downhill, with short uphill stretches not exceeding 10 percent. Sidehilling, or going across a slope, is out because of the danger it presents to the horse if a log begins to roll.

Perhaps the most important limit is skidding distance. Even a low-overhead horse logger can't turn a profit if the skidding is more than 600 to 800 feet. It simply takes too much time.

Finally, log size is important. Scott says 16-foot logs over 18-24 inches in diameter are too much for Duke. They take too much energy and time to make them worthwhile. When Scott can afford it, a team of horses may help the situation some, but in large timber, as in clearcuts or seed-tree harvest cuts, mechanized logging is best.

The only cloud Scott sees over horse logging is the few bad apples that can spoil the reputation of any profession. Many horse loggers have proven to be unreliable. They will start the job and not finish, take too long, or switch to a tractor half way through the operation. These kinds of things endear them to no one, including professional foresters who might otherwise recommend horse logging to more landowners.

Scott, however, is building a good reputation. Once he accepts a job, he camps there and works from 6 a.m. to 5 p.m. except for occasional days off, usually "to fix something." Moving horses is a chore and an expense, so Scott prefers to keep Duke on-site until the job is done. By camping there, Scott protects Duke not only from people, but as he says, "It's amazing the ways a horse can find to get into trouble."

What about buying a horse to help out on your land? Scott doesn't think it's a good idea. Using a horse logger or buying horses to become a contractor is one thing. But if a person already has a tractor or other means of doing the heavy work in his woodlot, it usually won't pay to buy a horse. A work horse is just that, argues Scott. Most people buy horses as a hobby for riding, sleighing and other pleasure purposes, but Scott claims that training for pulling logs through the woods is too specialized for the all-around pet. In fact, he allows no one else to handle Duke for fear of confusing the five-year-old. "Later, he'll be too set in his ways to let careless commands or movements mess up the job, but right now he's too young."

For the intrepid who would like to try horse logging as a business, the only way to learn is by apprenticeship. For a partner, the commonly used breeds are Belgians, Percherons, Clydesdales and Shires. Mules are also used, their owners claiming they can pull more for their size and are easier to keep. Like most owners, Scott thinks his horse is the ideal. Duke weighs 1,600 lbs. and stands 16 hands high (about 64 inches), which is on the small side as draft horses go. But his smaller size means greater coordination and stability in the woods, less feed needed, and easier transport from job to job.

The prospective horse logger must also weigh his costs. In addition to the horse and feed, there are vet bills, collars, harnesses, skidding chains and tongs, special slip-resistant shoes, a trailer or truck for transport, and various other expenses that can add up quickly.

Horse logging is not for everyone, but contrary to the opinion of some professional economists who snort at horse logging, in many cases it makes both dollars and good sense. True, if you are not a do-it-yourselfer and you own a stand of timber with enough volume and value to attract the bids of mechanical loggers, you may not get as high a stumpage price if you choose horse logging. Some loggers, in fact, offer the choice and will do it for you either way. But the reduced daily production of horse logging will require you to accept a lower price for the slower, more careful and less damaging approach. On the other hand, for small jobs, a businessman like Scott may be the only person interested, and his bid will seem very attractive.

Horse logging does have its niche in the woods, both economically and aesthetically. If the thought of dozers or giant wheeled monsters is too much for you, remember that a Scott Barbour and Duke are probably not far away, peacefully pulling logs to the roadside. You might want to give them a try.

For More About Horse Logging...

Draft Horses and Mules in the 1980's. Draft Horse and Mule Association of America, 521 Elden Dr., Cary, IL 60013.

This free, 30-page booklet describes the association as well as the many ways true horsepower is being revived on farms and in the woods. Well illustrated.

Small Farmer's Journal. 3890 Stewart St., Eugene, OR 97402.

This is a quarterly that frequently includes news and helpful information on logging with horses. There is also plenty of other information useful to woodland owners.

Draft Horse and Mule—Youth and Beginners Manual. Available from the Draft Horse and Mule Association of America, 521 Elden Dr., Cary, IL 60013.

Thirty-two pages packed full of basics on the breeds available, determining age and condition, feeding, general care and other valuable information.

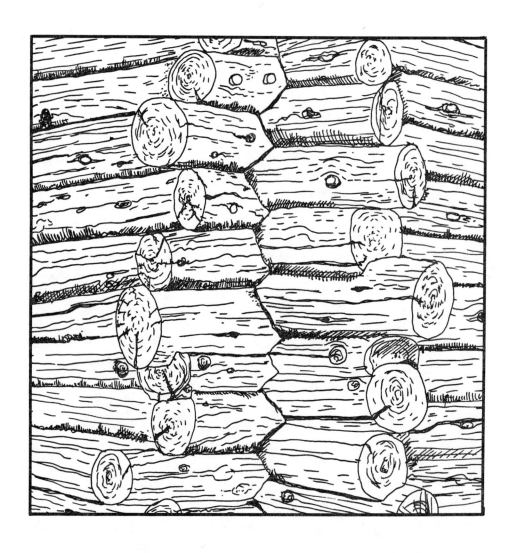

9 A Crop of Timber
is
More than Logs

> *Some of the best relationships come from*
> *working together in the woods...*
> —George Freeman
> Award-winning Woodland Steward

The woodlands of North America are a cornucopia of products. At last count the flow of products numbered more than 5,000, ranging from lumber to chemicals for toothpaste. Predictions are that consumption will more than double in the next three decades, further strengthening this industry which is now the sixth largest in the United States and a leading exporter in Canada.

The value of forest products is well known to the men and women I interviewed while touring private woodlands across the country. All wanted to make a profit from their land, from their crop of trees. But there was, also, down to a person, an expressed desire for something from their woodlands not measurable in dollars. The reward of woodland stewardship was clearly recognized as something more than logs.

In the pages that follow are some of these woodland stewards. In the spirit of kinship common in forestry, they have freely shared their ideas and their solutions to the problems they encountered trying to manage a forest. They also embody the essentials of success—optimism, a desire to learn, the will to work hard, and a sense of responsibility to others and the land.

Hardwoods Are Special

George Freeman says with a blink that his fascination for oak may have begun with his principal's oak paddle. Or, like the first pioneers of forestry in America, perhaps it was the carefully groomed forests of Germany that sparked his interests, a sight he recalls from his military service in that country.

George now owns 711 acres of woodland in the hills of western Pennsylvania. He is the winner of a county conservation award from the Soil Conservation Service, a regional winner of the Outstanding Tree Farmer of the Year award from the Pennsylvania Forestry Association, and the winner of Pennsylvania's prestigious Maurice Goddard Forestry Award. Not bad for a guy who makes his living managing the truck fleet for Quaker State Oil and negotiating labor agreements.

George began assembling his forest land in 1957 with the purchase of a 60-acre parcel made possible through a partnership. Unfortunately, the partner wanted to strip mine. George's interest was the trees. His next purchases were made on his own—usually parcels that had been logged off and were available at a good price. Finally, he picked up an old adjoining farm after its house burned down. Today this is the center of his idyllic retreat. The barn sports a fresh coat of red paint, a one-acre pond provides for fire protection, and a cozy living quarters-shop-workroom has been added for weekend use. The old fields now grow red pine, larch, Norway spruce, the most delicious of blackberries, and 11 acres of corn. There is a picnic area, too, and a large mowed lawn, for the Freeman Farm is as much a social center as it is a tree business.

"I wouldn't call this a hobby," says George. "You don't work this hard at a hobby! I want to build it up and someday make it a full-time occupation. I enjoy it that much. And you'd be surprised at the market value of the trees on this land."

Trees grow rapidly in the moist hills of Pennsylvania, and even abused acreage can be molded into a fine forest with the right kind of attention. George Freeman gives it that attention. For example, the one real curse of the place is a jungle-like invasion of wild grapes. Clearcutting and high-grading during earlier ownership created ideal conditions for the creeping canopy of grape vines. They smother the regeneration and climb into the highest limbs of residual trees, gradually choking the life out of them.

To George, the grapes have almost become an obsession. As soon as I arrived he showed me the scourge of gray mats plainly visible in his aerial photos. We visited those spots first in his Jeep. The problem is common throughout the East, but this was the worst I had ever seen. What makes George stand out as a tree farmer is that he is one person who is meeting the challenge head on. Never have I seen a more aggressive, nor a more successful, one-man campaign against an enemy of the forest. It is truly hand-to-hand combat.

The method George uses to control the vines is direct, safe, painfully slow, and highly effective. He simply cuts each vine stem, not just once so it is free to swing down and start new roots, but twice so that a section several feet long is removed. Then, to make certain the old roots do not send up new shoots, he coats the "stump" with a herbicide from his sidearm applicator that hangs like a gun from his belt.

The goal is to completely eradicate the wild grapes from all 711 acres. It is largely George's fight, but sometimes he hires local boys or out-of-work laborers. It has also helped put spending money in the pockets of his three sons as they worked their way through college.

As a family the Freemans kill vines, plant trees, cut about 10 cords of firewood each year for their own use, mark trees for selective cutting and maintain the network of roads they planned and developed themselves with the help of a Case 350 bulldozer. Through it all, strong family bonds were formed. Says George, "When the boys were growing, these woods were invaluable. We could talk. Some of the best relationships come from working together in the woods or sitting down to lunch over a peanut butter and jelly sandwich." And now, he added, the young men are beginning to realize the economic value of their old daddy's madness, and this bodes well for the future of Freeman's Farm.

The object of these efforts is a mixed hardwood forest rich in red and white oaks, black cherry, tulip poplar and sugar maple. Oak is George's favorite and along with sugar maple, is favored in selection cutting. Yellow poplar is also desirable, but it requires larger openings or group selection cutting to get the greater amount of light needed for its regeneration. That, unfortunately, would also favor the accursed grapes.

An exception to selection cutting on Freeman Farm is a 10-acre clearcut made in 1981. It is ugly, like most clearcuts, but local foresters convinced George it was the best method. The trees there were generally on the decline but a good understory of sun-loving cherry was present. Reluctantly, George gave the go-ahead. "It was a hard thing to do, to cut such beautiful trees," George told me with an anguished expression. But there were plenty of 18- to 24-inch veneer logs that brought income that helped ease the pain.

Harvesting is not a favorite activity with the Freemans. A local service forester considered it a great accomplishment when he finally convinced George it had to be done. The first loggers he employed did little to assuage his fears. He said with a laugh, "My dad always said to be cautious of anyone with oil or sawdust on their boots."

So, when he began to allow logging, he was cautious, but not cautious enough.

"I required a performance bond," said George, "but it was not large enough. They backed a truck into my gas pump and left ruts all over the place. They really tore up the land."

He also found it necessary to coax them along and to spend a lot of time waiting for the job to get done. Now he gladly pays a consulting forester to ride herd on the logging and things are going a lot easier.

Much of the acreage needs improvement cutting, and this George pursues with enthusiasm. It is like a handicraft

to him, using his saw to shape a forest of tall, thriving hardwoods. Normally this would suggest a good opportunity to sell firewood, but George doesn't want the trouble of overseeing cutting by others or the liability of people hurting themselves. He gave away an area of blowdowns to a local family, and once he tried making a few extra dollars by hauling a load to Pittsburgh for sale. There a bizarre thing happened, perhaps a "first" in the history of forestry.

"I had just come out of the Liberty Tunnels and was going down Saw Mill Run Boulevard with my truck full of firewood. Some guy starts blowing his horn at me, so I pulled over. He comes up, mad as hell, and informed me I was in his territory! Would you believe, a firewood Mafia?"

George seems to have no desire to be on the wrong side of anyone. To keep deer under control, George and his family share their hunting privileges with others, but he limits it to 70 people, using a rigid permit system. This way he not only controls the deer, but also the hunters, and even illegal hunting. "I've found my permittees actually patrol the area for me," George grinned. And to give the deer a fair shake, he compromises his dislike of grapes and leaves some as a screen along many of the roadsides.

He also gives permission for motor biking if people ask first, but he restricts it to the roads. On that point he says, "I've found kids to be no trouble at all, it's the parents who come in without asking or ride all over the place!"

In visiting with George Freeman, it quickly became apparent that he is a man of foresight. His view toward mineral rights serves as an example. To the grief of some land purchasers, they discover they own the surface rights to a parcel but someone else owns the rights to drill or dig for the minerals that underlie it. This can wreak havoc on management plans, to say nothing of what it can do to the land's future value. George always buys the mineral rights for each parcel he acquires. But he cleverly went beyond that in one case. This was the day he sold a desirable 80-acre parcel next to a local reservoir. The sale was to a minister for a boys' camp, and it was a piece of land that figured prominently in George's own boyhood. To be certain the property and the lake would not be abused, he retained the mineral rights. Sure enough, he later found out the good minister had actually intended to strip mine the place to raise funds.

Strip mining is an old plague to many eastern woodlands. "Skinnin' n' guttin' the land" they called it in West Virginia when I was in school. As forestry students we visited many of those areas, usually with an eye toward what could be done to rehabilitate the scars and impoverished soil called "overburden." Black locust was the big hope, with its ability to add nitrogen to the soil from tiny nodules on its roots. It did well on those awful places, quickly starting the decades-long process of rebuilding the spongy humus and duff to hold moisture and form a bed for new growth. But a strip-mined area is never the same.

Today new laws have forced operators to restore some of the original contour to the land, getting rid of the ugly step-like cliffs and deep troughs that mar the forests in so many places. Some reclaimed sites are actually impressive. But it still takes a lifetime to restore the forest, and in many cases the cover type may never again be the same.

Despite the enticing cash offers from mining companies, George will have none of the coal blight. He won't even allow them to do test drillings. But like salesmen who won't take "no" for an answer, the coal people keep coming. In some cases, they even sneak onto his property and sink test holes.

Another aggravation is a quarter-mile of township road that crosses a piece of his land. Uncharacteristic anger comes to the surface when George talks about it. The problem is the universal one of road crews who are insensitive to the beauty and usefulness of trees. In this case, numerous trees along the edge of George's forest were cut or gouged during the installation of road drains.

His own road building is done with more care. A Case 350 bulldozer has provided him with good access to all of his land, allowing the kind of intensive treatment George wants for his oaks.

Careful, far-sighted and methodical are probably the traits that sum up George Freeman, the hardwood grower. Of all the woodland owners interviewed for this book, George was the only one who kept such good records that he could actually give an estimate of the financial returns on his total investment. Today it stands at a fantastic 25 percent, a figure enviable in any enterprise. Some of this, of course, is the result of buying land when its price was low due to the previous owner's short-sighted highgrading, then nurturing it back to a healthy forest. Part is also from the high-value lumber and veneer logs sought by local furniture factories. But most is simply from George's love of his woodland and the superior management he brings to it.

As we headed toward the blackberry patch before our trip back to Pittsburgh, I asked George what advice he might offer someone who has just acquired a woodlot. With little hesitation he offered this: First, be sure you know and mark the boundary lines exactly. Second, determine your stand volumes by species. Third, get some of that free advice from local service foresters and the Soil Conservation Service. He added, "I don't know how they pick those guys, but I've never run into a bad one. They give you alternatives. Finally, do your own research!" In George's case, that research is paying off handsomely.

Walnut—Black Gold

Black walnut! It has been called our best friend in times of war and peace. Its strength, resistance to decay and wonderful workability have made it the standard for gun stocks. Its fine, dark grain has also been treasured for three centuries as perhaps the premier wood for furniture and cabinets. So valued is its wood that buyers will sometimes bid for a single tree in an urban backyard, paying prices that virtually make walnut trees the gold mine of forestry.

It was a hot afternoon in July when Dawn and I stopped in to visit a walnut woodlot in the heartland of America. The place was an old farm on the outskirts of Crawfordsville, Indiana, almost dead center in the range where walnut grows best. It was pleasantly situated on the mounds that pass for hills in Indiana, with a lazy stream called Sugar Creek meandering through a valley west of the old white farmhouse.

BLACK WALNUT
JUGLANS NIGRA L.

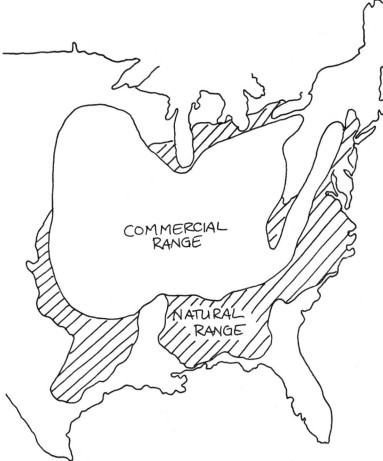

COMMERCIAL RANGE

NATURAL RANGE

Soil Maps and Planting

The senior Moore began planting, both in the alluvial soil of the bottomland and in the upland fields that were once planted in corn. We walked through the results of these efforts, row after row of beautiful walnut trees interspersed with rows of white oak, red oak, white ash, black cherry and sweet gum. There were also poorly formed butternuts, which Raoul said were a mistake to plant.

We saw other mistakes, but mistakes are just part of woodland management. Raoul views the mistakes as learning experiences. For example, not all the walnuts were 15-inch DBH beauties with straight, clearly-pruned trunks. Some were scraggly and short, and the reason was poor soil. "The first step," stressed Raoul, "is to get a soil map."

As premier trees, black walnuts deserve premier soil. There, growth will be rapid. On sites of lesser quality, it may be better to plant oaks, pines or some other species. Walnut sites should have deep, fertile, well drained soil. Look for a uniform dark- or yellowish-brown color sandy loam, loam or silt loam to a depth of at least 24 inches. The Moores' 3-acre sand bar is not the place for walnut. Neither is clay soil or any soil with a hard layer hidden near the surface. Where there is a choice in aspect, the moist north and east sides of slopes, especially near the bottom, are the best places for black walnut.

Planting can be done rapidly with a dibble bar, shovel or the heel of a boot, using seeds easily prepared at home. Or, one-year-old nursery stock can be planted in the usual manner. With either seeds or seedlings, rodents are a big problem. To keep them at bay, use wire cones or large tin cans with their tops perforated. Putting cans in a bonfire before using will remove the tin coating and allow them to disintegrate as seedlings grow beyond their most vulnerable stage of life.

Aside from its visual beauty, the day was horrible. It didn't seem to bother our host, but to us mountain folks the heat and humidity were staggering. We dripped sweat in the shade, and flies and mosquitoes came at us in waves. There was poison ivy as well, covering the ground so densely it was impossible to avoid as we made our way toward the woods.

But as we left the path next to the hayfield and entered the woods, we entered a scene as exciting as I have ever encountered in a privately owned woodlot. Suddenly, we were surrounded by walnut trees. I had grown up in country where they could be found in a scattered array, but never had I seen so many in one place. It was a bit like walking into the vaults of Fort Knox. Our host, Raoul Moore, agreed, calling his woodlot "the ultimate in deferred gratification!"

Raoul's woodlot was his father's hobby farm. John Moore was an English professor at nearby Wabash College. But he loved hardwood trees and in 1956 bought 40 acres of farmland where he began a vigorous improvement and planting project. Apple trees were his real penchant and he soon had 120 different varieties. However, he also had enough foresight to almost immediately do an improvement cut on Sugar Creek's rich flood plain. At the time it was an unmanaged jungle of vines, brush, and low-grade trees overtopping young walnuts and other high-value hardwoods.

"The place was a mess, but we were lucky," Raoul said. "The farmer who owned it before us paid a dozer operator to clear-cut the flood plain. But, when the guy got half done, the farmer paid him and he never came back to finish the job!"

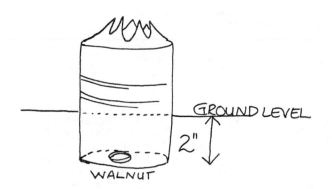

GROUND LEVEL

2"

WALNUT

WALNUTS FROM SEED OR SEEDLING

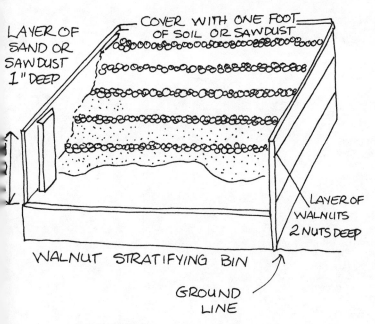

LAYER OF SAND OR SAWDUST 1" DEEP

COVER WITH ONE FOOT OF SOIL OR SAWDUST

WALNUT STRATIFYING BIN

LAYER OF WALNUTS 2 NUTS DEEP

GROUND LINE

WHEN PURCHASING FROM A NURSERY, LOOK FOR...

1 YEAR OLD

TOP AT LEAST 10"-14" LONG

IDEAL WALNUT SEEDLING

STEM AT LEAST 1/4" IN DIAMETER 1" ABOVE ROOT COLLAR

ROOT SYSTEM LARGE, FIBEROUS, UNBROKEN AND SHOWING NO ROT

WALNUTS CAN EASILY BE PREPARED AT HOME FOR SPRING PLANTING. COLLECT THE NUTS FROM A LOCALLY GROWING TREE. BE SURE TO SELECT ONE OF EXCELLENT FORM AND VIGOR TO TAKE ADVANTAGE OF HEREDITARY TRAITS. THEN...

1. HULL THE WALNUTS
2. SELECT A COOL, MOIST PLACE FOR A STRATIFYING BIN OR WELL-DRAINED PIT AS ILLUSTRATED.
3. PROTECT FROM RODENTS, BUT PLACE YOUR BIN OR PIT WHERE IT WILL BE SUBJECT TO THE VARIATIONS OF WINTER TEMPERATURES.
4. IN SPRING, REMOVE THE NUTS AND PUT IN A TUB OF WATER. HOLLOW ONES WILL FLOAT AND SHOULD BE DISCARDED.
5. PLANT THE OTHERS 2"-3" DEEP. OVER PLANT TO ASSURE ADEQUATE NUMBER OF SURVIVORS

Other enemies of young walnuts are grass and other competing vegetation. When planting, strip back any sod cover for several feet around the seedlings, or cultivate two to four times a year. These intensive grass and brush control efforts should be continued for about four years, or until the walnuts are well above their neighbors. The result can be gratifying when you consider that walnut growth can be doubled during the first five years by such measures.

Being sun lovers, walnuts need large openings if interplanted within an existing stand of trees. The diameter of the opening should be at least equal to the height of the surrounding trees.

Many landowners use chemicals to control grass and brush, but Raoul will have nothing to do with them. "I'll do it by hand or accept the slower growth," says Raoul.

Pruning is Key to Quality

The trees are a memorial to Raoul's father. They are also a tribute to Raoul who feels a responsibility to carry on what his father began. John Moore's dream was to have a crop of walnut of which 80 percent would be suitable for veneer. Raoul works toward that objective by visiting each tree during the dormant season and practicing the essential art of pruning.

There is no single method of pruning, but there are two guiding principles. The first is that a single, straight stem should be developed. As illustrated, this begins when the seedling is only a few feet tall, usually in the tree's third year of life.

113

CORRECTIVE PRUNING

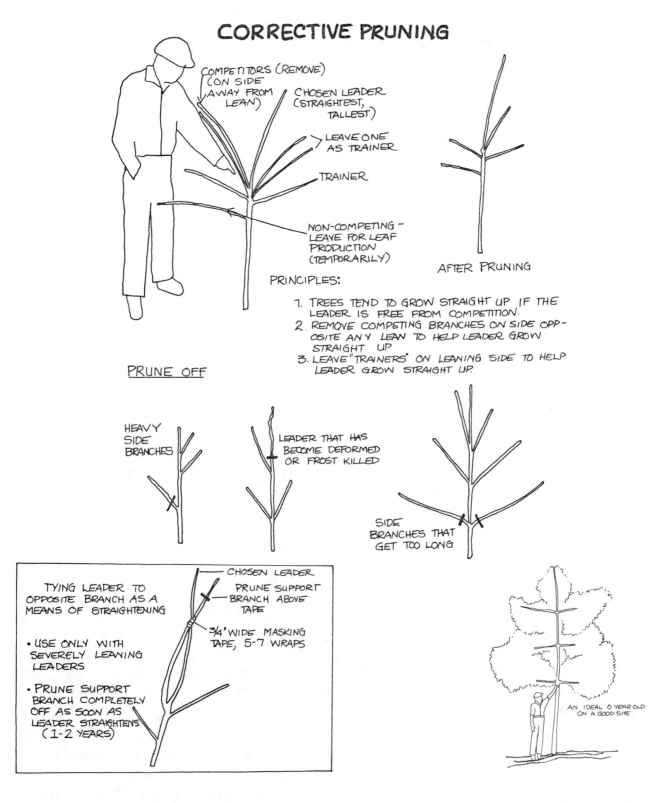

COMPETITORS (REMOVE) (ON SIDE AWAY FROM LEAN)

CHOSEN LEADER (STRAIGHTEST, TALLEST)

LEAVE ONE AS TRAINER

TRAINER

NON-COMPETING - LEAVE FOR LEAF PRODUCTION (TEMPORARILY)

AFTER PRUNING

PRINCIPLES:

1. TREES TEND TO GROW STRAIGHT UP IF THE LEADER IS FREE FROM COMPETITION.
2. REMOVE COMPETING BRANCHES ON SIDE OPPOSITE ANY LEAN TO HELP LEADER GROW STRAIGHT UP.
3. LEAVE "TRAINERS" ON LEANING SIDE TO HELP LEADER GROW STRAIGHT UP.

PRUNE OFF

HEAVY SIDE BRANCHES

LEADER THAT HAS BECOME DEFORMED OR FROST KILLED

SIDE BRANCHES THAT GET TOO LONG

TYING LEADER TO OPPOSITE BRANCH AS A MEANS OF STRAIGHTENING

- USE ONLY WITH SEVERELY LEANING LEADERS
- PRUNE SUPPORT BRANCH COMPLETELY OFF AS SOON AS LEADER STRAIGHTENS (1-2 YEARS)

CHOSEN LEADER

PRUNE SUPPORT BRANCH ABOVE TAPE

3/4" WIDE MASKING TAPE, 5-7 WRAPS

AN IDEAL 6 YEAR OLD ON A GOOD SITE

Through careful cutting with sharp clippers, corrective pruning can take advantage of a tree's natural tendencies and produce straight trunks free of crooks or forks. Few woodland trees other than walnut warrant the time-consuming care demanded for quality form. But by annually inspecting and carefully shaping each tree in its first few years of life, the owner will be rewarded well.

The second principle of pruning is not very different from that covered in Chapter 6. Beginning at about age five, all side branches should eventually be sawed off, flush with the trunk, to a height of at least 17 feet. In walnut, it pays to

go even higher. Branches should be pruned before they reach 1 to 1½ inches in diameter, and no more than half the living crown should be pruned in any one year.

As we walked through Raoul's woodlot, trees were noticeable that obviously had gotten beyond the point where pruning could help.

"I didn't listen to Dad as much as I should have," my host explained. "There was a period of years when some of them got away from me. It really takes constant attention and learning."

Raoul now attends workshops occasionally and some

forestry courses at Purdue University. He is also visited by a service forester every five years for re-certification in Indiana's Tree Farm System, which keeps his property taxes at a remarkably low rate.

Spacing

Spacing is an important issue with walnut growers. The Moores used approximately 15 x 15-foot spacing, taking their cue from spacing they observed in natural stands. But the experts suggest starting with 10-foot spacing if tractor cultivation is to be used or even 8-foot with chemical weed control. The closer spacing is initially more expensive but gives you more potential crop trees to select during thinning. Eventually, only about 75 trees per acre should remain when they are 12 inches DBH. This means that if a happy medium of 12 x 12 feet is used, three-fourths of the original planting of 300 trees per acre can be lost or thinned out while still ending up with the optimal final spacing.

Since the foliage of walnut is rather thin, pure stands allow large amounts of light to penetrate to ground level. This aids sod growth and tends to promote limb growth, making more work for the pruner. To counter this, some growers interplant other species to provide a thicker canopy but without competing with the walnuts. Raoul's father used this method, selecting species for alternate rows that grow at about the same rate as walnut. Fast growers like cottonwood, sycamore or yellow-poplar would soon overtop the walnuts, creating more problems than they would prevent. Black locust and autumn olive are sometimes recommended since these species add nitrogen to the soil, which is then used by the walnuts. Christmas trees are also sometimes interplanted, not so much for natural shading as to use the soil and space for a profitable crop while the walnuts are still saplings.

Extra Care and Extra Cash

The high value and intensive management of walnut suggest that it is a tree crop well suited for small properties. Raoul's walnuts cover 30 acres, and some plantations are even smaller. The right site and proper devotion to the trees each year are more important than extensive acreage. A small, successful plantation is better than a large failure.

Raoul is striving for quality veneer and growth of ½-inch in diameter each year. In ten more years he anticipates his first large harvest of logs of 18- to 20-inch DBH. After that, he expects trees planted later or growing slower to provide a continuing cycle of cuts that will keep the cash flowing. In the meantime, he supplements his income with occasional sales of soft maple, cottonwood, and other logs removed in thinnings, improvement cuttings, or from areas not planted in walnut. He even uses the branches from harvested trees, trucking them himself to the ready firewood market in Indianapolis.

Nuts offer another opportunity. Raoul explained that Indiana's walnuts are not good enough for the large, commercial industry, but he does sell some locally each year. What wonderful trees to provide annual cash crops while adding wood for the ultimate payoff as veneer!

These precious trees require special protection. The monetary value of a mature walnut is so great that the theft of individual trees is not uncommon. In fact, shade trees have even been stolen from front lawns! Some ways to help safeguard against theft include limiting access roads to points that go past occupied dwellings, strong, locking metal gates, and good relations with neighbors who can help watch for thieves.

Raoul has also found it necessary to carefully control hunters. "One bullet can change a $4,000 veneer log into a $50 sawlog," he said, without much exaggeration. "And a shotgun can wipe out a sapling. But deer can wipe them out, too."

Raoul, who doesn't hunt and who is only gradually coming to condone it at all, estimates that for a time 20 trees a year were lost or damaged due to hunting. His solution is to allow hunting only by bow and arrow, a condition that attracts a sufficient number of enthusiastic hunters, goes easy on the trees, and helps keep deer numbers under control.

Raoul takes life pretty easy, working with his trees, growing some corn and asparagus for cash, dabbling in the sale of solar technology, and building his own house on a wooded bluff overlooking peaceful Sugar Creek. Without question, he is enjoying life and his woodland is a central part of his existence.

BEST SOURCES ON WALNUTS

Planting Black Walnut for Timber by F. Bryan Clark, USDA Forest Service Leaflet No. 487. U.S. Government Printing Office, Washington, D.C. 20402.

A short, authoritative summary that provides good tips on soils, site preparation, seeds, seedlings and spacing.

Growing Walnut for Profit and Pleasure. Fine Hardwoods/American Walnut Association, 5603 W. Raymond St., Suite "O", Indianapolis, Indiana 46241.

This booklet contains some of the above plus information on how to cut and market logs for maximum value. This industry association is worth knowing about for a variety of information and advice.

Corrective Pruning of Black Walnut for Timber Form by Walter F. Beineke. Purdue University, Cooperative Extension Service, West Lafayette, Indiana 47907.

Purdue is a leader in walnut research and this is just one of several pamphlets that will help with your woodlot. For example, one on "Grafting Black Walnut" introduces an interesting topic that is beyond the scope of this book. Ask for a list of their other publications.

Walnut Council, PO Box 41121, Indianapolis, Indiana 46241. Landowners, industry types, foresters and researchers belong to this organization. It is dedicated to encouraging the culture, planting, management and utilization of walnut. It has a reasonable membership fee and is well worth joining.

Logs for a Home

If there is romance in growing forest trees, surely the epitome is using your own logs for your own house. To most of us this is only a dream, but to Al and Daryl Kyle it is reality.

Al and Daryl have carved their niche in the woods of northern Idaho. They and their four adopted children share part of the family farm where Daryl grew up. They returned there to settle after seeing the world as a military family and getting advanced degrees in their professions. Their education, however, led them to the conclusion that the real values in life are to be found on the farm and in the forest—not in the pursuit of riches or status. Today their lives revolve around a happy combination of family, sheep, cows, chickens, hay, garden crops, and the best meals imaginable, all as natural as possible and mostly coming from the labor of their own hands. Life for the Kyles is subsistence farming, or as close to it as is practical, and happiness is a full woodshed and a fire in the hearth of their own log house.

The family's three-bedroom house is built on three levels, the first and second floors connected by a spiraling wood staircase. Wiser now from the mistakes, triumphs and discoveries of their first building venture, they will eventually add more to their house. Al built the house on his own, learning from books like the ones suggested on page 118. The dream may be more possible than you think— all of Al's logs came from only 30 acres of his adjoining woodlot.

The log-gathering process took two years, fitted between chores and odd jobs. Like most visitors to the farm in those days, Dawn and I lent a hand with the logs one warm spring day. Al did the felling and skidding, then the rest of us worked on peeling. Using garden hoes, pulaskies, or a drawknife, we stripped the wet bark down to the shiny white core of the log. These were then piled in criss-crossed layers and covered with straw and a tarp for the long, slow period of drying. Seasoning the logs in such a manner for several months or a year will reduce splitting and eliminate later shrinking and twisting which can virtually pull the house from its foundation.

Al used top quality trees for his house logs, tall and straight and naturally pruned from the dense shade of a bottomland site. The fewer knots, Al knew, the fewer the problems with shaping and rot. The trees were mostly Douglas-fir, which offers the great strength needed in a two-story house and easy workability that is increasingly appreciated as each log is grooved and trimmed to fit the one beneath it. Al's logs measure 12- to 14-inches in diameter, but next time he'll go to 16-inches to help speed the wall building. Also, the difficulties of working with a heavier log are balanced by the added insulation it offers.

The box on page 117 can be used to roughly compare the insulation values of logs. To standardize the comparison, figures are for 12% moisture content. R-values vary greatly with moisture content; wetter wood loses more heat. To figure the total insulating value of a solid log wall, multiply its thickness times the R-value. Assuming the logs fit tightly and most of their diameter is used, this will be slightly on the conservative side since there is an accumulative insulating effect of adding more inches to the thickness.

For estimating more precisely at a range of moisture levels, consult the *Wood Handbook* published as Forest Service Agriculture Handbook No. 72. For comparison, a frame wall, typically insulated with a 3½-inch bat of fiberglass, has an R-value of about 11. You will also find that because a material's insulating value depends on tiny air spaces, the lighter the wood, e.g., balsam poplar, the higher its R-value. Unfortunately, the tradeoff is less resistance to decay.

Al learned something he did not find in any of the books. It is easier to work with short walls than with long spans. This is good news for the woodland owner that may not have the long 20- to 30-foot lengths common in the log house business. When he adds to his house, Al plans to break long walls with a jog so he can use the more workable lengths. This method is also a way to use lower quality logs, since short but good wood may be left after defects are cut off.

Logs from Your Land

In many areas of the country buyers of house logs are becoming an important market for woodland owners. Nearly 1,000 companies are now scattered around the country. A few, like Mountain Gem Log Homes in Sandpoint, Idaho, specialize in dead, dry snags which are higher in R-value and eliminate the shrinkage problems that can create major problems for home builders. Mountain Gem specifies a minimum diameter of 10 inches.

More commonly, green logs with diameters as small as 6 inches are purchased. Your local forester, Roger Hard's book, or a look at ads in country living-style magazines, will provide leads on log buyers in your area.

The preferred species for house logs in the East are eastern white cedar, red pine and white pine. In the West they are Douglas fir, redwood, spruces, true firs, western redcedars, white pine and lodgepole pine.

In planning your own house, you can easily determine if you have enough trees for the job. From a blueprint or other estimate, determine the total linear log lengths necessary for the building. Then review your cruise data or make an actual count in your woods to see if you can match the required number. Roger Hard estimates you will need 6,000 to 6,500 lineal feet of 8- to 12-inch logs for a 20 x 40-foot, 1½ story, cape-style log home. This comes out to at least 300 trees, averaging one 20-foot log each.

Boards and Awards

Like so many of the people we interviewed, Al and Daryl Kyle are intensely involved with their woodland. They know its resources and are continually thinking about its potentials. The economic contribution their woods makes to their lifestyle is not taken lightly.

Besides using house logs, they have their lumber custom sawed from logs they provide to a mill. Some woodland owners are even doing the sawing themselves, selling the excess to neighbors. This has been made possible by a simple, inexpensive portable sawmill that is

SOME VALUES OF COMMONLY-USED HOUSE LOGS

Species	R-Value (per inch at 12% moisture content)	Workability	Bending Strength	Resistance to Decay
Aspen	1.22	Fair	Week	Poor
Balsam Poplar	1.33	Good	Weak	Poor
Balsam Fir	1.27	Good	Weak	Poor
Basswood	1.24	Good	Weak	Poor
Black Spruce	1.16	Fair	Weak	Poor
Cedars-				
Red (Eastern)	1.03	Good	Weak	Excellent
Red (Western)	1.09	Good	Weak	Excellent
Northern White	1.41	Good	Weak	Excellent
Cottonwood	1.23	Fair	Weak	Poor
Cypress	1.04	Fair	Weak	Excellent
Douglas-fir	.99	Fair	Strong	Good
Hemlock	1.16	Fair	Weak	Poor
Pines-				
Jack	1.20	Good	Fair	Fair
Ponderosa	1.16	Good	Fair	Fair
Red	1.04	Good	Fair	Poor
White	1.32	Good	Fair	Fair
Redwood	1.00	Good	Weak	Excellent
Tamarack	.93	Fair	Fair	Fair
Yellow Poplar	1.13	Good	Fair	Poor

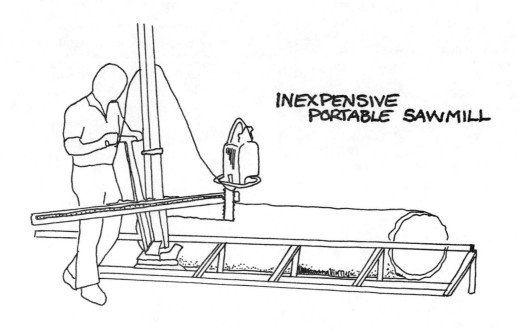

INEXPENSIVE PORTABLE SAWMILL

little more than a heavy duty chainsaw mounted vertically and pushed along a track. One such rig is available from Portable Sawmill Systems of LaGrande, Oregon.

The drive and tenacity necessary to build a log house shows up other ways in Al Kyle. In fact, he tends the 160-acre family forest as intensively as anyone I have ever known in the West. Al has mapped, measured and planned. He spends about 100 hours a year pre-commercially thinning some stands, with the Agricultural Soil and Conservation Service compensating him for his labor as part of their cost-sharing package. He harvests other areas for sale of the logs at roadside; sorts and sells or uses his cuttings as lumber, fence posts, barn poles or firewood; piles and burns the slash; and, of course, carefully protects and marks the best Doug firs for future walls of his expanded house.

With an eye to the future and a mind curious about how trees grow and respond to his labors, Al even has a series of research plots in his woodlot. He keeps careful cost records on these areas—some are thinned as needed, others have had the lodgepole pine removed to favor ponderosa, while still others are allowed to remain in their original condition. By measuring growth rates and values over time, Al will have an account of what pays off and what does not. The research will be of help to other landowners in the area and is providing the Kyles with one more dimension of enjoyment and learning from their land.

Best References on Log Houses

The Wilderness Cabin. Calvin Rutstrum.
  Collier Macmillan Publishers, New York.

  More text in proportion to illustrations.
This one also goes into non-log structures, and its 194 pages are full of useful insights ranging from acquiring land to living in a log house.

Building a Log House in Alaska. Axel Carlson
  and Sandy Jamieson. Cooperative Extension
  Service, University of Alaska, College, Alaska
  99701.

  From the land where log buildings are
serious business, 75 pages of illustrated tips and plans for buildings and furnishings.

The Log House Book. Jack Kramer. The New
  American Library, New York.

  Photos, drawings and brief but authoritative explanations on all aspects of planning, building and protecting a log home. 142 pages.

Build Your Own Low-Cost Log Home. Roger
  Hard. Garden Way Publishing, Charlotte,
  Vermont 05445.

  Detailed, practical and clearly illustrated.
Its 200 pages cover all aspects including a list of manufacturers of log home kits for landowners lacking enough trees of their own.

Other Products

Lumber, veneer, chemicals, and woodcrafts—with the ever-growing number of products from wood, it pays to explore markets and match the species and condition of your trees with the best buyer for each product. It is important not to view your trees as the raw material for only one kind of product. Buyers may prefer that you do, because they then may pay you the lowest common price. Instead, if there is variety in your timber, sort your logs by their best potential use and sell or use them that way.

At the Kyle farm, Al routinely separated logs as he cut them into stacks of saw logs (lumber), house logs, barn poles, fence posts, firewood, and cedar logs for fence rails or roof shingles. In other areas of the country, pulpwood, veneer, railroad ties, mine props and even stumps for chemical distillation suggest possible categories for sorting.

Explore local markets, then ask buyers for specifications and prices. If the price is right and your products can meet the "specs," you may have new opportunities for making the most of your woodlot. Following are a few of the more common products and general specifications. These vary widely, so be sure to check markets locally and have a buyer before you cut.

Pulpwood

If veneer logs are the premium wines of the woodlot, logs for pulpwood are the bread and butter. Particularly in Canada, the South and the Lake States, it may pay to consider trees for pulpwood as your main or even your only crop. In southern pine coastal areas, a crop may be produced in as little as 20 years! In many areas, trees from thinnings and improvement cuttings, and small-diameter trees in a clearcut can be marketed as pulpwood. In some areas in recent years, wood once only considered for pulpwood has brought a better price as firewood. Still, for landowners who prefer minimum involvement in sales, or who want someone else to do all the work, pulpwood buyers are by far the easiest to find.

Specifications:
- Minimum diameter, small end, usually not under 4-inch, but 7-inch is more practical.
- Lengths commonly are 4-foot or tree length (sometimes specified as 40-foot); 5-foot in the Appalachian region and west of the Mississippi in the South; 5-foot 3-inch in much of the Southeast; and 100-inch in the Lake States.
- Hardwoods and conifers are used, but the same mill may not use both.
- Limbs must be trimmed flush.
- Sticks must be free of metal, char and extensive ro[t]

Charcoal

Charcoal plants are scattered around the U.S. and Canada, but are located principally in the Lake States and south with a few in the West, mostly in California. The market for charcoal is limited, due to the low value

118

of the end product, the seasonal and relatively low consumer demand, and the problem of smoke produced by charcoal kilns and ovens. However this is a product to watch. Recently, Mark Solomon, an innovative blacksmith at Idaho Forge and Fabricators in Moscow, Idaho, has invented what he claims is a virtually smokeless kiln. It is light and portable, easily transported into the woods on a truck. There, limbs and tops are placed in the oven, and after a few days, pure charcoal results. Solomon hopes to rekindle interest in pure charcoal for cooking, blacksmithing and even as a replacement for firewood for heating the home.

Specifications:
- Solomon's method, currently being tested in cooperation with the U.S. Forest Service, utilizes almost any size or species of logging slash.
- Otherwise oak, maple, hickory, birch, beech, Virginia pine, shortleaf pine and lodgepole pine are used most.
- Logs 3 feet to 4 feet long and 2 inches to 6 inches in diameter, round or split are of optimum size.

Railroad Ties

Massive quantities of railroad ties are needed to replace those rotting under the thousands of miles or our nation's rails. Generally, ties offer an outlet for short but sound trees of low grade.

Specifications:
- Usually 9-inch DBH minimum and approximately 7 feet to 8 feet in length.
- Straight and sound.
- Hardwoods preferred, but some conifers accepted.

Mine Timbers

Another use for short, sound wood in some localities is mine props. In mining areas, large quantities are needed, and a sale might be made directly to the consumer, especially if round props are acceptable.

Specifications:
- Minimum diameter usually 4 inches.
- Lengths and species variable, but strength and rot-resistance are important.

Poles

High-value uses of tall, straight conifers are for electric and telephone poles and for building. Only a small percentage of trees qualifies for poles, but the price received makes it worth the search. Be careful: Poles are closely graded, and what you will be offered for low grade poles is often less than for what you would get for the same log used for lumber or pulpwood. High grade poles are a different story.

Specifications:
- Minimum DBH usually 9 inches; length 25 feet to 75 feet (in 5-foot increments), with special orders sometimes made for larger ones.
- Species vary, but common ones are longleaf, shortleaf, loblolly, slash, lodgepole and white and red pines; eastern white and western redcedar; Douglas-fir; and western larch.
- Sweep or bend allowed only in one direction and not more than about 1 inch per 6 feet in length.
- Splits, rot, metal, spiral grain and numerous other defects are not allowed; allowable knot sizes are usually specified.

Pilings

Like poles, logs for pilings have special requirements. Pilings for docks, wharves, bridges and foundations command prices even higher than for poles, but steel has reduced the demand in recent years. If your land is near coastal or lake areas, pilings could still be the best use of tall, straight trees that do not qualify for veneer.

Specifications:
- Usually 12-inch minimum diameter; 14 inches for higher grades.
- Straight and sound.
- Commonly used species include pine, cypress, oak and elm in the South; Douglas-fir, larch, cedar, and spruce elsewhere.

Fence Posts

Fence posts are a good use for small diameter trees in all areas of the country. Industrious landowners with highly durable species may even be able to sell directly to consumers. More often, however, mills purchase the logs, remove the bark and smooth the surface, then treat the wood with preservatives.

Specifications:
- Minimum size usually 2 inches in diameter and 6 feet to 8 feet in length.
- Rot-resistant species necessary for untreated use; pines are particularly good for treatment because they are easily penetrated by the preservative.
- Reasonably straight and sound.

Shakes, Stakes and Other Things

For the woodland owner with enough interest, there is an almost endless number of specialty uses for trees. For example, have you ever pressed the blister on a balsam fir to watch the resin squirt? If you don't mind tedious work, this sticky liquid can be collected in glass vials and sold to biological laboratories for slide mounts or medical purposes. In case you are interested, it takes about 150 blisters to yield a pint!

More practical examples include short chunks of cedar that can be sold for making roof shingles, or limbs and very small stems that can be turned into stakes or climbing poles for sale to garden shops and truck farms.

Even defects sometimes have a use. Abnormal swellings, called burls, are highly prized by novelty furniture-makers, and conks, galls, and witches' brooms are sought by craftsmen with a bent toward the rustic. Then, of course, there are always cones, pine boughs, and mistletoe at Christmas time.

The understory offers possibilities too. Euell Gibbon's classic, *Stalking the Wild Asparagus* (David McKay Co., New York), provides useful suggestions for the woodland forager, from recipes for huckleberry pie to sassafras tea. Some woodland owners even sell bark from harvested trees to garden shops, or logging slash to portable chipping plants that set up in the woods. The chips are then hauled to distant pulpmills. Tree and shrub transplants are often saleable items and can help pay for the thinning of over-stocked parts of the woodlot. In the Southwest, those fortunate enough to have the red, smooth-barked manzanita can find markets for its surreal branches in flower shops and with decorators.

It helps to be near urban centers if the sale of this kind of woodland bounty is your goal. But generally speaking, potential products and the development of markets are limited more by the imagination than by anything else.

SASSAFRAS LEAVES

Durability of Posts Made from Heartwood *

More Durable			Less Durable		
Species	Life Expectancy of Untreated Wood		Species	Life Expectancy of Untreated Wood	
	(years)			(years)	
Black locust	20-30 +		Red & jack pine	2-6	
Osage-orange	20-30 +		Hemlock	2-5	
E. and W. redcedar	20-30 +		Aspen and poplars	3-4	
Redwood	10-20 +		Cottonwood	3-4	
Baldcypress	10-20		Ponderosa pine	3-4	
Catalpa	10-20		Birches	2-5	
Burr oak	10-15		Beech	2-5	
Northern whitecedar	5-15		Spruces	3-4	
Tamarack	8-10		Balsam fir	3-4	
Red oak	6-8		Basswood	5	
Douglas-fir	4-6		Ashes	5	
			Willows	5	
			Maples	2-4	

*Sapwood of all species is relatively non-resistant to decay.

10 The Firewood
Phenomenon

*There are two spiritual dangers in not own-
ing a farm. One is the danger of supposing
that breakfast comes from the grocery, and
the other that heat comes from the furnace.*
—Aldo Leopold

Change is the essence of woodland management, both biologically as trees grow and take shape, and as technology develops to help us do the jobs from planting to harvesting. But the greatest change in recent times has been one of consumer demand. It has been the explosive new interest in firewood.

The firewood phenomenon began with the oil shortage and fuel scares of the early 1970s. It continues today because of rising utility costs, and because of a desire to be independent of the arrogant oil producers of the world, both foreign and domestic. There is some romance involved, too, as Americans see a certain "goodness" in wood and are attracted to the simple, sturdy stoves and hearths that have long been a tradition.

The result has been a ten-fold increase in the annual sales of wood-burning appliances since 1973! In fact, it is estimated that at least 26 percent of all occupied households now have wood burning units. New York State alone has over 1.3 million households that use fuelwood, and well over half the homes in some New England states heat with wood. Rates of use are increasing by as much as 30 to 35 percent per year in some areas of the U.S. and Canada. Total consumption in the United States currently is at the staggering level of 50 million cords annually.

The firewood phenomenon is significant to every forest owner. Studies have shown that as the percentage of firewood users increases, the number of users who supply their own wood decreases. This is because many of the first users had their own woodlots, but those now buying stoves are increasingly dependent on others to supply the wood. The "others" have been to a large extent public forests. But state and federal land is often far from urban centers. Also, public land can absorb only so much of the demand. As a consequence, where the demand is high, wood is no longer freely available. In Connecticut, and New York, for example, lotteries have been established to determine who gets permits to cut on state lands. Even in the remote forests of Idaho, the U.S. Forest Service now charges for the privilege of cutting dead trees or hauling away the wastes of logging operations.

All this has opened up new possibilities for just about anyone who owns a woodlot, and it has created two schools of thought. The pessimists foresee indiscriminate cutting that can only ruin a forest. They fear an irresistible temptation for quick cash that will bring an end to long term management for lumber and veneer. The optimists, on the other hand, see this demand for small-diamater trees as an unprecedented incentive to plant, thin, and make improvement cuttings. For the first time, many woodland owners can indeed improve their stands and do it profitably.

The Firewood Forest

Any woodland needing thinning or improvement has the potential for firewood as a byproduct. But for firewood as a principal crop for your own use, an area of at least 10 acres will be needed, depending on your species and the productivity of the site. A well-stocked eastern hardwood stand will grow at least one-half cord per acre per year under average conditions. A moist, hardwood site with species suitable for coppice cutting will yield more than a dry, southern exposure site limited only to conifers. The condition and potential of your woodlot, and your objectives, will determine how much firewood can be removed each year.

The following are two examples that show the extremes of possibilities—one where lumber-quality trees are the ultimate goal and firewood is a compatible byproduct, and the other where the land is planted and used solely for firewood.

Firewood as a Byproduct

The following is provided by Thomas Stone, a forester in Michigan's northern Lower Peninsula, as reported in *National Woodlands*. Stone works on land that is being brought under intensive management for the first time and could be typical of similar tracts in many areas:

"On a typical 10- to 40-acre woods we can plan for the owner's immediate needs as a means of achieving long term management. In the first year a road system can be laid out where it *should* be. Depending on the size of the woodlot, several years' fuelwood supply could be produced just from where the road is built. The road could be built in stages on larger tracts. In all cases it can provide immediate incentive and can increase long term management possibilities and property value.

"In the second to sixth years (or others, adjusted for woodlot size) owners could take out weed trees and trees that overtop potentially better crop trees on two or more acres per year. It is common in a crop tree-weed tree thinning to remove from 35 to 45 sq. ft. of basal area per acre. That produces a lot of firewood per acre! It is possible to get 1.95 standard cords per acre for each 10 sq. ft. of basal area where 8-inch diameter trees are the average. Assuming 20 sq. ft. of basal area are to be cut per acre, this yields 3.9 standard cords per acre.

"By releasing the potential crop trees early in management, we plan for long term, high-value logs as always. The weed trees and the undesirable species which are not competing with crop trees are left to be cut later. From the seventh year on, owners can cut these weed trees for their firewood use or sale.

"In theory, after 10 to 16 years have passed, the woodlot should be ready for the first harvest of saw-logs. Then, tops from this harvest will provide firewood for several years."

The Firewood Plantation

If you have an open area that you want to plant in trees solely to provide firewood, you first need to determine two things: (1) the best species to use, and (2) how much firewood is needed, so you can estimate how many trees to plant to get this yield annually. Here is an example of how this has worked in eastern Nebraska, according to a study conducted by Kansas State University:

A. Six species were selected based on: (1) ability to sprout after harvest, (2) fast rate of initial growth, (3) heat production (BTU's) and (4) suitability for Nebraska sites.

These were:

Species	Million BTU's per cord of air dry wood
Honeylocust	20.0
Green Ash	18.0
Black Walnut	22.5
Siberian Elm	16.6
Silver Maple	19.0
Cottonwood	13.9

B. The number of trees needed to annually yield a cord of wood was determined. (A service forester can help estimate this for your area and possible species. In this example, the trees attained 6 to 8 inches DBH and about 30 feet in height in 6 years.)

Desired Yield (in cords)	Honeylocust	Green Ash	Black Walnut	Siberian Elm	Silver Maple	Cottonwood
½	180	210	210	200	170	140
1	360	420	410	400	340	270
3	1,090	1,260	1,220	1,770	1,020	820
5	1,820	2,090	2,020	1,940	1,700	1,360

C. The number of acres needed to grow the desired amount of wood was then determined through stocking tables. Various spacings are shown to allow for the use of different sized equipment for weed control.

Spacing (ft.)		Number of Trees						
Within Rows	Between Rows	200	400	600	800	1,000	2,000	3,000
6	10	.28	.56	.84	1.12	1.4	2.8	4.2
8	8	.30	.60	.90	1.20	1.5	3.0	4.5
6	12	.32	.64	.96	1.28	1.6	3.2	4.8
8	10	.36	.72	1.08	1.44	1.8	3.6	5.4

These figures will vary by as much as 25 percent depending on soil fertility; that is, better than average sites in this same area will produce 25 percent more on the same amount of space. Also, the second harvest from stump sprouts can be expected 2 to 3 years sooner than the first harvest from plantings.

With local growth data and due consideration of site characteristics and species involved, you can use these steps to determine the size and yields of your own firewood plantation.

SOME FIREWOOD CHARACTERISTICS

Species	Heat	Gross Heat Value*	Ease of Splitting	Ease of starting	Coaling qualities	sparks
Alder	M-L	16,480.0	easy	fair	good	moderate
Apple	VH		difficult	difficult	excellent	few
Ash	H	22,513.0	easy-mod	fair-diff	good-exc	few
Aspen	L	15,467.7	easy	easy	good	few
Beech	H	24,457.9	difficult	poor	good	few
Birch	M	20,884.2	easy	easy	good	moderate
Boxelder	M-H		moderate	fair-diff.	excellent	many
Cedar	M-L		easy	easy	poor	many
Cherry	M	20,437.4	fair	poor	excellent	few
Cottonwood	L	15,858.6	easy	easy	good	moderate
Douglas-fir	M	22,732.4	easy	easy	fair	moderate
Elm	M	20,046.6	very diff	fair	good	very few
Grand & subalpine firs	L	17,400.0	moderate	easy	poor	moderate
Hemlock	M-L	16,483.0	easy	easy	poor	many
Hickory	VH	28,422.6	easy	fair	excellent	moderate
Juniper	M		difficult	fair	good	many
Larch (tamarack)	M	25,833.6	easy-mod.	easy	fair	many
Locust	VH	29,260.2	very diff	difficult	excellent	very few
Maple, Red	M	19,209.0	fair	poor	fair	few
Maple, Sugar	H	23,787.8	easy	poor	excellent	few
Oak, Red	H	24,681.3	easy	poor	excellent	few
Pines, Southern	M	22,196.2	easy	easy	fair-poor	moderate
Pine, others	L	19,000.0	easy	easy	fair-poor	moderate
Poplar	L	14,071.0	easy	easy	fair	moderate
Spruce	L	15,272.8	easy	easy	poor	few
Willow	L	16,800.0	easy	fair	poor	moderate

*Gross Heat Value is expressed as 1000 BTU's per air-dried cord. 1 BTU=amount of heat required to raise the temperature of 1 pound of water (about 1 pint) by 1 degree F. It takes about 10,000 BTU's to heat a load for laundry; and about 150 million BTU's to heat the average Massachusetts home.

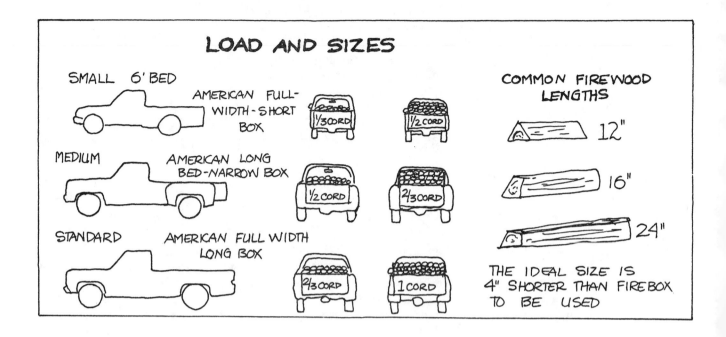

Firewood for Pleasure and Profit

The firewood phenomenon is bringing strangers to the woods. Traditional wood users are being joined by weekend cowboys in their flashy pick-up trucks, and trendy urbanites filling their trunks and backseats with wood for an evening's entertainment. Firewood has even spawned social movements in the form of government-subsidized cooperatives.

There is an increasing number of ways both owners and users are finding to get wood from forest to stove or hearth. It may be worthwhile to be aware of the kinds of operations that work—or don't work.

Wood for Your Own Use

For Dawn and me, firewood is recreation. Just as we don't keep track of costs when we go fishing or camping, we have few concerns about what it costs to bring home a cord of wood. Our time in the woods is both mental relaxation and physical exercise that is a welcome relief from jogging. Splitting a piece of roundwood to me has all the allure of cutting a diamond, and the feel of wood in my arms is a sensual relationship with the forest. I am sure we would cut our own wood even if we won a free, life-time supply in a state-run lottery.

Not everyone views firewood as rhapsody. In fact, the groundswell of interest is overwhelmingly economic. Often, this interest in saving a buck is misguided, and it is actually more economical to pay the gas, oil, or electric bills. Interest in burning wood may also be misguided if firewood becomes the main use of a woodlot at the expense of longer term objectives such as lumber or veneer. My friend Don Hanley, a savvy extension forester at the

University of Washington, has come up with a handy guide for figuring how economical it really is to use firewood to heat your home. All you need to follow these steps is a pocket calculator, a pencil, your highest utility bill, and the form on page 130 .

Firewood Production As A Business

The manufacture of forest products after they leave the woodlot is beyond the scope of this book. However, since firewood production for wholesale or retail purposes may be a temptation to owners of larger tracts, we call your attention to a study done on this subject by the U.S. Forest Service. It is reported in the booklet:

"Prospectus: Firewood Manufacturing and Marketing" by Ralph T. Monahan and Jeffrey L. Wartluft. USDA Forest Service NA-FR-17. Northeastern Forest Experiment Station, 370 Reed Road, Broomall, PA 19008.

In brief, the report indicates that you *can* make money at large scale processing of firewood. However, it is difficult. Of three small companies studied, only one seemed to be on firm footing. Also, at its highest rate of production (17.4 cords per 8 hour shift and 1.8 man-hour per cord) it made only a 12 percent return on fixed assets after taxes. Finally, red oak was used in this study, a relatively high value firewood. In all, not a rosy picture for the business-minded.

The Forest Service discovered two keys to success beyond the usual expectations of efficient labor force, preventive maintenance of equipment, and low down time. These seem applicable regardless of species or location:

SOME CONSIDERATIONS IN FIREWOOD PROCESSING

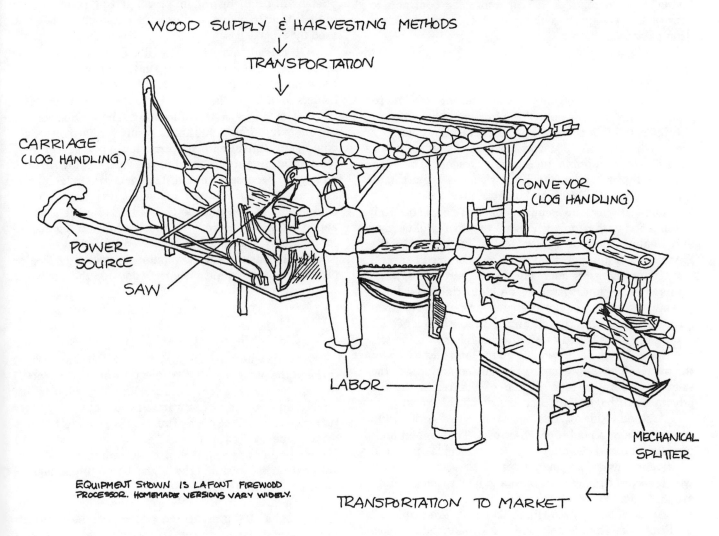

WOOD SUPPLY & HARVESTING METHODS
↓
TRANSPORTATION
↓

CARRIAGE (LOG HANDLING)

CONVEYOR (LOG HANDLING)

POWER SOURCE

SAW

LABOR

MECHANICAL SPLITTER

EQUIPMENT SHOWN IS LAFONT FIREWOOD PROCESSOR. HOMEMADE VERSIONS VARY WIDELY.

TRANSPORTATION TO MARKET

1. Rigidly specify that logs in the woods be bucked to an exact length that allows later cutting into the preferred fireplace sizes of 12", 16" or 24".
2. Favor logs between 7" and 14" in diameter. Efficiency in handling and processing below and above those diameters fell dramatically.

For anyone contemplating processing firewood as a business, here are four additional considerations that are essential before making an investment:

1. Carefully assess your market. How many houses are there in your community (advertising agencies and chambers of commerce usually have such data). From a random phone survey, what percent use wood? What species do they prefer and where do they currently get their wood?
2. Assess your supply of raw material. Can your woodlot continually supply enough or can it be supplemented from other reasonably priced sources?

3. Estimate production capability. Given your raw materials, transportation system, equipment and manpower, how many cords can you produce? There is a tendency to overestimate this important factor.
4. Estimate financial returns, weighing fixed assets, labor and operating costs against potential income. Also consider alternative uses of your trees and whether or not firewood enhances or interferes with saw log production, aesthetics or whatever else might be important.

A 'Cut Your Own' Operation

As we roamed the country looking at woodlots and their management, the most impressive firewood operation we found was on Dave Houston's Pleasant Acres Farm near Cabot, Vermont. His way of selling firewood is described on page 159 along with his maple syrup operation. Here is a person who uses the sale of firewood both to increase the production of his

127

maples—his main objective—and help finance the operating costs of converting sap to syrup. By carefully laying out sale zones each year and using contracts to control "do-it-yourself" cutters, he does it with hardly a drop of sweat.

Firewood Finders, Inc.

Need breeds ingenuity, and one of the more promising services born out of the firewood phenomenon is Firewood Finders, Inc. This northwestern company came into being in 1981 and has spread its operations from British Columbia to Eugene, Oregon. The idea could easily be implemented elsewhere as a benefit to firewood users and woodland owners alike.

Quite simply, the company matches people desiring to sell wood with people who want the savings of cutting and hauling their own. Bob Matthews, owner of the Olympia, Washington firm, says he operates in several ways. One thing his company does is purchase salvage rights after logging operations on industrial forest land, private woodlots, or government property. He then advertises and sells the firewood-sized slash or culls through permits issued on-site, through local businesses, or through the mail, depending on the land and wishes of the owner. The landowner can specify conditions for the sale to exercise a high degree of control, with the advantage of having someone else do all the work.

A second side of this operation is a "notification service" to a mailing list of subscribers. These individuals pay a nominal annual fee and receive postcard notification describing new sales. Species, condition of wood, access, cutting dates, cost and how to get a permit are all indicated on the card.

At the time of this writing, 20 people are employed by Firewood Finders and business is booming. Yankee ingenuity is not limited to New England!

Cooperatives

In recent years fuelwood cooperatives have been springing up around the country like mushrooms. Like mushrooms, they first emerge full of energy and promise, but in many cases they quickly disintegrate and eventually vanish. Co-op organizers seem to be the social "do-gooders" of forestry, often attracting idealistic young people full of enthusiasm for grass-roots social action. Usually they are at least initially supported by a government grant or other subsidy. When they fail, large amounts of public money are wasted; but any that succeed offer yet another opportunity for improved woodlot management by providing ways to thin or remove low quality trees from your stand.

In theory, co-ops allow people in a community to band together and help each other obtain firewood. There is usually a nominal member fee plus a requirement to contribute so many hours of work for each cord obtained. The work is either done en masse or individually with the help of a common truck, chainsaws, splitters and other equipment. There are

sometimes allowances in the rules to help the poor or aged obtain their quota of wood, and there is always a phalanx of problems ranging from getting people to put in their time to trying to maintain equipment owned and used by everyone.

Of special interest to woodlot owners is that most co-ops also face a problem of finding enough wood for their members. In Ulster County, New York, co-op leaders found that they could solve their supply problem by offering a service to landowners. The service consists of removing low-grade trees using only lightweight equipment and human power. Through a survey they found that almost one third of the local landowners did no logging because of their dislike for commercial loggers and most of the rest did not allow the use of heavy equipment. When the co-op seized upon this as an opportunity, 63 percent of the landowners agreed to cooperate by allowing free or low cost removal of trees. The result was improved woodlots, a source of free or inexpensive labor, and cheaper wood for the fuelwood cooperative.

The Problem of Hauling

Anyone who has worked with firewood can see right through the old adage that "firewood warms you twice." By the time the wood is cut, skidded, hauled, split, stacked and carried, it has warmed you many more times than twice. This is also why firewood is a difficult way to make money. It is heavy, bulky and labor-intensive, and offers little opportunity for automation. Where automation is possible, the high capital investment is difficult to earn back.

In addition to the relatively low selling price of firewood, hauling presents the greatest barrier to profit. Long hauls from the forest to the consumer with gas-consuming weight and a relatively small payload make this prohibitive. Even in the woods, log skidding becomes a problem when looking at returns on the investment.

The only solution to long distance hauling is the sale of firewood at bulk prices for shipment to urban centers where the product is retailed in bundles through supermarkets at high prices. In parts of the U.S. and Canada, mass distributors are trying to make a business of this approach, and for some woodland owners, particularly those in remote areas, it might pay its way.

The problem of skidding can be handled through conventional methods, particularly with lightweight equipment such as that described on page 100. Some people have even modified equipment as light as an 8-horsepower garden tractor to haul firewood.

Michael Greason, a forester and woodlot owner in New York State, added metal racks to his tiny 14-horsepower tractor. By placing them both in the front and back, he reports excellent stability. At low cost and with reasonable operating care, Greason's racks have taken at least part of the sweat out of working with firewood. Here are some tips for making low-cost racks:

- Steel square stock, angle iron or pipe may be used; however, firewood will tend to slide off pipe unless something is welded on for texture.
- Design the racks for the length of wood you harvest. If you cut 16" wood, the frame of the racks should be about 12" wide.
- Take advantage of brackets, bolt holes, or other implement attachment features on the tractor for mounting. Then plan for rapid, easy installation and removal.
- Design the racks to slope outward and upward from the tractor. This will prevent hangup on stumps, rocks and depressions. However, close to the tractor, keep low to maintain a low center of gravity for stability.
- Use cross bracing for strength and places to hook rubber hold-down straps to prevent wood from falling off the racks.
- Strength is a big factor. Each rack may be carrying several hundred pounds of wood and be subjected to bouncing and twisting.

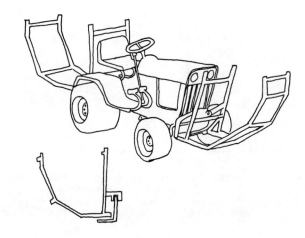

Wood Seasoning and Storage

The amount of water in wood is tremendous. Based on percent by weight, moisture content in wood ranges from 95 percent in aspen and elm to a low of 34 percent in the heartwood of spruce. When burned, moisture is the devil that can turn the pleasant task of starting a fire into an hour of frustration and raised tempers. It also adds to the build-up of dangerous creosote inside chimneys, and it is a subtle thief that steals heat. Up to 50 percent of the fuel value in wood can be lost in the process of converting fuel moisture to steam and spewing it out the chimney!

Ways to Speed Seasoning

The trick is to dry ("season") wood as quickly and thoroughly as possible. If dead wood is harvested, drying time of only a few weeks is necessary. For green wood, about a year is needed (outside, under cover) to reduce moisture content to 15-35 percent. The same wood dried in a heated house would be reduced to 5-10 percent water content. These are acceptable levels, because reaching even 4 percent requires the kind of oven-drying that is used for lumber, and this is just not practical for firewood.

Green wood with a natural moisture content of approximately 50 percent, if stored under cover, can reach the following fuel values in...

3 months	85% (of *practical* fuel value)
6 months	90%
9 months	95%
12 months	100%

To know when your wood is adequately seasoned, watch for small end cracks, or "checks." A more exact way is to periodically weigh on the bathroom scale the same piece of wood from a pile, or several sample pieces. When the weight loss is negligible, the wood is seasoned to a practical level.

WAYS TO SPEED SEASONING

- MAKE PIECES SMALLER BY SPLITTING AND CUTTING SHORTER
- REMOVE BARK
- ALLOW FOR AIR CIRCULATION
- STORE UNDER COVER
- IF CUTTING TREES IN LEAF, ALLOW THEM TO LIE ABOUT 2 WEEKS BEFORE CUTTING UP TRANSPIRATION WILL REMOVE UP TO 50% OF THE MOISTURE CONTENT.

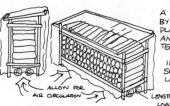

ALLOW FOR AIR CIRCULATION

A SOLAR KILN

LENGTH-WISE LOGS

A SOLAR KILN CAN SPEED SEASONING BY AS MUCH AS 75% USE CLEAR PLASTIC SHEETS AT LEAST 4 MILS THICK AND REPLACE AS IT WEATHERS AND TEARS (ABOUT 4-6 MONTHS)

IN WINDY LOCATIONS, SECURE WITH STRIPS OF LATHS LIGHTLY TACKED ON.

PREVAILING WINDS

2 SIDED WOOD SHED

ANY INEXPENSIVE WOODSHED PAYS HIGH DIVIDENDS IN REDUCING MOISTURE CONTENT, WEIGHT AND GENERALLY MAKING HANDLING MORE PLEASANT.

WARNING: BEWARE OF INSECTS AND SNAKES IN THE WOODPILE A CONCRETE FLOOR AND KEEPING THE PILE OFF THE GROUND WILL HELP CHECK FOR INSECT PROBLEMS PERIODICALLY, AND AVOID HARVESTING INFESTED TREES UNLESS THEY CAN BE BURNED QUICKLY.

How Much Does Your Firewood Really Cost?

STEP 1 - Determine the cost of heat from your present system:

Take your utility bill and divide the total amount paid by the amount used. This should include any fixed monthly charges. These costs/unit are normally expressed as:

$/gal. for heating oil $/gal. for propane
$/therm for natural gas $/ton for coal
$/KWH for electricity

My cost/unit is: $_____

> For example, if an electric home uses 1,780 KWH for a cost of $53.40, then $\frac{\$53.40}{1,780 \text{ KWH}} = \$0.0300/\text{KWH}$.

STEP 2 - Convert Step 1 costs to costs per 1,000 BTU (British Thermal Unit). These costs are expressed in dollars:

Select an alternative below. If you heat with:

oil   _____ ÷ 103.875 = $_____
natural gas _____ ÷ 80.0 = $_____
electricity _____ ÷ 3.413 = $_____
propane _____ ÷ 73.20 = $_____
coal _____ ÷ 15,000 = $_____

> For example, electricity
> 0.0300 ÷ 3.413 = $0.0088/1,000 BTU (rounded to 4 digits).

STEP 3 - Find the heat yield of the wood you burn:

The heat yield is simply the amount of heat that you can actually capture in your home. It is expressed as 1000 BTU/cord. Select the species of wood that you most commonly burn and the type of wood-burning unit you use. Multiply the gross heat found in the box on page ____ times the stove efficiency.

Stove Efficiency (examples)
high — 0.65 multi-chambered, airtight stove
0.40 single-chambered, airtight stove
0.30 Franklin type stove
0.15-0.25 improved fireplace (i.e., heatalator, glass doors, blowers, etc.)
low — 0.10 open fireplace

Heat yield = _____ x _____ = _____ BTU/cord
(gross heat value) (efficiency)

> For example, if Douglas-fir is burned in a single-chambered, airtight stove, the heat yield is:
> 22,732.4 x 0.40 = 9,092.96 BTU/cord

STEP 4 - Determine the break-even value (BEV) of the wood:

Multiply the heat yield value (Step 3) times the cost value determined in Step 2. The BEV is expressed in dollars per cord of wood.

BEV = _____ x $_____ = $_____/cord
(heat yield Step 3) (cost Step 2)

> For example, BEV = 9,092.96 x $0.0088 = $80.02/cord

The BEV is defined as the amount of money you could spend for a cord of wood to break even on your utility bills. If you spend less, the difference is how much you will save per cord of wood burned. If you are spending more for wood than the BEV, you would be better off economically to heat with other traditional fuels.

Step 5 is important if you plan to convert to wood heat from some other heat source. It takes into consideration the costs of the wood-burning unit. Add these costs to those found in Step 4.

STEP 5 - Determine the cost of purchasing and maintaining a wood-burning unit:

Price of wood-burning unit $_____
Maintenance + $_____
TOTAL $_____ (5a)

Expected lifetime of wood-burning unit (Expressed as the total number of cords burned) _____ (5b)

Cost per cord = _____ ÷ _____ = $_____
(5a) (5b)

> For example, assume 12-year life and 5 cords/year
> $ 700 fireplace insert
> $ 300 chimney cleaning (6 times at $50 each)
> $1000
>
> $1000 ÷ 60 cords = $16.67/cord OR
>
> $ 700 ÷ 60 cords = $11.67/cord (if you do maintenance yourself)

Steps 1-5 are valid whether you cut your own wood or buy it. If you cut your own wood, the following steps are necessary.

STEP 6 - Determine chain saw costs on a cost/cord basis:

Assume life expectancy at 12 years and 5 cords of wood cut per year.

Fixed Costs

Chain saw cost $_____
Maintenance, repairs and personal protective clothing + $_____
Salvage value - $_____
SUBTOTAL F $_____

Divide total fixed costs by number of cords cut.

Cost/cord = _____ ÷ _____ = $_____/cord
(subtotal F) (cords cut) (F)

> For example,
> Chain saw cost $250
> Maintenance, etc. + $150
> Salvage value - $ 50
> $350
>
> then $350 ÷ 60 = $5.83/cord

130

Variable Costs

Gasoline (3/4 gal./cord) $_____

Fuel mix (3 oz./cord)   + $_____

Bar oil (6 oz./cord)   + $_____

V = $_____/cord

```
For example,

     Gasoline      $1.00
     Fuel mix        .60
     Bar oil         .40
               V = $2.00/cord
```

Total Chain Saw Costs

Fixed costs/cord (F) $_____

Variable costs/cord (V)   + $_____

TOTAL = $_____

```
For example,

     Fixed costs    = $5.83/cord
     Variable costs = $2.00/cord
                       $7.83/cord
```

STEP 7 - Determine the total cost/cord:

Wood stove/cord $_____ (Step 5)

Chain saw total/cord   + $_____ (Step 6)

Wood cutting permit   + $_____
cost/cord (if any)

TOTAL   = $_____/cord

```
For example,

     Wood stove              $16.67/cord
     Chain saw             +   7.83/cord
     Wood cutter's permit  +    .50/cord
                   TOTAL   = $25.00/cord
```

As you can see, obtaining your own wood from a virtually "free" source will actually cost you more than $20/cord PLUS transportation expenses.

STEP 8 - Determine your transportation costs:

Transportation costs are those costs associated with hauling a cord of wood from the forest to your home. The amount will be figured on a cost per mile per cord hauled. You will need to know your total cost/mile to operate your truck (including depreciation, maintenance and fuel) and its capacity. Assume the following:

Truck Type	Capacity in Standard Cords
Import size	4/10
1/2 Ton (1-foot side racks)	1/2 - 3/4
3/4 Ton (2-foot side racks)	3/4 - 1
1 Ton	1 - 1 1/4
2 Ton	2 - 2 1/4

(A) Total cost/mile $_____/mile

(B) Truck capacity _____ cords

The total cost/mile/cord is found by dividing the cost/mile by the capacity (A ÷ B).

Transportation cost =

$_____ ÷ _____ = $_____/mile/cord
(A)   (B)

```
For example,

     Total cost/mile (A)        $ .30/mile
     Capacity (B)                3/4 cord
     Total cost/mile/cord = $.30 ÷ 3/4 - $.40/mile/cord
```

(NOTE: Repeat this step for any equipment used if you do your own skidding of logs for firewood.)

STEP 9 - Determine your maximum round trip mileage (MRTM):

The maximum round trip mileage that you can drive to gather your own wood can be calculated by subtracting your total costs from the break-even value of the wood. If you then divide this difference, called maximum allowable transportation cost (MATC), by your cost per mile, the quotient is your <u>maximum mileage</u>. Beyond that point it is not economical to haul.

MATC = $_____ - $_____ = $_____/cord
         BEV   Total cost
       (Step 4)   (Step 7)

MRTM = _____ ÷ _____ = _____ miles
       MATC (above)   Transportation
                      cost (Step 8)

```
For example,

     BEV              $80.02
     Total costs    - $25.00
     MATC           = $55.02

     MRTM = $55.02 ÷ 0.40 = 137.5 miles
```

11 Christmas Trees

'Tis the season for kindling the fire of hospitality in the hall, the genial fire of charity in the heart.

—Washington Irving

Few of us can resist an occasional fantasy about getting rich quick from our land. To many dreamers, the way to do this is by growing Christmas trees. After all, what other forest crop can you plant at 20 cents per seedling, then harvest seven or eight years later at $10 or more per tree?

Unfortunately, a closer look takes some of the glitter out of the ledger sheet and adds a lot of hard work to the seemingly simple prospect of growing a Yule tree. Still, for many landowners, Christmas tree production can be a profitable and rewarding use of rural land.

The most appealing aspect of Christmas tree production is the short rotation period, and therefore the short time between investment and profit. Another is that Christmas trees can be grown in almost any area of the U.S. or southern Canada, and on parcels of land ranging from hundreds of acres to as few as one or two. The major drawbacks are the investments of time and labor needed to produce a quality tree; the high risks of fire or other plagues (including theft); and in some areas, an over-supply from thousands of competitors ranging from industrial wholesalers to backyard hobbyists.

All told, Christmas tree farming is big business. In Canada, approximately 6 million Christmas trees are produced each year. In the United States, over 30 million are harvested each year, employing 100,000 people for an annual retail crop value in excess of $600 million. And Christmas tree growers are quick to point out that they are talking about real trees, not the fake ones of plastic or metal that are forever threatening to make inroads into the traditions of Christmas and the markets of tree farmers.

Choosing a Site and the Species

A good site matched with a good species makes the difference between success and failure in the Christmas tree business. Careful attention to this before planting can save effort and anguish in the years that follow.

In choosing a site, here are some important considerations:

- *Soil*—Sandy loam is best, but other soils may be suitable if they have good drainage and moderate fertility (soil classification site III or a low II is often ideal). Soil that is too rich can cause trees to grow too rapidly and be spindly. Avoid wet sites and areas that flood, and soils with subsurface layers of rock or clay that impede drainage or cause rapid drying of the soil.

- *Slope*—Gently sloping areas averaging up to 5 percent are best, giving enough slope to allow good air movement (to prevent late frosts), while being level enough so equipment can move about easily. Species can be selected to match any aspect. Avoid frost pockets, and where late spring frosts occur, select species that can withstand them.

- *Climate*—Sites where heavy, early or late snowfalls occur should be avoided. Extremely dry climates are also a limiting factor unless irrigation is feasible.

- *Wind*—Excessively windy sites can distort and dry trees, and cause damaging snow drifts. Plantations sheltered from constant wind or buffered by larger trees on the windward side are best.

- *Cover*—A bare field or one with vegetation that can easily be cleared (by plowing, burning or chemical treatment) is best. Over-topping trees, even if scattered, usually create damaging competition for sun and moisture.

- *Access*—For "cut-your-own" operations, a good (preferably paved) road and parking are necessary for customers. On other operations, roads must be adequate for late fall cutting and hauling.

- *Theft*—Especially near population centers, sites within view of houses will usually be safer than isolated ones. In some areas, an electric fence or alarm system may be necessary.

Once an appropriate site is selected, the next important decision is what species to plant. Some locations will limit this choice to only one or two, while others may allow a dozen or more. Nation-wide, 30 different kinds of conifers are used for Christmas trees, but the great majority are Scotch pine, Douglas-fir and balsam fir.

The Perfect Christmas Tree

According to Cornell University researchers, the tree most preferred by consumers has a compact, dense appearance; dark green or blue-green foliage; a symmetrical, pyramidal shape with the base no wider than 60 to 70 percent of the height; ability to retain needles (and color) indoors for at least two weeks; branches stout enough to hold ornaments, lights and small presents; nonprickly foliage; and a fragrant odor.

The Seedling Selection Scorecard can be used as a checklist for factors you need to weigh in deciding what to grow. Where the choice involves more than a few species, it can also be a handy tool as you try to decide. Local growers, foresters and nursery operators can also provide good information. However, be careful to sort bias from fact. Sometimes a grower's personal preference or habits can be cheating him out of trying a better-performing species and getting a larger share of the market.

It cannot be overstressed how important it is to pay careful attention to *strains* (seed sources) within a species. For example, on a relatively dry southern slope, Scotch pine will do better than firs. But Scotch pine from the northern latitudes of its native Europe has a tendency to turn yellow in the fall when planted in some areas of North America. In some of these same areas, seeds from the south (as in Spanish Burga or French Auvergne strains) have all the hardiness of the species but lack the unChristmas-like tendency to turn yellow. In Douglas-fir, one of our premium native species, three color strains are recognized—green, gray-green, and blue-gray. New York growers favor the blue-gray color, so those wishing to fine-turn their operations for color make sure their seedlings come from parent trees growing in the Rocky Mountains of Arizona, New Mexico and Colorado.

Strains are particularly helpful in overcoming site problems. An example of this is frost. Douglas-fir, for example, often meets both market and site requirements. Unfortunately, it also has a sensitivity to late spring frosts. The result can be stunted trees and a delay or loss of profits. Some strains, however, such as those from Vancouver Island (Duncan) and medium-elevation coastal areas, produce a late bud burst, thereby avoiding most frosts. Being aware of this, and making a seedling choice accordingly, can save much grief.

SEEDLING SELECTION SCORECARD

List the species in which you are interested in the left column. Then circle or write in the appropriate numbers.
Summing and comparing the scores will help you decide which species to plant.

Species:	Species does well in your area			Specific strains are available to match to your site.		Customer Preference*			Time needed to grow in your area			Average selling price for a 7-foot tree	Total Score:
	Yes	No	Mod. well	Yes	No	High	Low	Unknown	One of Fastest	Medium	One of Slowest		
	10	0	5	5	0	5	0	2	5	2	0		
	10	0	5	5	0	5	0	2	5	2	0		
	10	0	5	5	0	5	0	2	5	2	0		
	10	0	5	5	0	5	0	2	5	2	0		
	10	0	5	5	0	5	0	2	5	2	0		
	10	0	5	5	0	5	0	2	5	2	0		
	10	0	5	5	0	5	0	2	5	2	0		
	10	0	5	5	0	5	0	2	5	2	0		
	10	0	5	5	0	5	0	2	5	2	0		

*Customer preference can be determined by phoning or talking with a random sample of people within your target market. Circle "unknown" for specie with which the people in your survey are unfamiliar.

CHRISTMAS TREE SPECIES

FIRS

Firs (Abies)

Tradition, as well as the symmetrical shapes, attractive green color, softness and fragrance of these trees make firs the number one Christmas tree.

Balsam fir (Abies balsamea)

Especially in eastern U.S. and Canada, balsam is the leading fir. It is sometimes slow and difficult to grow outside its optimum range, but commands premium prices.

Douglas-fir (Pseudotsuga menziesii)

Taxonomically not a true fir, but it is similar enough in many features to make it one of the top three Christmas trees. It grows well both East and West on a range of sites.

Other favorite firs

California red fir (A.magnifica)
Fraser fir (A. fraseri)
Grand fir (A. grandis)
Noble fir (A. procera)
Pacific silver or silver tip fir (A. amabilis)
White or concolor fir (A. concolor)

PINES

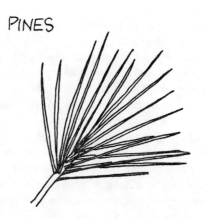

Pines (Pinus)

Fast growth, greater site tolerance and good needle retention have made pines popular with growers in recent decades. Some consumers, however, still harbor a bias toward short needled trees.

Scotch pine (Pinus sylvestris)

The number one Christmas tree pine. In addition to its rapid growth and site flexibility, it responds well to shearing and can be baled without damage.

Other favorite pines:

Austrian pine (P. nigra)
Red pine (P. resinosa)
Eastern white pine (P. strobus)
Western white pine (P. monticola)
Virginia pine (P. virginiana)

SPRUCES

Spruces (Picea)

A beautiful, symmetrical tree, but relatively slow growing, difficult to bale and transport, and loses its needles rapidly after cutting.

Blue or Colorado blue spruce (Picea pungens)

Its slow growth makes this a very expensive tree that will sell only in well-to-do or special market areas. In addition to its beauty, an advantage of this species is that little or no shaping is necessary. It is also popular for live tree sales either in burlap balls or potted as tiny table trees.

Other favorite spruces

White spruce (P. glauca)
Norway spruce (P. abies)

Planting and Care

Numerous extension publications are available on the details of Christmas tree culture. The major steps, however, are as follows:

Plan When You Plant

Besides following the rules of good planting as outlined in Chapter 6, you will need to pay special attention to roads and spacing.

Spacing depends mostly on when and how you plan to sell your trees, and the kind of equipment you plan to use for mowing. The idea is to strike a good balance between getting as many trees as possible on your parcel while having enough room to operate the plantation. Some general rules are:

- Plant closer than 5 feet between trees only when you have a market for very small trees.
- Trees to be marketed at 6 foot height can usually do well at 5½ x 5½-foot spacing.
- Pines need about 1 foot greater spacing than spruces and firs to be grown to the same height.
- Allow a little extra space in "choose and cut" operations so customers can walk easily through the stand.
- Garden-type tractors can be used with 5 x 5 foot spacing, but 8 feet between rows is needed for farm tractors.
- It is better to err on the side of wider spacing.

Since it is usually desirable to develop a plantation on a sustained yield basis, work out a plan for this before planting. Planting blocks in successive years is the easiest way to do this. Remember, too, that if you plant more than one species (which is always a good idea), they will probably reach cutting height at different times. Even within the same species, not all will mature in the same year, which means that it may take several years of harvests before a block is ready for replanting.

Allowing for roads is crucial to good management. Roads should surround the plantation and cross it at approximately 60- to 100-foot intervals. This provides for hauling, spraying, and fire protection. Parking or loading areas should also be left unplanted at strategic locations.

Planting Guide
(Seedlings Per Acre)

Spacing	Planted solid	After 10 percent reduction for roads or mortality
4½ x 4½ feet	2,150	1,940
5 x 5 feet	1,740	1,570
5 x 6 feet	1,450	1,310
5½ x 5½ feet	1,440	1,300
5½ x 6 feet	1,320	1,190
6 x 6 feet	1,210	1,090
6½ x 6½ feet	1,030	930

Fertilizing

The cost of fertilizer can take a big bite out of profits. Therefore, the best rule of thumb is: if growth rate and color are satisfactory, don't fertilize. In Scotch pine, even the color usually won't be improved by adding fertilizer. Some will argue, however, that by speeding up the harvest by even one year, the cost of fertilizing can be more than offset by earlier income.

If fertilizing seems appropriate, there are two ways to do it best. One is the slow release method used when planting. The other is to spread small amounts around each tree after it has been established for two or three years. This may be especially worthwhile on high value species, but even then some experimentation is advisable before going all out. The least logical method is helicopter or aircraft application, unless you enjoy mowing weeds and don't mind paying to help them grow faster!

If fertilization is believed necessary, contact your local extension agent or Soil Conservation Service office. Better yet, have a soil test made before you decide on a Christmas tree operation. If the site is infertile, you will probably be dollars ahead to plant elsewhere.

Shearing—The Essential Step

Some practices are optional in Christmas tree growing, but something that is absolutely mandatory is shearing. This is essential for producing quality trees, and it is a chore that must be done every year once it is started. It is hot, tedious work that is often done in the early summer months when high humidity can add to the misery. Because of the work involved, some novice growers try to skip or delay this operation. Perhaps I overstate the case by saying it is mandatory, but rare is the tree that will bring top dollar without shearing. With the possible exception of spruces and in some cases firs, it is better not to try Christmas trees if you do not have the time, means or interest to shear each year.

Usually the trees are ready for shearing in their third or fourth growing season, or as soon as the terminal leader exceeds 10 to 12 inches in length. The exact time of year will depend on the location of your plantation. For pines, the best time is when new spring elongation is about complete and the new growth hasn't hardened. The "candles" at this time are fresh and soft, but have grown as long as they will. This is only a two-week-long period and anyone without either a lot of time and energy or a large work force will need to begin a little earlier. Normally, pines only form buds (for next year's branch growth) at the *ends* of branches after their annual elongation stops. This is why internodes and whorls are so evident in pines.

Timely shearing of pines stimulates adventitious buds to form. These nearly invisible buds are located at the bases of needles along the branchlets. The next season, they sprout branchlets that fill in the open space. Shearing after the new growth stops and hardens can be counterproductive for improving the trees' looks. This because it may be too late for adventitious buds to form

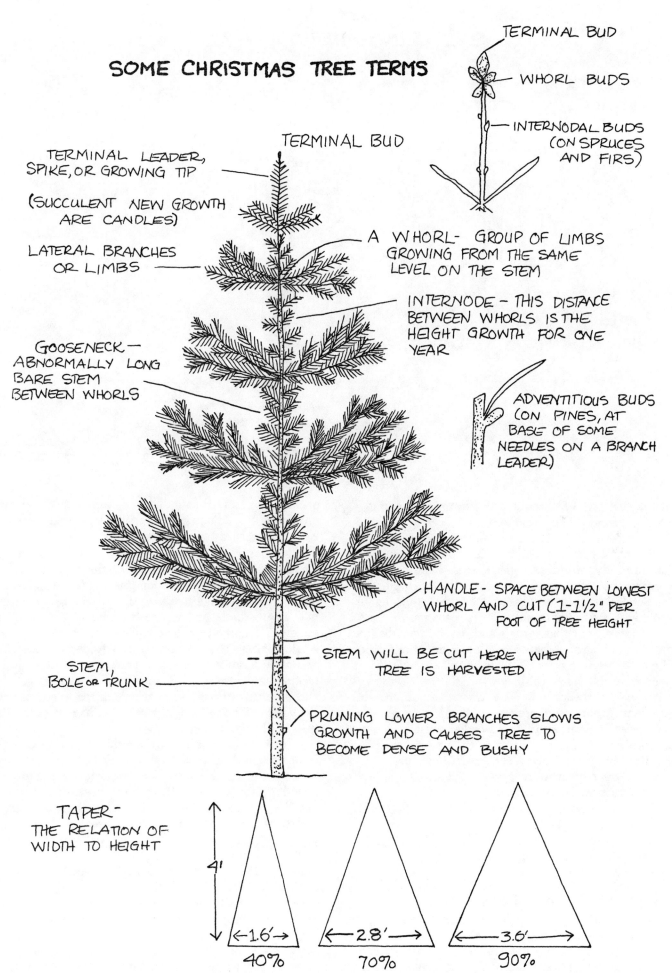

SOME CHRISTMAS TREE TERMS

TERMINAL BUD

WHORL BUDS

INTERNODAL BUDS (ON SPRUCES AND FIRS)

TERMINAL LEADER, SPIKE, OR GROWING TIP

(SUCCULENT NEW GROWTH ARE CANDLES)

TERMINAL BUD

LATERAL BRANCHES OR LIMBS

A WHORL- GROUP OF LIMBS GROWING FROM THE SAME LEVEL ON THE STEM

INTERNODE - THIS DISTANCE BETWEEN WHORLS IS THE HEIGHT GROWTH FOR ONE YEAR

GOOSENECK - ABNORMALLY LONG BARE STEM BETWEEN WHORLS

ADVENTITIOUS BUDS (ON PINES, AT BASE OF SOME NEEDLES ON A BRANCH LEADER)

HANDLE - SPACE BETWEEN LOWEST WHORL AND CUT (1-1½" PER FOOT OF TREE HEIGHT

STEM WILL BE CUT HERE WHEN TREE IS HARVESTED

STEM, BOLE OR TRUNK

PRUNING LOWER BRANCHES SLOWS GROWTH AND CAUSES TREE TO BECOME DENSE AND BUSHY

TAPER - THE RELATION OF WIDTH TO HEIGHT

4'

←1.6'→

←2.8'→

←3.6'→

40%

70%

90%

SHEARING METHODS

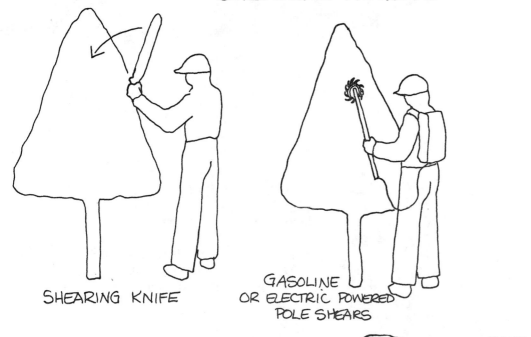

SHEARING KNIFE

GASOLINE
OR ELECTRIC POWERED
POLE SHEARS

HEDGE
SHEARS

HAND SHEARS

for the next year. The results will slow growth and give the tree a scraggly appearance.

Spruces and firs bud differently than pines. Unlike pines, they have internodal buds that send out branchlets that naturally "fill in" the open spaces. Shearing simply increases the density, and it can make the tree even more symmetrical than it would be otherwise. But, again, shearing is not as important in these species as in pines.

Some suggest that spruces and firs are best sheared after the new growth hardens in late summer or fall, or when the tree is dormant. Others believe that while late shearing won't hurt, fill-in growth the next season is better if the shearing is done when leaders are still succulent. Regardless of preference, this does suggest that the prudent operator will do his or her pines first, then the spruces and firs.

Remember, the reasons for shearing are to:
- develop compact foliage
- assure symmetrical form
- control height
- assure a single top
- eliminate deformities
- create a "handle" at the base

Protection and Other Management Needs

There is no easy way to summarize all the details that are part of a well-run Christmas tree operation. In some areas, long dry spells may make it necessary to irrigate; in others, combatting theft may be the big challenge. Fire

prevention and rodent control are nearly always problems, and no one in the business escapes the need to keep good records of expenses and income.

In most areas, another challenge is weed control. Especially in the first few years of the seedlings' lives, grass can be a formidable competitor for soil moisture. Similarly, aggressive hardwoods, vines or berry bushes will create shade and retard growth. Weed control is essential. Usually it can be accomplished by starting with a "clean" field, then following up with regular mowing and/or cultivation. Or, if you prefer, herbicides can be recommended locally. Rarely can a grower get by without using at least some chemicals for weed control. With care they can be used with no damage to either the trees or the environment.

Insects and diseases are another major challenge. Some are nearly always waiting to use Christmas trees as their homes, and when they are successful the landowner is not! Aphids, bagworms, midges, weevils, moths and sawflies are among the flying invaders that can reduce growth rates or deform trees. Diseases that uglify Christmas trees include brown spot needle disease, needle cast and rusts, and various cankers. Early detection followed by application of insecticides or fungicides is usually necessary. Some non-chemical controls, such as cutting out diseased or cankerous branches, or introducing ladybugs to prey on aphids, offer limited help. The best alternative to chemicals is prevention; check with local experts before planting, then avoid planting species that are especially vulnerable to local

Steps for Shearing Christmas Trees

As with skinning the proverbial cat, there are many ways to shear a tree. Here is the procedure recommended by the Cooperative Extension Service at the University of Wisconsin:

Pines

1. As you approach each tree, look it over to determine its potential for a good Christmas tree. Look for: deformities, too little or too much taper, unbalanced crown, and gaps in foliage. Decide which whorl of branches will be the lowest on the tree. This lowest whorl should have at least four well-spaced lateral branches. Think about the taper you want.
2. Shear the terminal leader back to the length you want, usually 6 to 12 inches. Cut it at an approximately 45-degree angle.
3. Shear the laterals around the terminal leader to ½ to ¼ the length of the leader—or to fit your plan for taper.
4. Shear the rest of the tree to fit the taper you want. Remember, to grade "premium," the final taper must be between 40 and 90 percent. A rule of thumb during the early years is to try for 60-70 percent taper (a 3-foot tree about 2 feet wide at the bottom).

Spruce and Firs

1. Same as for pines.
2. Cut back the terminal leader and its laterals to fit within your taper limits. Be sure to leave the terminal leader longer than other leaders.
3. Shear the sides of the tree to fit within taper limits: 40-70 percent. Shear only current growth. If you must cut older wood to improve balance, taper, or to remove a deformity, clip back to a branch axil with hand clippers.

---

problems. When spraying does become necessary, county extension agents or service foresters are usually the best sources of advice on what to use and how to use it safely.

Rabbits, mice and pocket gophers—all irreverent feeders on the roots or bark of Christmas trees—require a combination of controls depending on how much of a problem they are. A good preventive measure is to keep the area free of brush piles or anything that serves as their habitat. In the case of rabbits and deer, hunting is the growers' friend. Encouraging hunting can also be used for good public relations, or in some cases as a source of extra income through leasing or entrance fees.

Trees from the Wild and Stump Culture

Once upon a time all Christmas trees came from the wild. As late as 1959, over half the trees coming from the Pacific Northwest came from natural, wild stands. Now, relatively few trees are used commercially unless they come from plantations. The reason, of course, is that few trees under natural conditions have the form and foliage density that people have come to expect. From the growers' standpoint, treating or favoring trees for a Christmas tree crop in a natural stand is often inefficient and is not likely to be the best management of the forest. There are some exceptions, however. Some old fields, cutover areas and even a few older forests may have enough seedlings of high enough quality to be suitable for Christmas tree management. Some properties in the balsam fir region of Canada, New England and upstate New York provide examples.

From the various attempts at producing Christmas trees in natural stands, one interesting lesson was learned that has some application in plantations, around the home, and to some extent in the woods. This is stump culture. As illustrated, it simply means leaving a whorl of lower branches below the cut when a tree is harvested (or culled), then selecting one or two branches to become future Christmas trees. Especially in Douglas-fir, the true firs and most pines, the branches will turn up and can be sheared for eventual harvest. Sometimes the process can be repeated again, creating a third crop from the same root system.

Harvesting and Marketing

The most popular tree height is 6 to 8 feet, but there is always a need for some very tall trees, and there is an increasing demand for 2- or 3-foot "table trees" as more people move to apartments and townhouses. Wise growers research the market and plan their sale strategies when they are planting, not harvesting the trees.

Seasonally, the time to cut depends on when snow may block access to the stand, or how far trees must be shipped to market. The later you postpone cutting, the greater the risk of snow but the higher your assurance that the trees will be fresh. On the other hand, studies have shown that if stored properly, trees can be cut in late October and retain as much moisture as those cut in December. The big *if* in this matter includes:

- storing the cut trees in cool shade
- keeping their butts in water or wet soil
- protecting them from wind

Common harvesting methods include the use of hand saws (bow or pruning saws), lightweight chain saws, gasoline-powered brush saws, and tractor-mounted hydraulic shears.

How you sell your trees makes a big difference in how much you will make from the time, sweat, money and worry you put into growing them. The possibilities range from wholesaling to "choose and cut" (sometimes called "U-cut"), with several combinations in between. Whether it is cutting, loading or selling, the more you do yourself, the more money you will make. As a general guide, here are the ranges of how much of the final retail price you will receive depending on how you sell:

To a wholesaler—you receive 30 to 50 percent
To a retailer—you receive 50 to 60 percent
Cut & retail yourself—100 percent (less retailing costs)

STUMP CULTURE

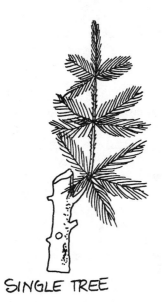

SINGLE TREE

"TURN-UPS" - A YEAR
OR TWO AFTER CUTTING

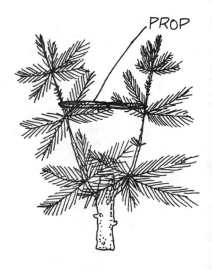

PROP

DOUBLE TREE

Stump Culture
1 . Select tree with vigorous, well shaped whorl near bottom.
2 . Harvest or cull the tree, cutting at a 45-degree angle about 4 inches above the remaining whorl.
3 . Alternate A: Select one or two of the best branches in the whorl and cut off all others.

   Alternate B: In steps 1 & 2, leave about 10 percent of the tree below the cut. Two or 3 years later select the best potential new tree (or trees) and cut off all other branches.
4 . After a year or two, shear like other Christmas trees.

Stump Culture Advantages...
- No need to buy seedlings
- Saves planting time & expense
- Overcomes problems of seedling establishment such as mice, drought, etc.
- Established root system may mean faster growth

Disadvantages...
- In plantations, it moves the row off center, sometimes making mowing more difficult
- The curved trunk must be cut off, thereby wasting a couple years' growth
- If two trees are to be produced, they usually need to be propped apart

"Choose and cut"—100 percent (usually with lower retailing costs and sometimes at higher prices)

When selling to a wholesaler or retailer, a clear, tight contract plus advance payment is a good idea. A sample contract is in the appendix. Selling by consignment is the worst of all possible worlds since the risk of not selling the trees is high, and if the trees do sell, the income is shared. By whatever method, arrangements should be concluded by October. And when the buyer or unskilled labor is to do the cutting, it is a good idea to use color ribbon or tags to identify those trees to be taken .

For someone with land in the right place (near a large population center and accessible by good roads), and who enjoys dealing with people, the most lucrative method of sales is probably the choose and cut operation. In fact, it may well be the single best method of obtaining the highest possible income from rural woodlots. Here is one couple's experience to help you decide if growing Christmas trees is for you.

A "Choose and Cut" Farm—For the Love of It

Janesville, Wisconsin is a bustling little city that could be Anywhere, USA. On its western edge, the town gives way quickly to old, neatly painted houses with large gardens, lawn ornaments and a rural past. I remarked to Dawn that the urbanizing farmland reminded me of southern England. But like Janesville itself, these suburbs could be almost anywhere.

Three miles from town, the road curves south and a house appears that is different from the rest. Behind it, the owners' 10 acres are clearly delineated, not by a fence or a cornfield, but by a nearly solid block of small conifers. The trees stand in straight lines, but their sizes range widely and gaps appear here and there. Grassy lanes bisect and circle the plot, and in the center looms a small hut two stories high on wooden stilts. A sign out in front, swinging in the wake of passing cars, confirms that we've found the Utzig Christmas Tree Farm.

The Utzig Farm, known as Tannenbaum Acres, is a family-run, part-time operation that specializes in allowing customers to choose and cut their own trees. A small number of trees are also cut and sold at roadside. The whole family—David, Mary, and their two sons—pitches in to make it work, just as they do at their body shop a few miles down the road. The Utzig Farm is in many ways a typical U-cut operation, but in many ways it is unique. Most important, it is highly successful.

As we walk with David through the lanes of neatly sheared trees, he recalls that Christmas trees have always been a family interest. "When I asked the wife to marry me, that was part of the bargain—that we'd find 10 acres to buy, live in the country, and grow Christmas trees. And talk about dummies! That was *all* we knew back then. We wrote all over trying to get information and it wasn't easy."

That was in 1953. By 1955 they found and planted their parcel outside Janesville, and in 1964 they began

harvesting and selling a couple hundred trees each year. Today people come from as far away as Chicago and carry off over 1,000 top-quality trees at prices any grower would envy.

The Utzig reputation is built on four things: quality trees in a variety of sizes and species; a little bit of well-placed advertising; friendly service that provides an experience, not just a Christmas tree; and a unique reservation system that allows people to select their tree early, then cut it or pick it up closer to Christmas.

Sales Methods That Appeal

There are many ways to operate a U-cut farm. Basically, the customer selects a tree, cuts it, and pays so much per foot on the way out the gate. According to David and Mary, that system leaves much to be desired, including high stumps that cheat the grower out of profits, and trees cut but left in the field when a "better" tree is spotted.

At the Utzig Farm, each tree ready for harvest receives a numbered tag (with a bright color spot so it is visible in snow!) with the price written on it. Tagging is the key to a system that allows close control over cutting and price. It also provides for a highly popular "reserve-a-tree" system. On Thanksgiving Day, the first day Tannenbaum Acres opens to the public, the crowds begin arriving at dawn! "It's now a tradition around Janesville," says David. He also grumbles about the "paperwork" and threatens to do away with the system, but it is unlikely he will stop anything so popular with customers.

An essential factor in this operation is that the Utzigs love people. They do all they can to help when someone shows up to buy a tree, and to provide an atmosphere that is truly Christmas. It begins with a clean, cheerful sales shed that Mary begins decorating about a week before Thanksgiving. Outside, Christmas music wafts through the crisp air, and a Jeep-pulled wagon or sled takes people around the lanes. Refreshments have not yet become part of the offerings, but in the parking area tailgate parties are common. In the field, bright red stocking caps decorated with Christmas tree patches bob among the trees, identifying the hired help which may number as many as 12 at the height of the season. Plenty of help, according to the Utzigs, is another essential for good service. The workers talk with customers about tree quality, help them locate preferred species, provide saws, and will even help cut and carry the tree if that is desired. This also enables trees to be prepared for stump culture by instructing cutters to leave the lowest whorl of branches. As the customer leaves, the children receive a colorful storybook about how Christmas trees are grown.

In all, the experience at Tannenbaum Acres becomes a part of Christmas that keeps people coming back year after year. And not even considering the cost of gasoline, they also actually pay *more* for cutting their own. Where the demand exists, it is possible to charge a higher price for a tree on the stump because there is little or no loss if it doesn't sell by the end of the season. This adds up to a very profitable operation. Dave Utzig has never figured the exact return on his investment, but he says with a wink, "The closest I can figure is that it sure beats a corn crop!"

Advertising and Quality

Now that their reputation is established, the Utzigs spend little on advertising yet still outdraw their few competitors. Newspaper ads are purchased in the surrounding towns, and a permit is obtained to place an extra sign temporarily along the roadside. As members in the National Christmas Tree Association, they also receive referral service when people phone the headquarters office asking about places to cut their own tree. A similar service is provided by a Chicago newspaper each year, and Utzigs make certain their farm is included.

The best advertising of Tannenbaum Acres is the friendly service and enjoyable experience that customers remember and talk about. It is also the trees. The farm is predominantly rapid-growing Scotch pine of the "French green" strain. But Douglas-fir, white spruce and several others offer the variety that is important in a U-cut operation. Dave Utzig loves them all. He refers to them as persons—"He's looking good. He'll be ready this year." One of his favorite species is concolor fir. "People fight over 'em," he laughs. Fraser fir, he says, is also popular, and thrusts a sprig under my nose to show why.

It is apparent on this farm that quality trees come from the wise selection of planting stock, and the kind of painstaking care that means many hours in the field. For the Utzig family, the annual cycle begins in March. Old stumps are cut flush with the ground and the planting

A TAG SYSTEM

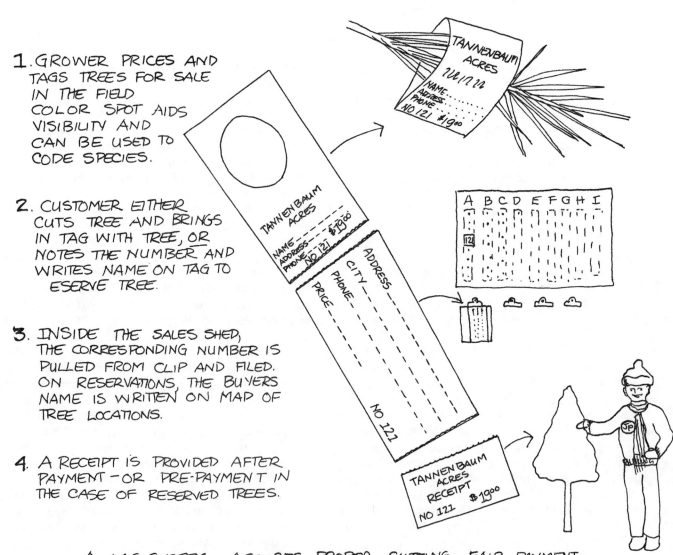

1. GROWER PRICES AND TAGS TREES FOR SALE IN THE FIELD COLOR SPOT AIDS VISIBILITY AND CAN BE USED TO CODE SPECIES.

2. CUSTOMER EITHER CUTS TREE AND BRINGS IN TAG WITH TREE, OR NOTES THE NUMBER AND WRITES NAME ON TAG TO RESERVE TREE.

3. INSIDE THE SALES SHED, THE CORRESPONDING NUMBER IS PULLED FROM CLIP AND FILED. ON RESERVATIONS, THE BUYERS NAME IS WRITTEN ON MAP OF TREE LOCATIONS.

4. A RECEIPT IS PROVIDED AFTER PAYMENT—OR PRE-PAYMENT IN THE CASE OF RESERVED TREES.

A TAG SYSTEM ASSURES PROPER CUTTING, FAIR PAYMENT, AND ENABLES CUSTOMERS TO RESERVE A TREE TO CUT NEARER TO CHRISTMAS.

operation is planned. In April and May, after weeds are killed with double doses of herbicide, the new trees—3-year-old transplants—are set out. Fertilizing is done sparingly, reserved only for some of the highest-priced firs. Late in June, shearing begins. "The four of us work every day for three weeks, mostly in the evenings when it's coolest," says David. Even so, the sweat drips and mosquitoes rise in hordes from the grass.

The trees are sprayed for insect protection when necessary, and a contracted helicopter spreads a fungicide to keep the plantation free of brown spot disease. In August, David Utzig hooks up paint barrels to his spraying rig and gives the trees an artificial coating of green. "People go boogie over painted trees. They're sophisticated buyers who want perfect shape and perfect color." This canned perfection takes about two or three minutes per tree to apply, using a special tree paint available from suppliers who advertise in the Christmas tree journals.

In September, the weeds are cut one more time so the place looks in top condition when the Thanksgiving Day opening rolls around. Next, trees are selected and tagged, some are bought wholesale from plantations to the north for roadside retailing, liability insurance is renewed, and a computerized cash register is rented to handle the cash and to help keep the books. Finally, lower limbs are cut for wreaths and bough bundles which, along with white birch table tree holders, supplement tree sales.

Imagination and Learning Pay Off

In the course of developing their highly successful operation, David and Mary have encountered just about every problem that any grower may face. Typical of these is thievery, but with their usual flair for innovation, the problem has been all but eliminated. The Utzigs' system begins with a rose hedge around isolated sections of the parcel. A hidden trip wire connected to a siren adds to the protection during the most vulnerable period of the year, though this has its shortcomings, as wandering foxes sometimes discover! Most effective is a scarecrow-like observation tower in the middle of the farm. We rarely man it," says David, "but people think we do and who is going to try to steal a tree that is watched?"

Other problems include muddy parking areas the Utzigs have corrected with gravel, and potential accident situations which they've eliminated by prohibiting chainsaws and snowmobiles. They have even found a way to keep birds from breaking the tips of trees in the spring. Throughout the plantation, bird perches protrude above the tops of the most valuable and most vulnerable trees.

BIRD PERCH

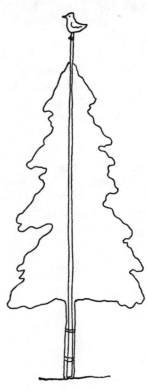

BIRD PERCHES PROTECT THE TERMINAL LEADER OF VALUABLE SPECIES.

TABLE TREE HOLDER

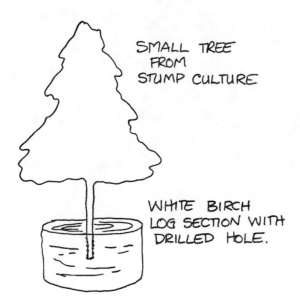

SMALL TREE FROM STUMP CULTURE

WHITE BIRCH LOG SECTION WITH DRILLED HOLE.

'TABLE TREE' HOLDERS ARE EASY TO MAKE, ADD EXTRA INCOME, AND PROVIDE A GOOD USE OF YOUNG TURN-UP BRANCHES FROM STUMPS.

If the Utzigs were really the "dummies" they claim to have been, there is no hint of it now. They attribute part of this to reading, but most of the credit goes to membership in the national and state growers' associations. "You can learn more in two or three days at the annual conventions than you can in ten years on your own," claims David. Going to the meetings has been a family affair, combining fun with learning and business. Christmas tree growers tend to be open and sharing, and they readily help new operators.

Yet growing Christmas trees is still a business, and the competition is tough. In the U.S., competition reaches its peak in annual, statewide contests in which growers can enter a sample tree. A panel judges the trees for shape, color, foliage density and uniformity, and other fine points of quality. The winner is given the honor of contributing a tree from his or her farm to the governor's mansion or capitol building. A grand champion winner from among all the states makes a presentation to the President and First Family in the White House.

In the sales shed on the wall is a yellowing newspaper picture of the Utzigs in the state capitol presenting their tree to the Governor of Wisconsin. David and Mary are obviously proud of it, but not as much as they are of other memorabilia that crowds one side of the shed. They point to one in particular. It's a huge thank you letter from school children who have visited the plantation. "We even have blind kids visit us," says David. "They circle a small tree and hang on to its branches while we cut it. You ought to hear them squeal as we cut through and it falls!" Many kids return later with their parents, some bringing cookies to Utzig as if he were Santa himself.

Perhaps this is the essence of a choose-and-cut operation. This kind of tree farming requires an eye for quality, a love of trees, and a real understanding of what the Christmas season is all about.

Does it pay? Probably more than any other kind of Christmas tree operation, and possibly more than any other intensive use of forest land. But David and Mary Utzig believe that they are probably working for about 25 cents an hour. Yet somehow that's not important. They love their work and they are proud of their product. And for thousands of people they make Christmas a little more memorable. To the Utzigs, that is important.

Best Guides to Christmas Tree Production

Profits From Christmas Trees. Cooperative Extension Service, Kansas State University, Manhattan, Kansas 66502.

This is only an eight-panel leaflet and it is free, but it contains some excellent investment analysis. It is certainly worth writing for.

Free information in every state!
In addition to the above, just about every Cooperative Extension Service at every land grant university in the country has a publication on Christmas tree growing specific to *that* state. Examples include:
Christmas Tree Production in Alabama
Christmas Tree Production in Iowa
Christmas Trees, a Profitable Crop for Georgia
Growing and Marketing Christmas Trees in Colorado
Growing Christmas Trees in the Pacific Northwest (Idaho, Oregon and Washington)
Growing Christmas Trees in Virginia

National Christmas Tree Association, Inc.
611 E. Wells St.
Milwaukee, Wisconsin 53202-3891

Dues to this organization are based on the size of a member's operation. They are quite reasonable and well worth the wealth of information in NCTA's quarterly journal and annual merchandiser magazine. Counselling, annual workshops and help on public relations and sales are among the other benefits. Statewide associations are valuable to anyone in the business and to those who are considering it.

The Ledger Sheet

Unless Christmas trees are grown strictly as a hobby or for family use, success or failure can be rather easily judged under the harsh light of economic reality. As a guide to estimating whether your investment in this land use is worthwhile (monetarily), plug your estimates into the following:

Notes and assumptions:

(1) It is assumed that you already own the land and must decide *how* to use it. Therefore, the cost of land and real estate taxes are not included.

(2) When you and your family provide the labor, you attach no dollar value to your time. Otherwise, add labor costs of the same rate you include for any hired help.

(3) For any item requiring equipment you can figure costs one of 3 ways: (a) cost of contracting to have the job done, (b) amortize the purchase price over the expected length of its usefulness, less resale (salvage) value, (c) if you own and use the equipment for other purposes, you may want to list it as no expense.

Expenses

Item	Cost[1]	x	No. of times in rotation	+	Interest[2]	=	Total cost per Rotation
Site Preparation	_____		1		_____		_____
Seedlings	_____		1.1		_____		_____
Planting	_____		1		_____		_____
Weed Control	_____		_____		_____		_____
Insect/Disease Control	_____		_____		_____		_____
Other Protection	_____		_____		_____		_____
Shearing	_____		_____		_____		_____
Insurance	_____		_____		_____		_____
Color Spraying (Optional)	_____		_____		_____		_____
Harvesting	_____		_____		_____		_____
Shipping/Baling	_____		_____		_____		_____
Advertising	_____		_____		_____		_____
Other (Taxes, Attorney fees, fence, fertilizer, etc.)	_____		_____		_____		_____
A. Total cost per crop							_____

1 Including labor

[2] Use the compound interest rate you could obtain by investing the money in something else you'd feel comfortable with (pass book savings, bonds, etc.). For time, use year(s) of outlay to year of anticipated tree harvest.

Income

	Species		
	X	Y	Z
Number of trees planted less culls & mortality (10-25%)	_____	_____	_____
Total crop	_____	_____	_____
x Expected price	_____	_____	_____
= Income	(_____)	(_____)	(_____)
B. Total income per crop	_____		

C. Income less costs = _____ net return on investment

D. Divide A, B, or C by number acres and number of years in rotation for per acreage and annual costs or returns.

E. You may want to compare these figures with alternative investments. For a more complete investment analysis, you must also consider what you could get by selling your land and investing the money in other ways.

12   The Holly Buffs

Deck the halls with boughs of holly...

When I phoned Information in Baltimore, Maryland, and asked for the number of the Holly Society of America, the operator responded, "The *what*?!" This is the reaction of people unfamiliar with the world of holly—a world of nearly fanatical tree lovers dedicated to the genus *Ilex*. But for anyone with land in Eastern United States or on the West coast, holly is a tree well worth discovering.

Holly is a versatile tree deeply rooted in history. The early Romans presented holly boughs with gifts to their esteemed friends, and the Druids of ancient Britain and Gaul saw holly as the tree never abandoned by the sun they worshipped. In America, Indians brewed its leaves for a drink consumed at a ceremony that tested the worthiness of warriors by challenging the fortitude of their stomachs!

Religious beliefs and legends lace the history of this plant, but of greatest importance to woodland owners today is the pleasant happenstance that holly became entwined with the traditions of Christmas. As early as 1598, Stowe's *Survey of London* reported that at Christmastime every house, church and market place was decorated with the evergreen leaves and bright red berries of holly. By 1851, the commercial benefits of the tradition were noted by one Henry Mayhew who estimated that "250,000 bunches" were sold annually in London alone. Today, over 100 carload equivalents are shipped from the sprawling holly orchards of western Oregon and Washington each November and December; and in the East, both large and small growers have difficulty meeting the demand for holly sprays. To landowners looking for annual income from trees, here is an opportunity worth exploring.

One Couple's Start in Holly Production

At least 800 people have become so hooked on holly that they have joined together in what may be one of the most esoteric special interest groups in the world—the Holly Society of America. Under these auspices, the holly buffs publish technical information about the virtues of holly varieties, promote research and keep a list of official holly arboreta, publish a newsletter, promote the use of holly, and honor those people who make outstanding contributions to the culture of holly. Like horse clubs, they also serve as the official registry of new varieties, and as a conservation organization they try to locate outstanding natural stands of holly and protect them from destruction. One member in Millville, New Jersey, even maintains a small museum of holly memorabilia.

Each year about 100 of the faithful gather for an annual meeting and workshop. The sessions are crammed with technical presentations ranging from basic instruction for new members to the latest growing techniques for the experienced. They also include time for socializing and the trading of growing stock or marketing tips.

Two decades ago, Frank and Janet Lockhart attended their first meeting of the Holly Society. Today, they are officers in the group and highly successful growers who find holly to be a most interesting and profitable hobby. To get a better understanding of holly growers, we visited the Lockharts' property in the rolling farm and woodlands near historic Valley Forge, Pennsylvania.

The Lockharts are retired Philadelphia retailers who spent much of their lives in the shoe business. But with an eye toward retirement and a new-found love of holly, they purchased 7 acres of woods and fields within commuting distance of the city. It is not the size of the property that is important for growing holly. Frank and Janet plowed and planted 2 acres of old field and today this stand (called "orchards" by holly culturists) is all they can manage. Though small, its annual yield of decorative sprays and berries brings in roughly $2,000 in extra spending money.

"If we were younger, we could make a lot more of this," says Frank. "We just can't meet the market demand. I hate to do it, but we have to turn away customers each year," he added.

147

The Lockharts' customers are roadside nurseries so common in the suburbs of Philadelphia as they are in other cities. The product is a 1-pound bunch (spray) of holly twigs, tied at the base and carefully selected to include a group of red berries. Each spray is arranged as attractively as possible. Early in the venture, the Lockharts found careful packaging to be the secret of getting repeat sales. They also found that by dampening each spray and placing it in a polyethelene bag, it stayed fresh and held up better to the abuse of handling and displaying at the point of sale. All their business is wholesale with retail markup about three or four times the orchard price. The Lockharts' 140 trees easily yield about 1,500 sprays each season.

Although size of acreage is not critical for growing holly, the kind of site is important. Native holly, called American holly (*Ilex opaca*), was originally limited to the U.S. southeast and eastern coast where it reached maximum heights of 100 feet and 2 to 4 feet DBH. Today, its natural occurrence is largely as a small understory tree or shrub.

For most commercial purposes, one of some 30 species and more than 300 varieties ("cultivars," to holly buffs) is used. Each has unique physical characteristics such as height, leaf shape, leaf color and berry color. Each also varies in its ability to withstand cold that can serve as a guide to successful planting. The leaflet suggested at the end of this chapter and a hardiness zone map can be used in combination as a key to what species or varieties will grow in your climate. Then it becomes a matter of contacting nurseries or arboreta until a source of that cultivar can be located. The Holly Society can help in most cases.

The site chosen by the Lockharts is nearly flat. As Washington discovered a few miles away in the winter of 1777-78, this part of Pennsylvania can have brutal snows and wind. Going by the book, a good site will face away from prevailing winds and winter sun. Both can produce a deadly drying effect on small trees. But the low mortality rate in the Lockhart orchard proves that hollies are quite adaptable within their zone of cold-hardiness. Growers have also found that these trees thrive in a variety of soils, but tend to do best in those that are neutral to slightly acid, well-drained, light, and loamy to sandy. Clays are definitely not holly sites unless lightened with humus and carefully drained.

Frost pockets must also be avoided, because a late spring frost can wipe out the blossoms that produce the red berries that are such an essential part of the product.

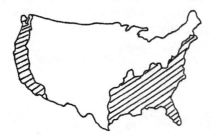

DISTRIBUTION OF HOLLY

Caring for Holly Trees

Fertilizing is extremely important. Nutrient deficiencies in the soil quickly show up in poor leaf color on the trees. It is the leaves people buy, so every effort must be made to keep them green and robust-looking. The Lockharts fertilize heavily each spring. For each tree, they follow a general rule of thumb, spreading roughly 1 pound of fertilizer for each inch of diameter (up to 3) in the tree's trunk. Above 3 inches, the amount should be tripled. What to spread can be determined by sending leaf samples to a commercial lab service such as offered by Agway, or to most land grant universities. By chemically testing for mineral deficiencies in the leaves, the percentages of a fertilizer mix can be recommended. The Lockharts have been able to change pale leaves to deep green first with a 12-12-12 mix, later settling for a less rich combination of 10-10-10.

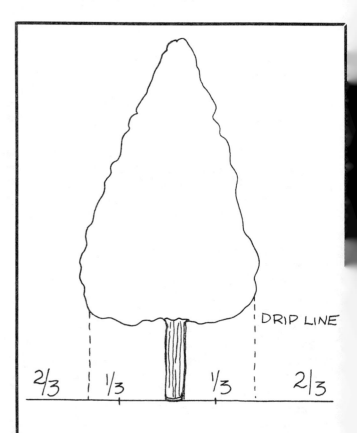

DRIP LINE

2/3   1/3   1/3   2/3

To Fertilize Holly

For the commercial production of holly, leaf color is almost everything. The key to good color is good soil nutrition. To fertilize:

1. Have leaf analysis conducted to determine soil nutrient deficiencies.
2. Obtain fertilizer in recommended proportions.
3. In early spring, spread in 2 bands around drip line. One-third of total quantity (see text for rule of thumb) should be just inside drip line; two-thirds in a wider band outside it.
4. Water thoroughly if no rain follows.

Leaves must also be protected from leaf miners, scales, grasshoppers, slugs, birds and a host of defacing diseases such as leaf blight and black spot. Each grower faces his own plagues and meets the challenge with a variety of chemical, biological, or physical controls. The Lockharts use chemicals judiciously once or twice each year, applying them with a gasoline-driven pump mounted on a 30-hp International Harvester Farmall tractor.

Mice can be a threat to holly production, girdling the trees at ground level. The best control for this, claims Janet Lockhart, is to keep mulching material away from the tree trunk. Mice often live in the mulch, and by keeping it away from the tree the chances of the mice snacking on the bark are reduced. The mulch—cow manure, straw, leaves—keeps the soil damp and controls yet another enemy, grass, the old competitor for soil moisture. Mowing is the other method of controlling weeds, which Frank does several times each summer with the help of his Farmall tractor, finishing the job by hand with a power mower. This is the part of holly production he likes least, and he is thankful he allowed 20 feet between trees so most of the job can be done by tractor.

Like most producers of forest products, Frank could only laugh when I asked him how many hours he puts in on his operation. It's a lot, especially at harvest time just before Christmas. At that time of year, help is sometimes employed to speed the daily cutting. But the Lockharts trust no one else with the packaging, so it means long evenings for weeks on end as the last step is taken to bring their product to market.

For the Lockharts, the annual cycle of work goes something like this:

Early spring (after frost and before growth starts)	Planting new areas or replacing dead trees. To assure berry production, one out of every 10 to 20 trees should be males and should be scattered throughout the stand. For quicker production, the larger the planted trees the better, with 4-year-old cuttings best if one can afford them. Harvest can usually begin during the seventh year.
April or May	Chemical treatment for leaf miners and some other insects and diseases.
May	Blossom time. If not enough bees are present naturally to assure pollination for berry production, it is necessary to contract with a local bee-keeper to bring in some hives.
May—September	Mowing for weed control
June—August	A second or third spraying of insecticides and fungicides if necessary.
Late November—the week before Christmas	Cutting, packaging and delivering sprays. Temporary storage should be in a cool place with an even temperature. Cartons are used to keep the bundles from being crushed.

Other than land, the investment needed to grow holly is minimal. The Lockharts list their tractor, mower and spray pump as their only equipment—and the tractor was needed anyway for snow plowing. Other expenses include the tree saplings and annual expenditures for fertilizer, pesticides, fungicides, and of course, society dues and meeting expenses. The profits seem well worth the investment, as there is a sense of satisfaction in producing near-perfect trees. As many growers discover, this is a measure of success that transcends monetary gains.

Other Uses of Holly

Christmas cuttings are not the only use of holly. Most holly buffs are simply fanciers of this plant in the same vein of genteel ferocity that roses or poodles are cultivated and shown. Others see holly as the epitome of tasteful landscaping. Much of the commercial trade involves nursery operations, the propagation of cuttings and the development of new hybrids. For these purposes, as in any involving sale of nursery stock, inspections and licensing are required by the government. This, of course, is to prevent the spread of insects and disease. In their early years, Frank and Janet supplemented their Christmas trade with the sale of greenhouse-grown container stock and transplants in burlap-wrapped root-balls. Lucrative as these sales were, root-balls are heavy and transplanting is a lot of hard work. Finally it was decided to leave that to younger nurserymen and focus instead on growing quality trees for Christmas sprays.

But what about those holly trees in the natural forest? You don't have to be a holly buff to appreciate the ivory color of what is said to be the whitest wood known. At one time, up to 75,000 board feet of wood was cut annually from the hills and river bottoms of the South, which found its way to specialty markets where it was prized in the manufacture of cabinets and furniture, mainly as decorative inlay.

Today, natural holly trees are generally small and sparce. They have fallen victim to destructive harvesting that in some areas has nearly eliminated this delightful tree. When asked about this, Frank Lockhart responds angrily, "It is disgusting. The trees are essentially gone. People just rip them apart."

For those fortunate enough to harbor holly in their natural stands, there is an opportunity to try spray production as part of forest management, or perhaps to favor some trees for the eventual production of a specialty wood. For others, the wide choice of cultivars can make interesting and profitable plantings in old fields or clearcut sites. Plenty of help is available, and the affinity for *Ilex* is contagious. In fact, without much effort at all, it is quite possible that you, too, will become a holly buff.

Getting Started in Holly

Handbook of Hollies edited by Dorothy E. Hansell. The American Horticultural Society, Washington, DC.

This 336-page publication is a special issue of the American Horticultural Magazine. Published in the fall of 1970, it is now slightly out of date on some of the technical data, but it is still the best single source on every conceivable aspect of holly culture. It is inexpensive and available from the Holly Society of America.

Hollies—Versatile Beauty for the Intimate Landscape by Fred Ebersole and Virginia Morrell. The Holly Society of America, Baltimore, Maryland.

Although only an 8-page leaflet, this is a handy summary—available for pennies— of the major hollies and their characteristics. Also included is a list of official holly arboreta and test centers, and a condensation of useful information on the culture of holly.

The Holly Society of America, Inc.
304 North Wind Road
Baltimore, MD 21204

A list of additional publications for holly growers as well as information on society membership is available from the society's secretary at the above address. Here is a pool of experts willing to answer questions and help you get started.

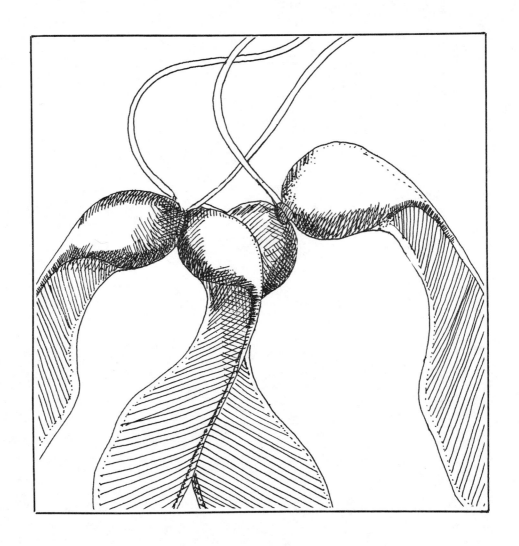

13 Sweet Maple

Though the snow is deep and frosty, Maple memories warm the heart.
—Alice Leedy Mason

In all the woods there is only one tree that rates a full ten on my personal scale of appreciation. That is the sugar maple—*Acer saccharum*. Here is a tree that is beautiful, infinitely useful, and steeped in the histories of Canada and the United States.

As wood, maple is hard and strong, producing the finest of furniture and floors. In the summer its shade is dense and pleasant. Later, its seedpods twirling earthward delight the children of every generation. In the autumn, it flames by day and glows in the crisp twilight. In the hearth it heats with intensity, and its ashes once gave soap to the pioneers. But in early America, as now, sugar maple was loved most for its sap. That sweet water of springtime, carrying new life to twigs and buds, is the epitome of epicurean delight—maple syrup.

Maple syrup (or *sirup* which is closer to the old French derivation, *sirop*) is a forest product which is undergoing a renaissance. In 1860, a record amount was produced— 6,612,500 gallons in the United States alone. Then, sugar and other sweetenings became more available, labor costs rose, and small farms began to vanish. Production dropped dramatically. Today, less than 2,000,000 gallons are produced in the United States. Canadian production has followed a similar pattern, but at higher levels. In about 1952, interest in syrup production began to increase. Prices have also risen, making this an attractive use of private woodlands for personal consumption or, under the right conditions, for income.

Maple Sugaring as a Hobby—A Family Affair

I was first introduced to maple syrup production— called "sugaring" by those close to it—on a visit to Dawn's family home in upstate New York. Springtime has never been the same since. If my work allowed, that's when I would take my annual vacation, not at Christmas or in the summer. Those March days in the woods were among the most pleasant imaginable. I long to be there, companion-in-spirit with the thousands of folks in the north woods who tap the maples, bring in the sap, and tend the boiling fires.

My wife's family runs a "backyard" operation that is about the simplest way possible to produce syrup. Their few hours of effort each day for a couple of weeks produce four or five gallons of good syrup each year. At this level of production, strictly for the fun of it, all you need are a few sugar maples, sap spouts (also called taps, or spiles), something to serve as buckets, and a large pan or pot for boiling.

Walter and Ann Chapman moved to the Adirondack Mountains in 1950 and found themselves surrounded by maples, so many maples, in fact, that even today the vast majority are not tapped. The Chapmans made their first gallon in their backyard and on the kitchen stove. The idea was only to show their children how it is done. To their surprise, the kids never stopped. In the years to come sugaring became an after-school event, then a home-from-college event, and eventually a delight to share with the extended family, including me.

The operation, if we can dignify it in such formal terms, begins in the fall. Firewood is cut and stacked in the woods behind the house. Happily, the maples adjoin a small cedar swamp, and white cedar burns quick and hot— important for good syrup. The cedar is cut thin, then covered with plastic to protect it from the snow that piles several feet deep in the winter.

In the garage hang the "buckets." In this case they are one-gallon plastic milk containers strung on a rope. They are not very romantic in appearance, but they are free and easy to clean, and when hung on the spouts they keep out the twigs, insects and other debris that rains down from the treetops. Old coffee pots, covered lard cans and similar containers work just as well.

In late February or March, the Chapmans keep a close eye on the weather. Like sugarers everywhere, they are alert for the signal to start tapping. It comes at different times, depending on location, but February through April is generally the season. No one wants to

SUGAR MAPLE
ACER SACCHARUM MARSH

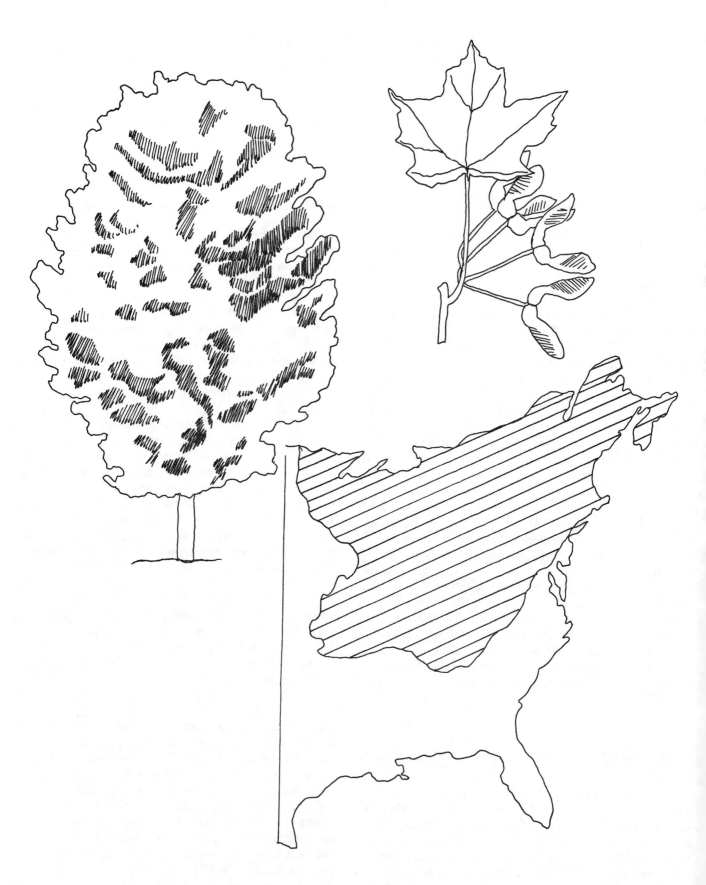

drilling into the outer 2 or 3 inches of the tree and inserting a spout, part of the flowing sap can be intercepted and used for our nourishment instead of the tree's.

With a little care, no harm comes to the maples from tapping. One precaution is to avoid tapping trees under 10 inches DBH. The following guidelines can be used for determining the number of taps per tree.

Inches DBH	Number of taps	Depth of tap hole
10-12	1	2"
12-18	1	3"
18-24	2	3"
24-30	3	3"
Over 30	4	3"

Under these guidelines the tree is deprived of only about 10 percent of its sap. Usually there is no harm from the holes that remain after tapping. Some people feel a need to plug the holes when the season ends. However, it is better to allow the tree to heal itself in the open air than to try closing the tiny opening and risk aiding fungi or other invaders of dark, damp places. Most tap holes will heal on their own within two seasons.

The Chapmans drill their holes with an ordinary hand drill. It is good exercise, reminding me of cranking homemade ice cream. We trade off regularly, also taking turns tapping in the spiles, which is more fun. Then the bottles (our "buckets") are hung—and we wait.

There is something lyrical about the dripping sap as it slowly fills each bottle. The whole process is magical, but this part is best. It is also fun to watch the differences between taps. Trees in the open tend to run faster, due mostly to their larger crowns, but a sunny southern exposure really helps the flow. Sometimes the differences are less apparent. This is because a tree's flow, like the sugar content of its sap, is in part hereditary. Serious operators go to great lengths testing their trees and thinning out the low producers. Most sugar maples range from ½ to 3 percent sugar content in their sap, but a few run higher. Each percent of change has a dramatic effect on the amount of syrup that can be produced from each gallon of sap. One champion in Madison, Wisconsin yields an incredible 14 percent! The Chapmans don't care. They tap the trees most convenient to their boiling fire. In fact, they even tap a few red maples as well. All of our native maples yield sugary sap, but the one that took on the descriptive name yields about 50 percent more.

The season lasts about two or three weeks, then the sugar begins to lose its sweetness and the sap yeilds dark, strong-flavored syrup referred to as "buddy." For commercial producers, these are busy days of "gathering" sap in the daylight and boiling it down long into the night. For hobbyists, the pace is usually more leisurely. Yet even with a hobby operation, once you tap the trees, the sap must be collected regularly or it will spill over and be wasted. When other activities interfere, or when constant cool or warm weather slows the run, someone is ap-

miss the first days of a run, those days when the natural pumps first bring the water skyward from the roots. At this point, the sap is at its sweetest.

What happens in the tree is this: each year the green leaves of a maple convert water and carbon dioxide to sugar. A by-product is oxygen, the gift of trees we so often take for granted. The sugar is the tree's nourishment, used for its twig, root and flower growth, new leaves, and its increase in diameter. Some sap is used immediately, but much is converted to starch and stored in the root system and lower trunk of the tree. Since starch is not water soluble, it cannot be carried through the tree's cellular transmission network. So, it stays there in the roots and trunk, stored through the long winter like a well-stocked larder.

Gradually the starch becomes sugar again, available for movement through the tree and for new growth when dormancy ends. In late winter, the conversion has reached its peak and sugar content is highest.

Next comes the pumping action of freezing nights and the first warm days of the year. The rising temperature in the tree's living cells creates a positive pressure. The pressure then falls when the air cools. As the nightly freeze sets in, a vacuum (negative pressure) develops and sap (water, sugar and various other organic compounds—some of them contributing to the distinctive maple taste) is drawn from the roots ready for the next flow. The greater the difference between daytime and nighttime temperatures (and thus between the positive and negative pressures), the greater the rate of flow. By

155

FROM SAP TO SYRUP IN THE BACKYARD

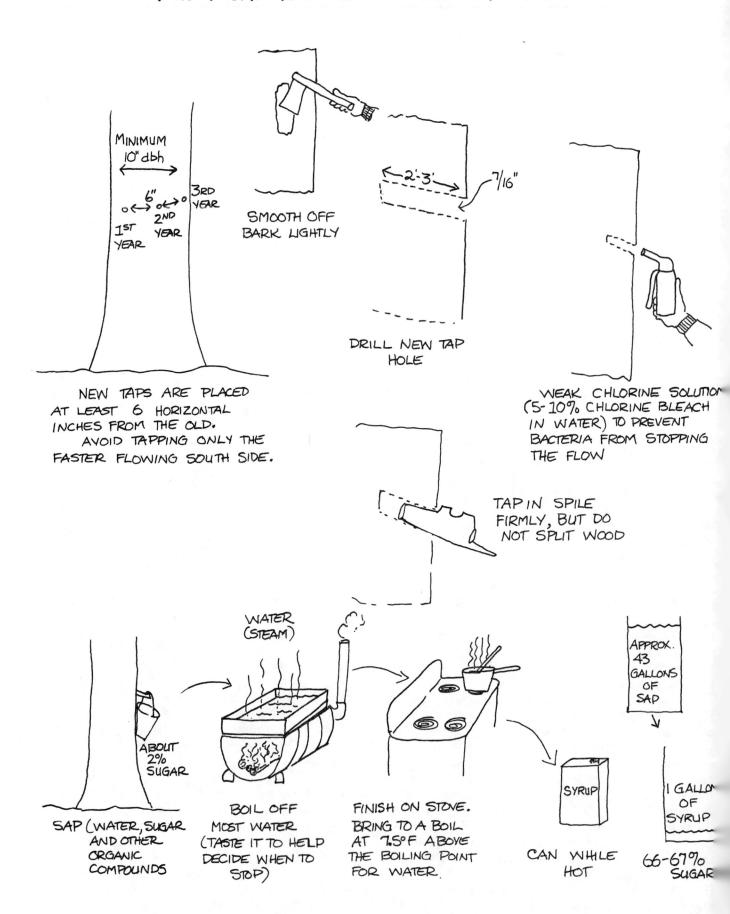

MINIMUM 10" dbh

6"

1ST YEAR
2ND YEAR
3RD YEAR

NEW TAPS ARE PLACED AT LEAST 6 HORIZONTAL INCHES FROM THE OLD.
AVOID TAPPING ONLY THE FASTER FLOWING SOUTH SIDE.

SMOOTH OFF BARK LIGHTLY

2'-3'
7/16"

DRILL NEW TAP HOLE

WEAK CHLORINE SOLUTION (5-10% CHLORINE BLEACH IN WATER) TO PREVENT BACTERIA FROM STOPPING THE FLOW

TAP IN SPILE FIRMLY, BUT DO NOT SPLIT WOOD

WATER (STEAM)

ABOUT 2% SUGAR

SAP (WATER, SUGAR AND OTHER ORGANIC COMPOUNDS

BOIL OFF MOST WATER (TASTE IT TO HELP DECIDE WHEN TO STOP)

FINISH ON STOVE. BRING TO A BOIL AT 7.5°F ABOVE THE BOILING POINT FOR WATER.

SYRUP

CAN WHILE HOT

APPROX. 43 GALLONS OF SAP

1 GALLON OF SYRUP

66-67% SUGAR

pointed to collect the sap, and it is stored in large, plastic garbage cans with lock-on lids to be boiled at a more convenient time. Storage should be in a cool, dark location.

On good days when the run is steady, boiling takes place on an open fire. No one could make money this way, but that's not the purpose. Our hearth is a 50-gallon drum cut lengthwise and steadied in a cradle of soil and rocks. An opening in one end provides a door for the wood and a length of stove pipe at the other end gives an outlet to the smoke. Keeping the fire hot and spread evenly beneath the pan eats up the woodpile quickly. Cutting more helps pass the long hours. So does laughter, pleasant conversation, watching squirrels and spring birds, and even reading or letter writing if the day is warm enough. Periodically we make the rounds to the trees, and slowly pan after pan yields its water to the heavens.

It is difficult to know when to stop boiling. Without a hydrometer to measure sugar content, experience becomes the best guide. Color and depth of the remaining liquid, along with some friendly debate about taste, seem to be the best clues. What remains is then skimmed to remove any ash, bugs or other flotsam, and poured ever so carefully into containers and carried home. The process would kill a true syrup producer, but to us it's like Christmas.

The final step takes place in the kitchen. Actually, the entire boiling procedure could be done there, but the cost of gas or electricity, plus a house full of steam and sticky vapors is less than desirable. However, by doing the final boiling in a pot on the stove, temperature can be watched closely as sugar content nears its optimal level of 65 to 67 percent. Anything less is likely to ferment and sour; anything higher might crystallize. Before this final step, it is necessary to use a thermometer to determine the boiling point of water since it is dependent on elevation and atmospheric pressure. The latter may change daily or more often. Using a special syrup thermometer works even better. Then, when the concentrated, boiling sap shows a temperature of just over 7.5 degrees above the boiling point of water, we proclaim, like producers everywhere—"*Now* we have syrup!"

A Vermont Sugar Bush—Syrup as a Business

The joy of sugaring extends far beyond the hobby level. I have seen this at the annual meetings and tours of syrup producers, and I saw it again when Dawn and I visited the Vermont farm of David Houston and family.

Among commercial operators, a woodlot of maples used for syrup production is called—with a touch of affection—a sugar bush. The Houston sugar bush is a 100-acre parcel of woods on their 200-acre farm near Cabot, Vermont. Dairy products provide the mainstay of the family, but syrup production is also a large part of their income. It has been this way since 1935 when Dave's father, Donavan Houston, settled the place. At

75, Donavan still mans the boiling fire. Dave's son, once ready to give up life on the farm, returned from the military and decided that cows and the sugar bush were not a bad life after all. Dave's grandson—a fourth living generation of these hardy New Englanders—may well follow suit.

Like all Vermont producers at the commercial level, Dave Houston aims for large-scale production, efficiency, and perfect quality. But Dave retains some of the romance of sugaring by using his two beautiful Belgian work horses. We watched them graze in a summer meadow across the dirt road from Dave's cow pasture.

"I still tap about half my trees using those two," Dave pointed out.

Knowing this is not efficient in today's world of plastic pipelines in a sugar bush, I could not understand this inconsistency. From a business standpoint, I still can't. But Dave is not ready to capitulate entirely to technology. He has one of the best managed sugar bushes and evaporating systems in New England, but he also intends to have horses.

He tried to explain. "We work like a team and it's a real pleasure. Besides, I just plain like horses. In the sugar bush I walk to a tree for the bucket, and those two know to move up the road closest to me and stop."

With that the subject closed. If I couldn't understand that was my problem.

When horses are used, workers carry sap buckets to the sled, which is actually a large box on runners. A lid on the top keeps the sap from sloshing out. A valve at the bottom discharges the liquid into a holding tank back at the sugar house—the building where sophisticated evaporation equipment replaces the simple pans of hobbyists.

The only problem with horses, claims Dave, is finding workers who know how to use them. In fact, finding reliable labor for the other tasks of sugaring is also a problem. Ready as always with an example, Dave said, "I had one guy who was all enthused. He put on the snowshoes and lasted ten trees and that was it."

Low wages and hard work is the lot of temporary help at sugaring time. Letting Yankee sagacity illustrate the problem from the farmer's standpoint, Dave laments, "It takes you five days to teach them what to do, then they quit on the sixth." Consequently, Dave and his son do most of the outdoor work, and Dave's father manages the sugar house.

As he shows us his sugar bush, Dave offers his views on some other social issues. As we walk, it becomes apparent there are two things in life he really hates—the square-tailed flies (read deer flies) he slaps and discusses, using one's corpse for a visual aid; and free-loaders who won't work. He has no problems with the many back-to-the-land types who are moving into the hills of Vermont—as long as their intended self-sufficiency doesn't include sustenance from the taxpayers. Any able-bodied person who *can* work, *should* work. And if it's a New York City librarian who moves to the hills and can't find a library to work in, then he ought to do something else.

Government is too generous in Dave's opinion, and should help only those who are really down and out. One of the services he mentions is one that touches close to home. It is the local service forester provided by the state's Agency of Environmental Conservation. But, Dave admits, since the service is available, he figures he may as well use it. The result is evident in his stand of maples, a woodlot as beautiful as it is useful. We look at it with the respect due a cathedral. But the quiet this summer morning belies the noise of chainsaws on other days. To shape a stand this uniform in species, this widely spaced, and so productive in terms of income to the Houstons, intensive forest management is necessary. For anyone seriously considering maple syrup production, there are many excellent lessons in these woods.

Managing Maples for Syrup

There is an inherent conflict in managing a maple stand for lumber *and* syrup production. Tap holes cause one problem. Each hole results in a strip of dead wood equal to the depth of the hole, a little wider than its diameter, and extending below and one to two feet above the hole. If this were a tree for lumber, the defect would be in the butt log, usually the most valuable portion of the tree.

More important, management for lumber requires sufficient density to maximize yield per acre, and it should result in tall, branchless trunks with high crowns. This is achieved through spacing that assures a tight canopy. For maximum sap production, however, wide spacing is best, with full crowns extending almost to the ground. This conflict must be resolved as a first step toward maple management. If it is in favor of lumber, sugaring should probably be kept to the hobby level. If, as in Dave Houston's case, the decision is in favor of syrup

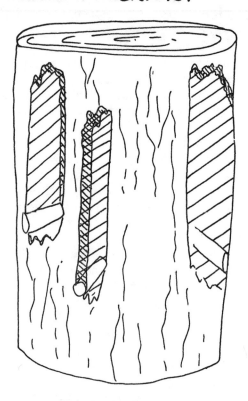

TIMBER AND SAP PRODUCTION CREATE A CONFLICT

DEAD WOOD FROM TAP HOLES

IDEAL TIMBER TREES

BEST FORM FOR SAP PRODUCTION

production, lumber is relegated to a by-product. As we will see, however, wood products still have an important role to play in a well-managed sugar bush.

A productive sugar bush is usually created within existing forests with the aid of selection cuttings. Maple plantings in old fields, like fertilizing sugar bushes, have not proven economical. Neither has natural seeding. Either way, it is a very long wait to get into business, although weeding and restriction of grazing can eventually bring the stand to production status. But in the natural stands, especially on good sites, maple has some very nice characteristics that work in favor of the grower and make intensive management pay off.

A good sugar bush site has deep, moist, well-drained soil with medium or fine texture. The glacial tills and benches of New England and the Lake States are often ideal. The best aspect is usually southeast, which along with moist, lower elevation sites protected from cold winds provide earlier and sometimes heavier sap flows. But maples grow on other sites, too, and if they are on your parcel, improvement through management is possible.

On the Houston farm, the site is higher and colder than ideal, but otherwise moist and rich. The flow often starts weeks later than on the farms of friends just 20 miles away, and perhaps the run is not as generous, but to Dave, this just makes it all the more important to manage carefully and operate efficiently.

In the sugar bush, the way to good management is selective thinning. When the service forester began marking the Houston woodlot, he chose many timber-quality maples, white ash, and yellow birch. Favored to stay were the most vigorous maples in a size class suitable for tapping but not overly mature with deterioration beginning to show. Those initial selection cuts provided immediate income, as well as improvement of the stand. Now, each year the forester marks a portion of the woodlot for thinning.

One of the maple's fortunate characteristics is its tolerance to shade. Beneath an old stand, regeneration is usually abundant. When the stand is thinned or an opening is created when an older tree blows down, young maples respond quickly. Even in middle-aged trees, if relatively open growing conditions have provided a crown over most of the trunk, additional space will usually lead to an even fuller crown and better sap production. Eventually, under ideal conditions, thinning will leave about 25 to 40 large, productive maples per acre, spaced about 35 to 40 feet apart.

The reason for successive thinnings instead of a single one-time cut to reach optimal spacing is to keep out competitive species. Large openings can invite intolerant species such as cherry and birch. Gradual thinning gives the maples an edge over the others, while at the same time reducing risk of various environmental "shock factors" to the favored trees (sunscald, maple borer, wind damage, etc.). Repeated thinnings also control the excess of new maple regeneration, while at the same time allowing future tap trees to be selected.

According to extension foresters, the objectives of thinning in the commercial sugar bush:

- To convert the area to a pure stand of sugar maples, including the elimination of red or silver maples.
- To develop the best sugar producers (those with the best crowns and best diameters).
- To hasten diameter growth (so new trees reach tappable size—about 10 inches—quickly, and so older trees produce more sap).
- To facilitate seedling growth as future replacement of older trees.
- To remove conifers that shade tap holes, thereby slowing sap production.
- To obtain usable wood products.

A Profitable Firewood Byproduct

On the Houston's 100 acres, their forester tries to get to each of several units of the stand every 5 years. He then marks for thinning about 5 to 10 cords of standing trees per acre

In most sugar bushes, thinnings represent the essential fuel for the gargantuan appetites of the evaporator fires. Dave Houston, however, has found it is just as profitable and far more efficient to sell the thinnings as firewood and boil his own maple sap using fuel oil. Oil as a sugar house fuel is usually slightly more expensive than the labor required to cut and store firewood. However, oil is far easier to use, heats the sap quickly and evenly, and reduces the almost unbearable heat in the sugar house by efficiently burning within insulated walls. Oil also reduces the problem of having to constantly rake the burning wood into a hot, even bed of fire.

Dave Houston sells his thinnings to finance the purchase of fuel oil. The price he receives is several times higher than the going rate for pulpwood, and most of the operation is on a "cut-your-own" basis. Using a contract shown in the appendix, he assigns each permittee to part of the unit that has been marked for thinning by the forester. Each cuttable tree has a paint swath both on its trunk and below stump level to prevent the illegal removal of trees to be left. Colors identify the area

159

marked in a particular year. His clientele come from a radius of about 15 miles around the farm and they haul off 100 cords each year. For quadruple the price, Dave or his son will do the cutting and splitting, which adds yet another source of revenue from the woods.

Technology in the Sugar Bush

Although the bucket and horse tradition lives on at the Houston farm, the sugar house and the tapping of half their bush follow the path of high technology. It begins with tapping the trees using an electric drill powered by a generator mounted on the sled. (Some operators use a drill attached to a modified chainsaw.) More striking, however, is a strange network of tubing strung like low telephone wires throughout the stand. This tubing, similar to that made for medical uses, links the trees to a collecting tank like one giant spile and bucket.

Dave leaves the tubing in place from year to year to save the time and expense of rolling it up. You should plan on about 3,000 feet for each 100 taps and on replacing it every 5 or 6 years. Each spring when the run ends, it needs to be flushed with a chlorine solution.

The use of tubing began in the 1950s. The tubing is commonly 5/16-inch at the inside diameter, and made of soft vinyl. Sometimes it is dark-colored to absorb sunlight and help keep the sap from freezing. In the Houston sugar bush, the tubes drain into ½-inch plastic pipes, and these empty into a 1-inch mainline. While some operators labor to keep their tubing warmed by the sun, Dave paints his large tubes white to reflect the sun, and he plans to bury the mainline so the sap stays cool. There is balance needed here, since the sap must get warm enough to flow, but warmth increases the growth of bacteria that destroy flavor and grade.

Constant slope and straight lines must be engineered into a tubing system to help create a vacuum and reduce friction. Constant slopes at about 10 percent gradient tend to create a natural, gravity-induced vacuum that can actually increase sap production as much as 50 percent. Vacuum pumps can increase it even more and can help overcome friction on low slopes.

Dave uses these techniques to bring the sap to a low spot in his sugar bush. There it pours into a huge tank he dismantled from an old milk truck. On a good day, he says, the tank will be full in 6 hours.

Because of terrain, the Houstons must pump their sap uphill from the collecting tank to the sugar house. They found this more convenient than building the sugar house in the woods so far from the main house and barns. The wooden sugar house with its metal roof and smoke stacks is as picturesque as any that ever graced a Vermont calendar. Inside, however, it reflects a state of the art that puts commercial syrup production on par with most other efficient factories. First the sap enters from holding tanks and is pre-heated in pipes built over the hot steam of the boiling pans. The steam is then condensed to yield hot water for use in the sugar house. The sap, meanwhile, passes under ultraviolet lights to kill

bacteria, its temperatures and sugar content closely monitored on the dials of thermometers and hydrometers. Pipes and valves control the flow from pan to pan as water is driven off and sugar content rises. The final heating is done over bottled gas to assure close control.

Finally, the syrup is packaged and sealed in clean metal cans. Dave doesn't like the plastic jugs that are cheaper and more common these days because their translucency doesn't protect the high quality he strives to produce. His cans, carrying the Houston label—Pleasant Acres Farm—are retailed at the farm and through other local outlets. About two-thirds of it goes into large barrels for shipment in bulk to a wholesaler.

The Future

Dave Houston's advice to anyone considering a commercial sugar bush is—"Count up your costs before you invest." He complains about the constant flow of government surveys that ask him for his production figures. Apparently they don't ask about his costs. "The next thing you know, they put out a news release saying how much farmers make." Dave believes it gives a false impression. He suggests that with the cost of labor, metal cans, fuel, evaporators, and other equipment, a person is lucky to break even.

Dave may be stretching it a bit, but certainly the sugar bush offers no easy road to riches. As attractive as the product may be, the high price that is necessary to compensate for its production is a real barrier to its widespread consumption. In fact, the Houston's wholesaler will accept no new producers because he currently receives all the syrup that the market can absorb. This, of course, could change, and local retailing through outlets ranging from farm stands to motel lobbies offers additional opportunities. Still, Dave's advice is well worth considering.

Dave, like many other producers, faces another problem. At the time of my visit an onslaught of forest tent caterpillars was only 15 miles away. When defoliating insects strike a sugar bush the sweetness of sap can be cut in half. Reluctantly, the Houstons face the prospect of spraying insecticides, something they have resisted and don't wish to do. It will also add yet another cost to the ledger.

The problems of efficient production have soured some of the romance of sugaring, but there are rewarding challenges in engineering a modern sugar bush. When it is all said and done, Dave Houston—like thousands of other sugarers—would rather work with his maples than his cows, or probably anything else for that matter. "It never gets boring," he told me, and he hints that his maples, and the syrup they yield, give a richness that cannot be measured in dollars alone.

SUGAR BUSH TUBING SYSTEM

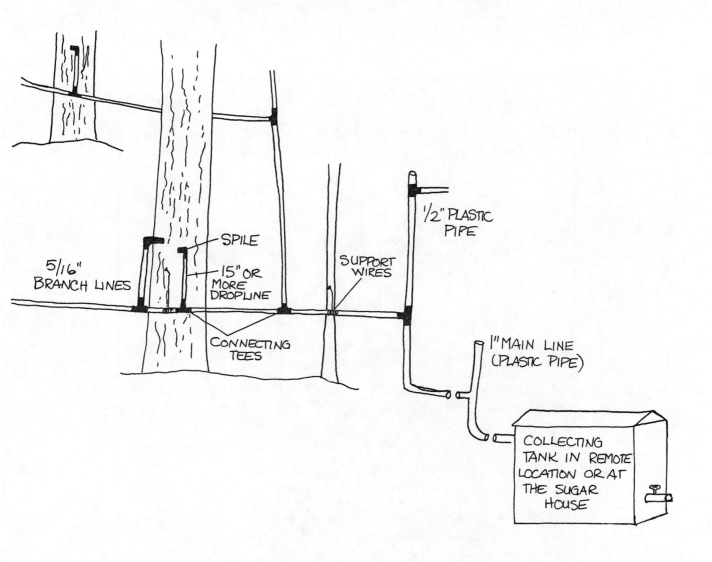

5/16" BRANCH LINES

SPILE

15" OR MORE DROPLINE

SUPPORT WIRES

½" PLASTIC PIPE

CONNECTING TEES

1" MAIN LINE (PLASTIC PIPE)

COLLECTING TANK IN REMOTE LOCATION OR AT THE SUGAR HOUSE

Best Source for More Information

"Maple Sugaring Field Manual" by Thom J. McEvoy. The Extension Service, University of Vermont, Burlington, VT 05405-0088.

Here is the best single source of information on maple sugaring. It is written in clear language, uses the latest findings of research projects, and covers a range of topics from evaluating a potential sugar bush to operating an efficient sugarhouse. The 40-page booklet also offers a valuable guide to recommended reading, including periodicals, and where you can purchase maple supplies.

14 Woodlands
For
Wildlife

The forest is far more than a collection of trees.

—Gifford Pinchot

Americans are intensely interested in wildlife. According to a 1980 survey made by the U.S. Fish and Wildlife Service, 60 million people in the U.S. alone participate in wildlife-related activities. And that does not count young people under the age of 16!

The government began surveys of wildlife users in 1955 and has found that except for waterfoul hunting and saltwater fishing, there has been continued growth in what are termed the "consumptive" uses of wildlife.

The total amount of hunting and fishing continues to rise. In 1980, a new category was added to the survey. This is what is called "nonconsumptive wildlife use" and it was designed to tally the bird watchers, photographers, wildlife feeders and others who simply enjoy seeing wildlife. People were counted in this category if they actually involved themselves with wildlife in some way; simply visiting a zoo or noticing birds while on the way to work did not count. As it turned out, 93 million U.S. citizens were counted as nonconsumptive users. About 30 million of these also hunted and fished during part of the year.

Canadian statistics are just as impressive. Surveys there have found that one of every ten Canadians hunts and one of every five makes a special effort to observe, photograph, feed or study wildlife.

It all underscores our tremendous interest in wild creatures, and few people are more interested than woodland owners. In the Berkshire Mountains of Massachusetts a study found that about as many nonindustrial woodland owners considered wildlife conservation as the most important use of their land as those who viewed timber production as number one. In West Virginia, a similar study found that 33 percent of all private woodland owners listed timber production as their primary objective, while 57 percent said hunting and wildlife-related recreation was their primary purpose for owning forest land. In Pennsylvania, timber production was rated first with only 1 percent of the owners; 27 percent cited aesthetics and recreation (including widlife-related activities) as their primary objective.

Interest in wildlife is apparent in almost every landowner I visited. Some hunt and fish, others simply want to share their land with wildlife and experience the satisfaction of watching and learning. A few even see wildlife as an aid to good forest management.

For example, forest farmers in the South are finding that by using management techniques that allow four species of woodpeckers to share the land, 65 percent of emerging adult southern pine beetles can be destroyed. Consider, as well, the following:

- A house wren feeds 500 insects to its young every summer afternoon.
- Swallows are said to devour 1,000 insects a day.
- A pair of redstarts feed their young approximately every five minutes for a minimum of 1,200 bugs a day.
- A pair of flickers might consider 5,000 ants a mere snack; and a Baltimore oriole can gobble 17 leaf-eating caterpillars a minute.

For whatever reason, if wildlife is important to you, there is much you can do to make certain it will always be part of your woodland.

Some Principles and Myths

The fundamental principle underlying management for wildlife is the relationship of an animal species to its surroundings. Like trees, each animal has evolved and adapted to live only within a well-defined geographical area. Along with the plants upon which they depend, wildlife species follow the changes of altitude, rainfall, temperature and other conditions that delineate life zones and biomes (Chapter 2). So, we think of mountain goats in alpine life zones and pronghorn antelope in lower elevation grasslands or shrub forests in the West. In the milder, rainier eastern woodlands we think of white-tailed deer, and in the swamps of the deep South, alligators.

What you can expect to have live on your land is controlled first by the limitations of natural range. Field guides show these ranges for each species. For identification of an unknown bird, or in planning to enhance habitat for a certain species, a look at a range map is a good first step.

The exception to this guideline is the ranges of some animals that have shrunk with the spread of civilization. Social factors rather than physical conditions control the range of these species. Thus, grizzly bears have retreated from the plains into mountain strongholds and even there they are being pressured toward oblivion. Conversely, some species are spreading beyond their former range as civilization creates favorable conditions. Examples of this are the northward movement of mockingbirds and the westward spread of eastern blue jays. No one knows for certain the reason for these changes, but plowed roads in

WILDLIFE AND SUCCESSION

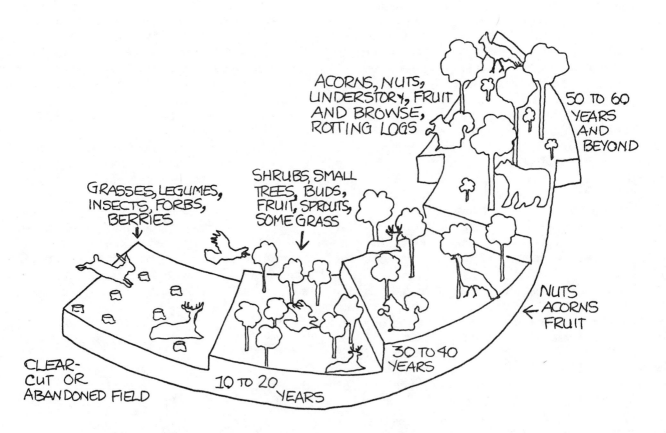

ACORNS, NUTS, UNDERSTORY, FRUIT AND BROWSE, ROTTING LOGS

50 TO 60 YEARS AND BEYOND

SHRUBS, SMALL TREES, BUDS, FRUIT, SPROUTS, SOME GRASS

GRASSES, LEGUMES, INSECTS, FORBS, BERRIES

NUTS ACORNS FRUIT

CLEAR-CUT OR ABANDONED FIELD

10 TO 20 YEARS

30 TO 40 YEARS

SUCCESSION IS ONE CLUE TO THE KINDS OF WILDLIFE THAT WILL BE ABUNDANT IN A WOODLOT.

the winter are suspected. Birds are dependent on small stones for grit in their digestive systems, and ground that was formerly snow-covered is now open year around, making it more favorable for birdlife.

Within its broad range, the occurrence of wildlife depends on habitat—the specific living conditions on the ground. Habitat is made up primarily of food, cover and water. Because of this, it is easy to see that there is a close link between the stage of plant succession that exists on the land and the wildlife species that can co-exist there. Thus, cottontail rabbits are more numerous in open fields of grass and shrubs (early stages of succession) than under the canopy of a forest at later stages of succession. In old fields or young plantations, they find the grass and succulent plants needed in their diet, and matted weeds or brush piles essential for protective cover and the rearing of young. Bears live at the other habitat extreme. They need the nuts and fruits of a mature forest and rotting logs they can claw apart to find insects and small mammals. Fallen trees provide a place to sleep, and the deep woods provide a secure place to hide and raise young.

Most species do best in a mosaic of living conditions. Deer offer a good example. Open areas such as a clearcut or field provide grass and the tender young shoots of new trees and shrubs, both important in a deer's diet. But deer also need dense cover for hiding during the day. So, a young stand of trees located next to an open acreage makes an ideal combination.

Woodland owners have many opportunities to affect the three keys to wildlife numbers—food, cover, and water. This chapter is devoted to some practical ways to create favorable conditions for wildlife, but first, let's consider some common myths I have encountered among woodland owners, and some principles that may help provide a better understanding of wildlife management.

Myth 1: Stocking Will Provide More Wildlife

Many landowners believe that if they buy and release game birds or other animals, they can increase the population of that species on their property.

Sometimes this can work; for example, re-introduction of a species, such as wild turkey, to an area from which it has vanished, but which is still suitable habitat, can be successful sometimes. This can work for an existing species, too, for a very short time. Shooting preserves operate on this basis. They grow 'em, release 'em and shoot 'em, often guaranteeing each hunter who pays his fee a given number of birds to shoot at. This is an expensive way to hunt and not the sort of thing most woodland owners have in mind.

Land will be as full of a species as possible when habitat conditions for that species are optimal. This principle is called carrying capacity. Beyond that optimal point introduced animals will either perish or move to other locales. Adding more animals to land that has reached its carrying capacity is like adding water to a cup already filled to the rim.

Carrying capacity will usually be high when there is plenty of food, cover and water. This varies with the

seasons, so when trying to improve these conditions, think of each factor during the most difficult time of the year. The worst season or the habitat element in shortest supply can be thought of as the limiting factor, which controls how many of any species can live on a particular piece of land.

The moral of all this is: work with the habitat and wildlife numbers will naturally increase.

In the case of herbivores, a species will sometimes temporarily exceed the carrying capacity of the land. Eventually, disease or starvation will reduce its population, or physiological stress will slow the reproduction process. In the meantime, much damage can be done to the woodland. This brings us to Myth 2.

Myth 2: Hunting is Cruel

To some people hunting is an ageless rite deeply ingrained in our culture. It takes on an almost sensual or religious attraction and is the annual highlight of life. To others, it is the unleashing of an army of boobs and ogres who drink, litter and resort to a form of anarchy that knows no respect for the property of others. Still others see hunting as mindless cruelty to animals.

I can not be an apologist for unethical hunters, but the charge of cruelty is groundless. Hunting is often necessary to control the numbers of animals before they exceed carrying capacity. The alternative of starving or dying from disease is more cruel than the relatively quick death by a hunter's gun. Hunting herbivores such as deer or rabbits is often essential to protect regeneration—the next generation of trees—from being eaten out of existence. By controlling *who* hunts on your land, and how they do it, you can keep out the slobs and at the same time keep wildlife in healthy balance with its habitat and your trees.

As for leg trapping, my unalterable opinion is that it *is* cruel. Leg traps of any kind, even the so-called painless ones that do not close entirely on the creature's limb, are terrifying to the animal, frequently trap the wrong species, and sometimes cause the animal to starve, drown, chew through its own leg in an attempt at freedom, or be preyed upon while chained in place before the trapper arrives to shoot it. Live traps, on the other hand, are cages that close harmlessly around the animal. These can be used to trap raccoons, porcupines, rabbits and other animals so they can be transported off the property if necessary.

Myth 3: Predators Should be Controlled

Thanks to decades of cultural influences ranging from fairy tales like Little Red Riding Hood to the propaganda of livestock producers and the attitudes of some fish and game departments, certain species of wildlife are labeled "bad." Coyotes, cougars and wolves quickly come to mind, and even foxes, eagles and bears might make the list. This prejudice has the mistaken idea that if you control predators, you automatically increase the numbers of "good" species.

Study after study has shown this is rarely the case. Usually predators harvest the excess that the habitat can produce. When habitat conditions are good, prey species are numerous and predators are also able to eat well. When habitat factors are poor, predator numbers decline right along with those of other wildlife. Predators serve the function of helping to keep numbers in balance with food and cover supplies. They perform a useful service and their control is better left to nature's food web.

Myth 4: "My Dog Wouldn't Hurt Nature"

These were the words of a local back-to-the-land suburbanite who added, "They love wildlife, too."

It is difficult to argue with an owner about the emotional inclinations of his dog, but at night and on the loose, the family pet is a terror for wildlife. The gentlest pet still harbors the natural instincts to hunt and chase.

Singly or in packs, dogs chase deer. In wintertime they can often travel rapidly over the snow while the long legs of deer punch through the crust. The end comes in an attack that results in the waste of a valuable resource. Even when wildlife escapes "harmlessly" from playful dogs, valuable energy reserves are used up that in the naked world of nature can mean the difference between life and death.

Dogs can be wonderful companions for the woodland owner, but letting them run loose is an act of irresponsibility toward both human neighbors and the native wildlife of fields and forests.

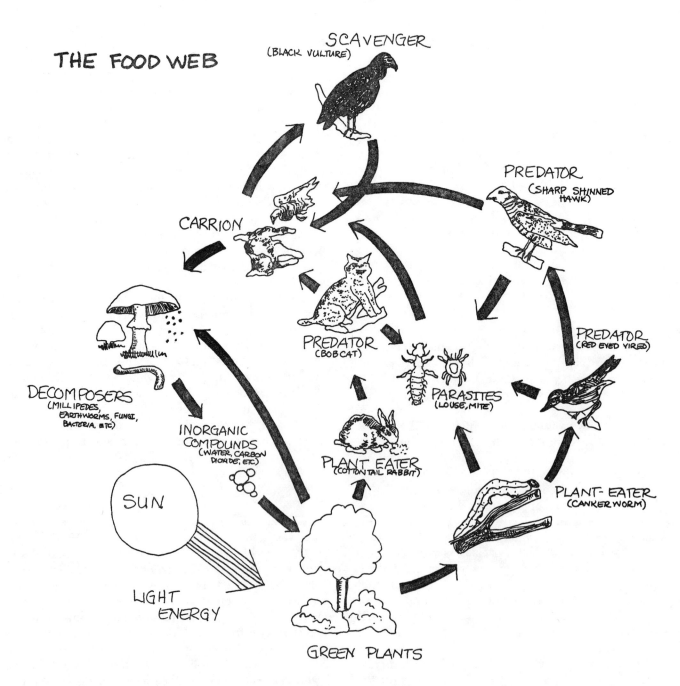

THE FOOD WEB

SCAVENGER (BLACK VULTURE)

CARRION

PREDATOR (SHARP SHINNED HAWK)

PREDATOR (BOBCAT)

PREDATOR (RED EYED VIREO)

DECOMPOSERS (MILLIPEDES, EARTHWORMS, FUNGI, BACTERIA, ETC.)

PARASITES (LOUSE, MITE)

INORGANIC COMPOUNDS (WATER, CARBON DIOXIDE, ETC.)

PLANT EATER (COTTONTAIL RABBIT)

PLANT-EATER (CANKER WORM)

SUN

LIGHT ENERGY

GREEN PLANTS

Managing for Wildlife

When the basic principles of wildlife ecology are understood, it becomes clear that the way to enhance wildlife on a piece of land is to improve the habitat for the species you wish to encourage. Therefore, the first step is to read all you can about that species and make notes on such things as:

- Does this species occur naturally in my part of the country and within the general kind of habitat provided by my woodland?
- What does it eat? (Martin, Zim and Nelson's book, listed at the end of this chapter, is a good start.) Note that food requirements may differ with time of year.
- What specific cover types are needed? This usually includes: escape cover, nesting cover, and "loafing" areas.
- What are its water needs?
- Is this species compatible with the other objectives for my land? (Consider cutting methods, human disturbances, potential damage to trees, etc.)
- Are there recommended management practices that are practical under my circumstances?

Wildlife Food

Food is the first essential you can help provide for wildlife on your land. As with humans, the right diet in both quantity and quality helps individual animals stay healthy and robust. Deer, for example, grow bigger antlers when they feed on farm crops and other vegetation produced on rich, fertile soils. Good soil is as important to wildlife as it is to tree growth. Obviously, an adequate diet also leads to greater numbers of wildlife if the other keys to habitat are present. If you will want twins born to doe deer each spring instead of a single fawn, or a clutch of 14 eggs in a bobwhite quail nest instead of five or six, then diet must be good.

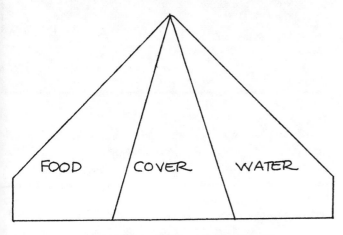

WILDLIFE HABITAT

Food requirements vary so widely among wildlife species that it is impossible to include them here. Fruits, nuts, twigs, leaves and even bark and roots provide nourishment to plant eaters; insects, carrion and the flesh of other creatures are the diet of the meat-eaters. You need to determine what you can supply that is useful to your favored species, then consider the best way to do this under your circumstances. Here are some common methods for achieving this.

Edge Plantings

Shrubs, vines and other vegetation important in wildlife diets can be planted (or favored from among existing vegetation) along the edges of fields, lawns, plantations, roads, lakes or other openings. These double as cover and many times add to the aesthetics of the property.

Edge plantings should be at least 20 feet across. Removing trees and letting succession take over is often all that is needed. Another trick is to plow the strip, then stretch a wire or strong cord between poles along the center. Birds resting on the line will do the planting! If more control over plant species is desired, transplanting from elsewhere on the property is an inexpensive solution. The more costly alternative is to order nursery stock. The list in the accompanying box will provide some ideas on what to plant, especially if your interest is in birds. Once established, the only maintenance required is to remove or girdle trees that get tall enough to shade out the understory of shrubs. However, some trees, such as cherries, apples or nut-producers, have such a high food value it is a good idea to leave a few scattered along the edge strips.

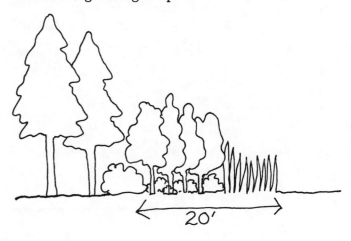

Food Plots

Providing food plots is a good but relatively expensive method to benefit game birds, rabbits, raccoons, deer and some other species. The size of food plots vary but are usually 1/8 to 1 acre in size. This method consists of planting old fields with grain, corn, legumes and similar plants having ultra-high nutritional value for wildlife.

Plantings can be done annually on an entire plot, but it is better to divide the field into strips, plowing and planting a different strip each year. On fields large

Excellent Shrubs and Trees for Wildlife Plantings

Species	Type	Site Requirements	Fruit
Autumn Olive (Elaegnus umbellata)	Large shrub small tree	Moist to dry; Sun to light shade	Sept.-Feb.
American Cranberrybush (Viburnum trilobum and other Viburnums)	Tall shrub	Wet to well-drained; Sun to light shade	Sept.-May
Bittersweet (Celastrus scandens)	Vine	Well-drained to dry; Sun to light shade	Sept.-Dec.
Cherry (various species of Prunus)	Tree	Moist to dry; Sun to light shade	Pin cherry: Aug.-Oct. Black cherry: July-Nov.
Crabapple and Apple (Malus spp.)	Tree	Moist to well-drained; Sun	Sept.-April
Dogwoods Flowering (cornus florida)	Small tree	Well-drained to dry; Sun to shade	Sept.-Feb.
Gray-stemmed (Cornus paniculata)	Thicket-forming shrub	Well-drained to dry; Sun	Aug.-Nov.
Eastern Redcedar (Juniperous virginiana)	Tree (conifer)	Moist to dry; Sun to light shade	Sept.-May
Firethorn (Pyracantha spp.)	Small tree	Moist to dry; Sun	Sept.-March
Hawthorn (Crataegus spp.)	Small tree	Moist to dry; Sun	Variable; Usually Oct.-March
Highbush Blueberry (Vaccinium corymbosum)	Medium shrub	Wet to dry; Sun	July-Oct.
Holly (Ilex spp.	Shrub to small tree	Wet to well-drained; Sun	Aug.-June
Honeysuckles Amur Honeysuckle (Lonicera maacki)	Large shrub	Well-drained to dry; Sun to shade	Oct.-April
Tatarian Honeysuckle (Lonicera tatarica)	Large shrub	Well-drained to dry; Sun to shade	July-Sept.
Mountain-Ash (Sorbus spp.)	Tree	Moist to dry; Sun	Aug.-March
Sumac (Rhus spp.)	Tall shrub	Well-drained to dry; Sun	Sept.-May
Virginia Creeper (Parthenocissus quinquefolia)	Vine	Moist to dry; Sun	Aug.-Feb.

enough for five strips, the recommended yearly sequence of working the strips is 1-3-5-2-4. As with farm crops, site preparation, suitability of the soil for the crop, and proper fertilization are necessary if the planting is to be successful.

If you produce farm crops on your land or lease a portion of it to a farmer, an alternative to planting food patches is to simply leave corners, ravines, or scattered "islands" of your crop unharvested. In biblical history, this was required as a tithe to be used by the poor. Today it is still a nice idea for the wild creatures that share our land.

For planting, consult your local fish and game department, the Soil Conservation Service or the Cooperative Extension Service for advice on what works best in your area, what site preparation is necessary, and how much seed should be sowed. They may also help with a soil test to determine the level of fertilizer needed. In the West, it is especially important to match the plant species with precipitation and elevation levels.

Some Common Food Plot Species

West

Grasses such as
    Russian wildrye and other wildrye species
    Crested wheatgrass and other wheatgrass species
    Smooth brome (in mountain areas)
    Tall oatgrass (in mountain areas)
    Reed canarygrass (in mountain areas)
    Meadow foxtail (in mountain areas)

Legumes such as
    Alfalfa
    Milkvetch
    Yellow sweetclover

Other broadleaf herbs such as
    penstemous, showy goldeneye, and cowparsnip, and a wide variety of shrubs.

East

Birdsfoot trefoil & Grass	6 lbs seed/acre; with 3 lbs orchardgrass. Plant early spring or late summer	Lime to 6-6.5 pH; 300 lbs acre of 5-10-10 fertilizer when seeding. later, 300 lbs 0-14-14
Buckwheat	1-1½ bushels/acre; plant early summer	Same as above but without second spreading
Corn	10 lbs seed/acre; 40" between rows; plant late spring	Same lime; 400-500 lbs/acre of 5-10-10
Japanese millet	25 lbs seed/acre; plant late spring	Same lime; no fertilizer
Lespedoza (Serica) 16 (Bicolor); plant anytime in spring	15 lbs seed/acre	Same as birdsfoot trefoil
Rye	3-4 pecks of seed/acre; plant early fall	Lime to 6-6.5 pH; 300-400 lbs/acre of 5-10-10 fertilizer
Soybeans	½-2 bu.seed/acre; plant late spring	Same as above
Wheat	1-½ bu. seed/acre; plant early fall	Same as above
Food patch mix #1 or #2	20 lbs/acre; anytime in spring	Same as above
Food patch mix #3	10 lbs/acre; anytime in spring	Same as above

Popular food patch mixes (with lbs of seed needed per 5 acres):

# 1		# 2		# 3	
Buckwheat	10#	Buckwheat	15#	Proso millet	17.5#
Grain sorghum	9	Foxtail millet	15	Grain sorghum	25.0
Foxtail millet	15	Sudangrass	15	Sunflower	7.5
Proso millet	15	Soybeans	25		50.0#
Kaffir	9	Cowpeas	30		
Sudangras	5		100#		
Soybeans	15				
Cowpeas	13				
Vetch	9				
	100#				

Maintaining Open Spaces

Deer, certain bird species (including bluebirds, meadowlarks and many upland game species), and other wildlife need open spaces. There they find grasses, insects and berries to eat, or the openness they need for territorial displays, nesting, or watching for natural enemies. As the fields of abandoned farms become woods, or the small trees of plantations grow up and close their crowns, habitat for these species becomes scarce, and numbers dwindle accordingly.

Especially in the East, lack of open spaces is a problem that is becoming significant. It is also one that is easily corrected simply by regularly mowing some open field areas. If planned correctly, these spaces might contribute to the visual qualities of the property by opening distant views, providing spaciousness around the house or other buildings and offering opportunities to watch wildlife. Open areas can also make good firebreaks.

When planting trees on large acreages, there are two good rules of thumb: (1) for areas of 5 to 10 acres, leave openings of about 66 feet between the planted area and the existing forest; (2) if planting more than 10 acres, leave numerous small openings scattered throughout the plantation.

Artificial Feeding

Feeding wild animals is always a subject of debate. On the negative side, feeding concentrates animals so they are more vulnerable to predation and the spread of disease. They tend to lose their natural caution and they become dependent on humans to provide their food. On the positive side, artifical feeding is sometimes needed to prevent starvation after ice storms or especially heavy

snows. In the case of elk in the West, feeding has become necessary in some areas as farms and houses have filled the valleys that once provided over-wintering grounds.

In general, artificial feeding should be kept to a minimum, limited to around the house where birds can be attracted for viewing and photography. Place feeders (ideally, more than one) near enough to conifers or other cover to provide birds with a comfortable route to and from the feeder. When corn or grain is supplied to pheasants, quail or other ground feeders, the open space should be close to cover, but not so close that the birds can be easily surprised by cats or other predators. Local Audubon Clubs can usually supply literature on bird seed, suet recipes, fluids for hummingbirds and other ideas for feeding.

Cover and Nests

Cover for escape, nesting or protection from weather is an essential part of total wildlife habitat that woodland owners can easily provide. Food plantings, particularly hedge rows and edge plantings, provide some cover. So does the forest, except in cases of pruned plantations on sites kept so neat that the ground is clear of branches and understory.

There are two ways to improve hiding or escape cover. One is to allow areas of trees or shrubs to grow more densely than good silviculture might otherwise dictate. Patches of conifers with branches reaching to the ground are particularly good, especially in generally open country or in what otherwise is a hardwood forest.

Another common practice is to provide brush piles for birds and small mammals. These can help with slash control as well, while removing only a small percentage of land area—if any at all—from tree production.

Location of the piles is important. For example, they should be on the edge or within a couple hundred feet of feeding and watering areas, or along travel lanes. By placing them at intervals between water and feeding areas, you may be able to create travelways and thereby make the area more habitable for wildlife.

Useful brush piles are not just heaps of branches—they must have space within for movement and yet keep out dogs and predators. Some suggestions are made in the illustration. Brush piles are also attractive to mice and rats. Although this may please local birds of prey, it illustrates again the type of tradeoffs that make woodland management so challenging. Does the possible increase in wildlife, including mice and rats, mean more to you than the additional number of small trees that may get girdled by gnawing teeth?

Wildlife managers have found nest structures to be a good way to attract some species and even to increase their populations. Some illustrations of these appear on page 172. Because cavity-nesting birds are quite particular about such things as height above the ground, size of the cavity, and size of the entrance hole, some dimensions are listed that will help you build bird houses that attract the cavity-nester you want.

BRUSH PILES FOR SMALL MAMMALS AND GAME BIRDS

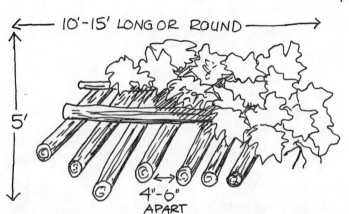

10'-15' LONG OR ROUND

5'

4"-6" APART

LARGER LOGS OR CULL LOGS, LAID PARALLEL. 6" DIAMETERS ARE IDEAL. NEXT LARGER SIZES AT RIGHT ANGLES ABOVE, THEN SMALLER LIMBS & BRUSH.

FOR:
QUAIL— KEEP WITHIN 200' OF OTHER ESCAPE COVER. IN WEST, ALSO WITHIN 1/4 MILE OF WATER.

RABBITS— PILES UP TO 50' LONG ARE USEFUL. IN WEST, PLACE IN RAVINES OR NEAR UPPER END OF BROAD ARROYOS.

TURKEY— PLACE WITHIN 1/2 MILE OF WATER AND AROUND BASE OF TREE OR OTHER LOGS

PHEASANTS— PLACE IN FIELD CORNERS OR ALONG FENCE ROWS

TOP-PRUNNED TREE WITH ATTACHED LOWER BRANCHES COVERED BY LIMBS AND BRUSH (ATTRACTIVE TO GROUND FEEDING SONG BIRDS)

LIVING BRUSH PILE

FROM PUSHING OVER PARTLY CUT CONIFERS (IF DONE PROPERLY, SHOULD LIVE ATLEAST SEVERAL YEARS)

PILE OF DISCARDED OR UNSOLD CHRISTMAS TREES

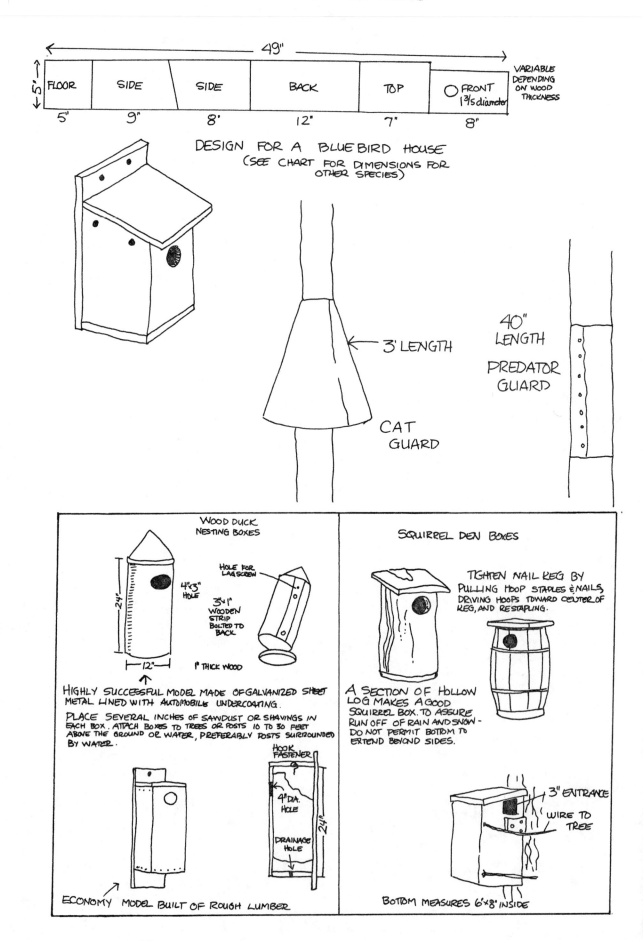

49"

5'

FLOOR	SIDE	SIDE	BACK	TOP	◯ FRONT 1 3/5 diameter

VARIABLE DEPENDING ON WOOD THICKNESS

5"   9'   8'   12'   7'   8'

DESIGN FOR A BLUEBIRD HOUSE
(SEE CHART FOR DIMENSIONS FOR OTHER SPECIES)

3' LENGTH

CAT GUARD

40" LENGTH

PREDATOR GUARD

WOOD DUCK NESTING BOXES

SQUIRREL DEN BOXES

24"

4"x3" HOLE

3"x1" WOODEN STRIP BOLTED TO BACK

HOLE FOR LAG SCREW

1" THICK WOOD

12"

HIGHLY SUCCESSFUL MODEL MADE OF GALVANIZED SHEET METAL LINED WITH AUTOMOBILE UNDERCOATING.

PLACE SEVERAL INCHES OF SAWDUST OR SHAVINGS IN EACH BOX. ATTACH BOXES TO TREES OR POSTS 10 TO 30 FEET ABOVE THE GROUND OR WATER, PREFERABLY POSTS SURROUNDED BY WATER.

TIGHTEN NAIL KEG BY PULLING HOOP STAPLES & NAILS, DRIVING HOOPS TOWARD CENTER OF KEG, AND RESTAPLING.

A SECTION OF HOLLOW LOG MAKES A GOOD SQUIRREL BOX. TO ASSURE RUN OFF OF RAIN AND SNOW - DO NOT PERMIT BOTTOM TO EXTEND BEYOND SIDES.

HOOK FASTENER

4" DIA. HOLE

DRAINAGE HOLE

24"

ECONOMY MODEL BUILT OF ROUGH LUMBER

3" ENTRANCE

WIRE TO TREE

BOTTOM MEASURES 6"x8" INSIDE

Species	Diameter of Entrance (inches)	Depth of Cavity (inches)	Floor of Cavity (inches)	Entrance Above Floor (inches)	Height Above Ground (feet)
Barn Owl	6	12-15	8 x 8	9-12	12-20
Black-capped Chickadee	1 1/8	8-10	4 x 4	6-8	6-15
Bluebird	1 3/8	8	5 x 5	6	5-10
Carolina Wren	1½	6-8	4 x 4	1-6	6-10
Crested Flycatcher	2	8-10	6 x 6	6-8	8-20
Downy Woodpecker	1¼	9-12	4 x 4	6-8	6-20
Flicker	2½	16-18	7 x 7	14-16	6-20
Hairy Woodpecker	1½	12-15	6 x 6	9-12	12-20
House Wren	1¼	6-8	4 x 4	1-6	6-10
Kestrel	3	12-15	8 x 8	9-12	10-30
Nuthatch	1¼	8-10	4 x 4	6-8	12-20
Purple Martin	2½	6	6 x 6	1	15-20
Red-headed woodpecker	2	12-15	6 x 6	9-12	12-20
Screech Owl	3	12-15	8 x 8	9-12	10-30
Tree Swallow	1½	6	5 x 5	1-5	10-15
Tufted Titmouse	1¼	8-10	4 x 4	6-8	6-16
Wood Duck	3 x 4(oval)	10-24	10 x 18	12-16	10-20

Structures can also be provided around ponds and marshes when natural cavities or platforms are lacking. Under natural conditions, waterfowl often use mounds of soil, beaver lodges, muskrat houses and large rocks. Whenever possible, these should be left alone in your wetlands. Where they are in short supply, you may want to try some of the substitutes illustrated here, but before you do, check with a local conservation officer. As these structures can be expensive and time-consuming, you want to be sure they have a good chance of success with the desired species. For example, black ducks require a lot of isolation when they nest, so only one pair will usually occupy a wetland regardless of how many nest sites are made available. Other species are more tolerant, but there is always a point at which added nests are only a waste of money.

Water

In Eastern Canada and United States, the availability of water is rarely a problem for animals. Open, standing water attracts a whole milieu of birdlife, and often increases opportunities to observe deer and other wildlife as they come to drink or feed along the shore. For these reasons, spring-fed ponds or creeks deepened and widened by small dams can add to the richness of your woodland. Then, too, if placed near a road, they can offer a source of water in case of fire.

In many areas of the West, the matter of water for wildlife is more crucial. Water may be the missing link in the total habitat, thereby keeping numbers low or non-existent. Watering tanks, impoundments and various catchment devices that trap precious rainfall are ways to bolster wildlife populations.

Other Management Practices

Depending on local wildlife and condition of the land, there are many other things a woodland owner can do to restore or increase wildlife. Some require no outlay of cash, just the awareness of animal needs as you go about planning for other uses of the land.

- Keep fire out of ravines, fence rows and other productive wildlife cover.
- Protect at least two dead snags or hollow trees per acre. In different stages of natural deterioriation they provide food and shelter for

SOME WETLAND NEST STRUCTURES

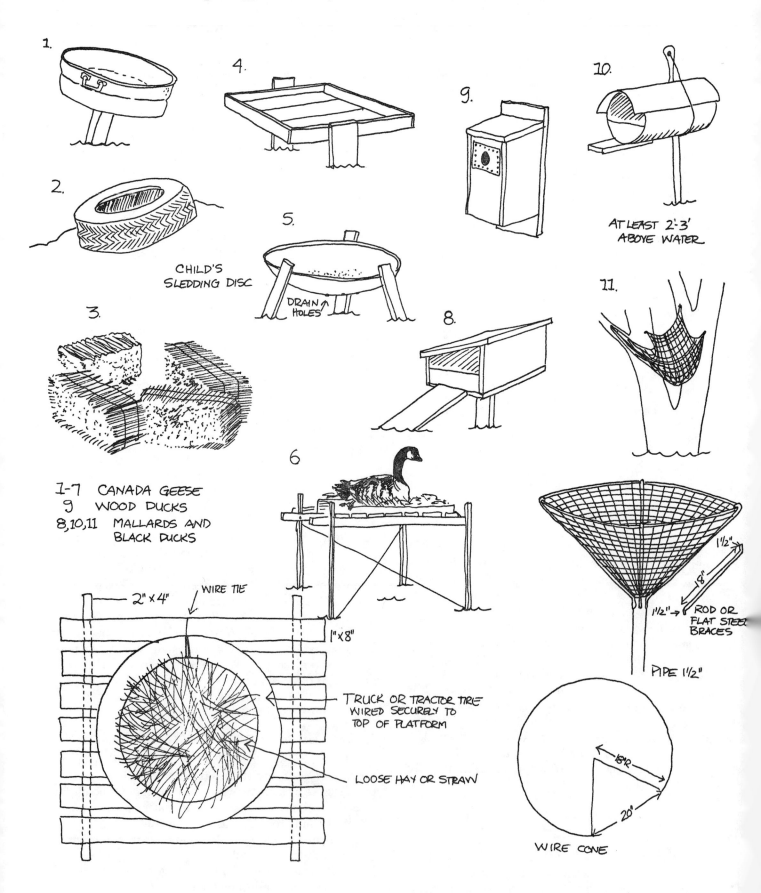

1.

2.

CHILD'S
SLEDDING DISC

3.

4.

5.

DRAIN
HOLES

6.

8.

9.

10.

AT LEAST 2'-3'
ABOVE WATER

11.

1-7   CANADA GEESE
  9   WOOD DUCKS
8,10,11   MALLARDS AND
        BLACK DUCKS

2" x 4"

WIRE TIE

1" x 8"

TRUCK OR TRACTOR TIRE
WIRED SECURELY TO
TOP OF PLATFORM

LOOSE HAY OR STRAW

1½"

8"

1½"

1½"

ROD OR
FLAT STEEL
BRACES

PIPE 1½"

18"R

20"

WIRE CONE

WATERING DEVICES

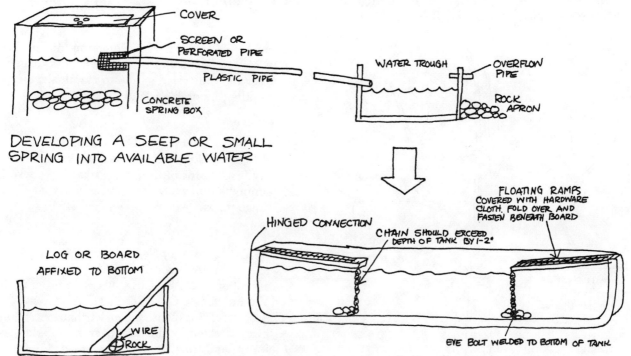

COVER

SCREEN OR PERFORATED PIPE

PLASTIC PIPE

CONCRETE SPRING BOX

DEVELOPING A SEEP OR SMALL SPRING INTO AVAILABLE WATER

WATER TROUGH

OVERFLOW PIPE

ROCK APRON

LOG OR BOARD AFFIXED TO BOTTOM

WIRE ROCK

FLOATING RAMPS COVERED WITH HARDWARE CLOTH, FOLD OVER AND FASTEN BENEATH BOARD

HINGED CONNECTION

CHAIN SHOULD EXCEED DEPTH OF TANK BY 1-2"

EYE BOLT WELDED TO BOTTOM OF TANK

SAFETY DEVICES (IN ALL OPEN TANKS) FOR SMALL MAMMALS AND TO ENCOURAGE USE BY YOUNG BIRDS.

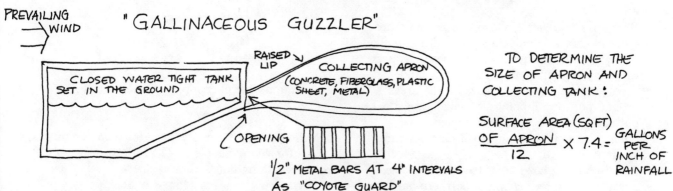

PREVAILING WIND

"GALLINACEOUS GUZZLER"

CLOSED WATER TIGHT TANK SET IN THE GROUND

RAISED LIP

COLLECTING APRON (CONCRETE, FIBERGLASS, PLASTIC SHEET, METAL)

OPENING

1/2" METAL BARS AT 4" INTERVALS AS "COYOTE GUARD"

TO DETERMINE THE SIZE OF APRON AND COLLECTING TANK:

$$\frac{\text{SURFACE AREA (SQ FT) OF APRON}}{12} \times 7.4 = \text{GALLONS PER INCH OF RAINFALL}$$

THIS DEVICE CAN BE USED TO COLLECT AND STORE RAINFALL IN DRY AREAS FOR QUAIL AND OTHER UPLAND GAME BIRDS (GALLIFORMES, thus the NAME).

Minimum Annual Rainfall (inches)	Square Feet of Collecting Surface Required			Apron Dimension in Feet					
				Square			Circular		
	600g.	700g.	900g.	600g.	700g.	900g.	600g.	700g.	900g.
5	192	225	290	14	15	17	16	17	19
6	162	189	243	13	14	15	15	16	18
7	138	161	208	12	13	14	13	14	16
8	121	141	182	11	12	14	12	13	15
9	107	125	161	11	12	13	12	13	14
10	97	113	146	10	11	12	11	12	14
11	87	102	132	9	10	11	10	11	13
12	80	94	121	9	10	11	10	11	12

different animals.

- Think in terms of giving up a little timber production for the sake of wildlife. For example, leave some "wolf trees" here and there, especially if they are acorn or nut producers. Don't thin all the way to the edge of the road, immediately next to fields, or along creeks.

- Recognize that cattle, sheep, horses and other domestic grazers compete with wildlife for food. To have both, restrict stock to fenced pastures rather than grazing all parts of your land.
- Protect cattail areas and leave brushy areas around portions of ponds and lakeshore; speak out against practices such as stream channelization and drainage of marshes and swamps.
- Avoid planting large areas to a single species.
- Slash from winter logging in northern hardwood areas or stands of eastern white cedar and some other conifers provides extra browse for deer at a time it may be badly needed.
- By all means, talk with local professionals—not just hunting and fishing buddies or local farmers— before making your wildlife management plans.

Some Good Sources of Wildlife Information

Identification and Range Maps

Peterson Field Guide Series. Houghton-Mifflin, Boston.
This excellent series is made for the layman and includes illustrated guides to mammals, birds, reptiles, amphibians and insects.

Birds of North America by C.S. Robbins, B. Bruun and H.S. Zim. Golden Press, New York.
My favorite for birds and constant hip-pocket companion in the woods. Particularly good for range maps.

Cavity-Nesting Birds of North America by Virgil E. Scott *et al.*, USDA Forest Service Agricultural Handbook 511. US Government Printing Office, Washington, DC. 20402.
A colorful, inexpensive booklet that focuses on the birds affected by the disappearance of old-aged forests and trees. A helpful reference for anyone interested in helping these species.

Periodicals

Audubon, Membership Data Center, P.O. Box 2667, Boulder, CO 80321.

National Wildlife or *Ranger Rick* (companion magazine for young people), 1412 16th St. NW, Washington, D.C. 20036.

Others

Enhancement of Wildlife Habitat on Private Lands by Daniel J. Decker and John W. Kelley, and
Wildlife and Timber from Private Lands: A Landowner's Guide to Planning by D.J. Decker, J.W. Kelley, T.W. Seamans and R.R. Roth.
Both of these valuable booklets are available at a small cost from the New York State College of Agriculture and Life Sciences (7 Research Park, Cornell University, Ithaca, NY 14850). The first is a detailed, well-illustrated instructional guide; the second concerns the integration of timber and wildlife management in eastern woodlands.

Planning for Wildlife in Cities and Suburbs by Daniel L.
Leedy. US Fish & Wildlife Service, US
Government Printing Office, Washington, D.C.
20402.
This includes much good information on food and
habitat needs, with the focus on keeping wildlife
production compatible with our expanding
suburban areas.

Ecology and Field Biology by Robert L. Smith. Harper
a n d Row, NY.
For the serious learner and none better can be
found. It is well illustrated and aimed at college-
educated readers, providing an excellent
grounding in the science behind both wildlife and
forest management.

Wildlife Conservation Principles and Practices edited by
R.D. Teague and E. Decker, and *Wildlife
Management Techniques Manual* edited by S.D.
Schemnitz. The Wildlife Society, 5410 Grosvenor
Lane, Bethesda, MD 20814.
These are only two of several books available from
this society of professional wildlife managers, so
ask for their current publications list. The first is
specifically for laymen; the second is a
comprehensive manual for practitioners that can
also be very useful to woodlot owners who are
serious about wildlife management.

*American Wildlife & Plants: A Guide to Wildlife Food
Habits* by A.C. Martin, H.S. Zim and A.L.
Nelson. Dover Publications, 180 Varick St., New
York, NY 10014.
An old classic and probably the most
comprehensive book on what animals eat. More
than 1,000 species of birds and mammals are
included. In one section, the animals are listed
along with what they eat; in another part, various
plants are listed along with the animals that use
them as food.

15 For Joiners & Learners

> *Let us share the promise and the joy, each in his own way, of the good and sweet earth, the woods and lake.*
>
> —Michael Frome
> Whose Woods These Are

The secret to happiness, said the sage, is having something to do, something to love, and something to look forward to. Your own woodland provides all of these intangibles plus what may be the greatest challenge and joy of all—the endless opportunity to learn.

Evelyn Stock and Her Forest Owners Association

In visiting woodland owners around the country, a remark I often heard was, "When I began, I had no idea what I was doing." It was also common to find that people had difficulty locating information, or at least in a form that could help in their circumstances or given their special goals and objectives.

One of the most inspiring people I visited was Evelyn Stock. Evelyn is a widow, with grandchildren, living on the outskirts of Syracuse, New York in a 200-year-old house. She is quick to point out this is not just any old house. This one is all wood, made from basswood. She would notice such a thing, for trees and wood are the center of her life.

Evelyn and her husband bought their house and 85 acres in 1946. It was a rundown farm with a dilapidated barn, 10 acres of woods and the rest weeds. Today she has hardwoods nearing prime lumber quality, firewood for fending off cold New York winters, and her son living nearby in a log house amid towering pines.

In many ways, Evelyn's story of good land management is the story of thousands of others who took over an old farm. She is typical of someone who went from zero to a very comfortable knowledge about her trees. The thing about Evelyn is that she lets nothing stand in her way, including age, and she is now helping others do the same.

Perhaps Mrs. Stock's interest in learning was helped by the coincidence of finding a job in the State University of New York College of Environmental Science and Forestry in Syracuse. She worked there for 13 years before retirement, editing publications and filling envelopes to meet the flow of requests for forestry information. Then, at age 50, she became a college student, pursuing her interests in English and the field of liberal arts. It took 13 years, but at last she had her degree.

New York Forest Owners Association

Somewhere along the way, Evelyn learned of the New York Forest Owners Association. There she found a most interesting group of people. Many had small woodlands like hers. Others managed large acreages or industrial forests. There were people who had just bought their first 10-acre plot and professors who held Ph.D.s in forestry. It was a wonderful mix, and they were all members so they could learn, share and grow.

"My goal," Evelyn told me as we sat in the shade of her maples, "is to manage these woods so that when I'm done with them they are as beautiful as possible."

The New York Forest Owners Association has a similar goal and several objectives to support it. I present them here because they represent the purpose of similar groups in nearly every state and throughout Canada:

1. To unite the forest owners of New York in a common cause of improving their forest resources and forest opportunities.
2. To join with and support private, state and federal programs that strengthen forestry, such as the New York Forest Practice Act and Tree Farm Program.
3. To help make ownership of forest land more attractive as an investment.
4. To work toward an economic climate favorable to permanent forest industry.
5. To maintain a balance between timber growth and cut to assure raw materials for industry and steady employment in forest communities and rural areas.
6. To encourage education and research in forest management, marketing and use of forest products and services.

7 . To manage forest land to enhance its natural beauty for the benefit of the owner, motorist, tourist and recreation.

The activities of this dynamic group increase every year. Members can do as little as read the bi-monthly newsletter or as much as participate in several woodland tours each year or lobby legislators for favorable actions.

Evelyn benefited from her membership in this organization, and virtually every woodland owner I interviewed suggested such a membership as being the best advice I could pass on in this book. For this purpose the list in the appendix was compiled to include the major groups in each area. Your membership would be welcome. In many areas there are also county or other local groups, or specialty interest groups such as those for holly growers or Christmas tree producers. County extension agents or local service foresters can usually put you in contact with these.

Inherent in woodland owner associations is the desire to share information and help others. Evelyn personifies this and clearly illustrates the old wisdom that he who gives receives.

For a long while, Evelyn felt inadequate to make any kind of contribution to the organization. As she put it, exaggerating a bit, "I didn't know one tree from another."

But the association soon changed that. She did know editing, and the newsletter was highly irregular since the editor was a busy guy and lived 150 miles from the printer. Evelyn saw this as a way she could help.

"I was 57 years old at the time and the employment people were trying to tell me I was too old to work. I had always loved to write, and I knew that many people live out their lives without really doing what they want to. Here, I thought, was something that suited me—both the people and the subject."

All Evelyn lacked was the nerve to volunteer. Then one Sunday morning she was listening to a radio minister who moved her to action.

"It was like he was speaking to me. He said, 'If there is something you've been wanting to do all your life, you had better do it now.' And I did. I phoned the editor right away and told him I'd like to give it a try."

She told me she loved her job editing the association's *Forest Owner*, and I have no doubt that the readers of this exemplary magazine felt likewise about having her do it.

As we parted, she told me that her association is working on a new project. They are trying to develop a land trust. She explained a concern I had heard many times before. When someone has invested a lifetime of work and love in their woodland, there is a feeling of uneasiness about what might happen to the land in the future. "So often," she said, "someone inherits the land and a logger comes in, pays them a lump of money and cuts down the trees. Promising veneer logs end up as pulp and its the end of the woodlot."

What the association hopes to do is provide a legal mechanism so today's woodland stewards can pass along property to heirs while at the same time assuring that the land will forever be managed as a woodland. Heirs get the property and a share of profits from forest products, and they can live on the land if they wish, but they can *not* subdivide it or do anything that would destroy its value as a productive forest. No method that I know of holds as much promise as this one for assuring the perpetual stewardship of private woodlands.

New England Forestry Foundation—Saving the Future

One organization that is already providing the service of perpetual stewardship is the New England Forestry Foundation. This organization has a membership of approximately 3,000 woodland owners, with an average property size of about 100 acres. The primary purpose of the foundation is to provide planning and a whole array of forestry services to its clients.

When it began in 1944, the intent of this organization was to help landowners protect their best interests while at the same time assuring that the forests of New England would be forever green and productive. Today, more than one million acres are being managed under the watchful eyes of foundation foresters. The whole effort is on a non-profit basis with the operating expenses coming largely from donations and a 15 percent commission on timber sales.

Besides being the stalwart protector of New England woodlot owners, the foundation has inherited numerous woodland properties, now totaling over 9,000 acres. Most carry the donor's name, such as the Lincoln Davis Memorial Forest. The land then continues to be managed as a woodland in perpetuity. Often it also serves as a demonstration area for other landowners, showcasing the practices of sustained yield forestry and wildlife management.

For more information, contact:
New England Forestry Foundation
One Court Street
Boston, Massachusetts 02108

The American Forestry Association

There are hundreds of organizations related to woodland management and most of them offer a good way to learn, meet people with similar interests, and get more enjoyment from your relationship with the land. Some groups are national or regional in scope, others are provincial or state organizations, and some are local. They range from the esoteric, such as the Forest History Society, to the oldest private conservation group in North America— The American Forestry Association (AFA).

Each group has its focus and its biases. It is important to look for these and join a group that is compatible with your own philosophies and interests. Of the many available, The American Forestry Association is probably the widest in scope and the most active. It also has a very reasonable membership fee, for which you receive *American Forests* each month. This magazine always has useful articles of interest to the owners of small woodlands. AFA sponsors an annual conference, a children's camp, horseback trips, an insurance program, legislative efforts, and other benefits for those who want more than the magazine. The address is: AFA, 1319 Eighteenth St. NW, Washington, DC 20036.

The Social Register of Big Trees

Another interesting feature of the AFA is its system of locating and recording the largest trees in the United States. Nearly 900 species are included in the register ranging from apple trees, paw paws and North Carolina's 26-foot devil's walking stick (*Aralia spinosa*) to California's 368-foot world champion redwood. Forty-three states and the District of Columbia have national champions, with Michigan and California having the most. California also has the oldest living trees in the world, the 4,600-year-old bristlecone pines.

You never know where a champion might show up. Generations of students and faculty rushed past the nation's largest Pacific willow right on the University of Idaho campus before a sharp-eyed forester decided to measure it.

Anyone can nominate a champ. The first step is to contact AFA for a copy of their nomination form and "Social Register of Big Trees." This lists the current record-holders, their sizes, general location and the individuals who discovered them. Next, measure the circumference at DBH, height, and spread of the crown. Compare with the current record, and if yours is larger, fill out the nomination form and send it to AFA. The tree will be checked by an expert, and if you were correct, your tree (and you) will be entered in the next register.

Some states and even counties have a local version of this. Your state forester will be able to tell you if your area has one, and if so, what procedures you should follow to get involved. The whole idea is to identify exceptional specimens, attempt to protect them from premature destruction, and to focus public attention on the role of trees in our heritage. And, of course, it is fun and definitely a learning experience.

AFI and the Tree Farm System

Honors for the greatest success story in private woodland management probably belong to the American Tree Farm System. The familiar green and white signs of its members mark the managed woodlands of some 55,000 owners who meet the standards set by the parent organization.

The tree farm system is a brainchild of the forest industries. It began as a public relations device to help make the public aware that commercial forest land is not too unlike a farm. A large tract of Weyerhauser land near

---

Getting Plugged In...
The Conservation Directory. National Wildlife Federation, 1412 Sixteenth St. NW, Washington, DC 20036.

This is a remarkable and valuable reference. Published annually at nominal cost, its 300 pages list virtually every major conservation group in the U.S. and Canada. Federal, state or provincial and private groups and agencies are listed, along with descriptions, names, phone numbers and addresses. You'll find organizations ranging from the Federation of Fly Fishermen to the Committee for National Arbor Day, and agency personnel in every state or province from the governor or minister to the editor of the agency's public magazines.

Grays Harbor, Washington was the first property to be designated. The idea worked. The public *could* understand—and appreciate—woodland management for the continuous production of forest crops.

Tree Farm Number 1 was established in 1941. It was soon followed by other timber companies designating their land as tree farms and by 1946 about half the states had tree farms. An interesting footnote to this happy development is that it was criticized by the U.S. Forest Service in 1943. Lyle F. Watts, the chief of the usually pro-forestry organization, viewed the campaign as an attempt by industry to avoid federal regulation of industrial land. The industry responded much as it would today—that indeed he was correct. They claimed that the system is a way to spotlight good forest management, and in so doing, to demonstrate the private sector's ability for effective self-regulation.

Through the years, two important features of the Tree Farm System evolved. First, the idea spread from industry lands to small private woodlands. Second, the emphasis shifted to the quality of management required before a tract could be included in the system.

Today, over 87 million acres bear the sign of a certified tree farm and 52 percent are woodlands of 100 acres or less. The program is sponsored and managed by the American Forest Institute, a non-profit, information and education organization supported by the forest products industries. Their goal, of course, is to keep wood flowing through the nation's mills. They view small, private lands as an important source of their raw material and good forest management as a way of perpetuating that source.

To promote the idea, there are 45 state tree farm committees that provide advice, select outstanding tree farmers each year, and encourage landowners to enroll. In addition, some 10,000 professional foresters volunteer their time to inspect the property of applicants and members, and to otherwise help manage the massive program.

Benefits from membership include the intangibles of public recognition and fellowship with others who see trees as a central part of their lives. Also, tree farm certification can help establish intent of holding timber for long-term growth and investment, serving to back claims to capital gains benefits at tax time. Just as important, it is one more way to learn and grow. Mandatory inspection upon application and at 5-year intervals after gaining membership guarantees contact with a professional forester. Woods tours and other events offer a chance to see how other people are using their woodlands and solving their problems. Two excellent publications, *Tree Farm News* and *Green America*, keep ideas from around the nation flowing into the homes of members.

One of the best features of this program is that it is free. It costs nothing to join and there is no obligation to maintain certification. However, to become certified, the following criteria must be met:

- Your woodlot must be 10 acres or larger.
- Practices on your land must include protection from fire, insects, disease and destructive grazing.
- You must be willing to include the production of timber and other forest products among your objectives.

For more information or to have your woodland reviewed for possible certification, contact:

American Forest Institute
1619 Massachusetts Avenue, NW
Washington, DC 20036
(Phone: 202/797-4500)

Guide Your Own Destiny

Those of us with land of any kind are blessed with a privilege and responsibility. The privilege is to have in our hands for a while a piece of land—and a chance to enjoy and perhaps gain financially from it. We are the envy of millions. With this privilege comes a responsibility. This is to use the land wisely, to protect it while it is under our temporary stewardship, and to pass it on as a wooded, natural heritage in an increasingly urban, artificial world.

So, I must close as I began. When all is said and done, the final decisions about your land and your trees must come from you. Help is out there, but so is an endless array of competing interests. The people I met while researching and writing *The Woodland Steward* love their land, learn all they can about it on their own, seek the advice of professionals, but in the end they make their own decisions. In virtually every case their decisions are as much for the benefit of others as they are for personal gain or pleasure. This is what woodland stewardship is all about.

Appendices

Appendix A
Forest Landowner Associations

ALABAMA

Alabama Forest Owners Assoc.
P.O. Box 104
Helena, AL 35080

Alabama Forestry Assoc.
555 Alabama Street
Montgomery, AL 36014

ALASKA

None

ARIZONA

None

ARKANSAS

Arkansas Forestry Assoc.
501 Woodlane Drive, Suite 203
Little Rock, AR 72201

CALIFORNIA

Forest Landowners of Calif.
3820 Auburn Blvd., Suite 90
Sacramento, CA 95821

Redwood Region Conservation
Council
224 Rosenberg Bldg.
Santa Rosa, CA 95404

COLORADO

Basin Forest Owners
8 Quarius Place
Durango, CO 81301
(Also other regional associa-
tions. Contact State Forest
Service.)

CONNECTICUT

Conn. Forest & Park Assoc.
Box 389, 1010 Main Street
East Hartford, CT 06108

Eastern Conn. Forest Landowners
P.O. Box 404
Brooklyn, CT 06234

DELAWARE

None

FLORIDA

None

GEORGIA

Georgia Forestry Assoc.
709 Cain Tower, Peachtree Ctr.
Atlanta, GA 30303

Forest Farmers Assoc.
P.O. Box 95385
Atlanta, GA 30347

HAWAII

None

IDAHO

Idaho Forest Owners Assoc.
P.O. Box 1257
Coeur d'Alene, ID 83814

ILLINOIS

Ill. Technical Forestry Assoc.
(Address not given)

INDIANA

Indiana Forestry & Woodland
Landowners Assoc.
Box 751
Jasper, IN 47546

IOWA

None

KANSAS

Kansas Tree Farm Committee
R.F.D. #5, 172A
Manhattan, KS 66502

KENTUCKY

Kentucky Forest Industries Assoc.
Department of Forestry
University of Kentucky
Lexington, KY 40546

LOUISIANA

Louisiana Forestry Assoc.
P.O. Drawer 5067
Alexandria, LA 71301

MAINE

Forest Products Marketing
and Management Assoc.
Vaughn Street
Dover-Foxcroft, ME 04426

Small Woodland Owners Assoc.
of Maine
P.O. Box 4960, RFD 1
Pittsfield, ME 04967

MARYLAND

Maryland Forests Assoc.
P.O. Box 1625
Annapolis, MD 21404

MASSACHUSETTS

None

MICHIGAN

Michigan Forest Assoc.
(Address not given)

MINNESOTA

Minnesota Assoc. of Farmers,
Landowners and Sportsmen
490 N. Snelling at University
St. Paul, MN 55104

Minnesota Forestry Assoc.
918 S. Fairview Avenue
St. Paul, MN 55116

Forestree Farmers of Minn., Inc.
Box 363
Park Rapids, MN 56470

MISSISSIPPI

Mississippi Forestry Assoc.
620 North State Street
Jackson, MS 39201

MISSOURI

Mo. Forest Products Assoc.
Suite 1, 611 E. Capitol Ave.
Jefferson City, MO 65101

MONTANA

None

NEBRASKA

None

NEVADA

None

NEW HAMPSHIRE

Society for the Protection
of New Hampshire Forests
54 Portsmouth Street
Concord, NH 03301

N.H. Timberland Owners Assoc.
54 Portsmouth Street
Concord, NH 03301

NEW JERSEY

New Jersey Forestry Assoc.
P.O. Box 304
Pennington, NJ 08534

NEW MEXICO

None

NEW YORK

New York Forest Owners Assoc.
c/o Northern Logger Magazine
Box 69
Old Forge, NY 13420

Catskill Forest Assoc.
Arkville, NY 12406

NORTH CAROLINA

North Carolina Forestry Assoc.
P.O. Box 19104
Raleigh, NC 27619
(Over half the counties have
County Landowner Forestry
Associations - contact
Cooperative Extension Service)

NORTH DAKOTA

None

OHIO

Ohio Forestry Assoc.
665 E. Dublin-Granville Rd.
Columbus, OH 43229

OKLAHOMA

Oklahoma Forestry Assoc.
Box 517
Broken Bow, OK 74728

OREGON

Oregon Small Woodlands Assoc.
c/o Robert Mealey, President
710 Thornton Lake Drive
Albany, OR 97321

PENNSYLVANIA

Pennsylvania Forestry Assoc.
410 E. Main St.
Mechanicsburg, PA 17055

RHODE ISLAND

Rhode Island Tree Farm Committee
Arcadia State Forest, RFD
Hope Valley, RI 02832

SOUTH CAROLINA

Black River Forestry Club
c/o W. Va. Pulp & Paper Co.
Andrews, SC 29510

SC/GA Wood Producers Assoc.
c/o Pat Hester
Mt. Carmel, SC 29840

SOUTH DAKOTA

None

TENNESSEE

None

TEXAS

Texas Forestry Assoc.
P.O. Box 1488
Lufkin, TX 75925

UTAH

None

VERMONT

Vermont Timber Land Owners Assoc.
Extension Natural Resources
Aiken Center, Univ. of Vermont
Burlington, VT 05405

VIRGINIA

Virginia Forestry Assoc.
One North Fifth Street
Richmond, VA 23214

WASHINGTON

Washington Farm Forestry Assoc.
1275 Hazell Dell Road
Castle Rock, WA 98611

WEST VIRGINIA

West Virginia Forests, Inc.
Ripley, WV 25271

WISCONSIN

Wisconsin Woodland Owners Assoc.
P.O. Box 188
Madison, WI 53701

WYOMING

Casper Mountain
Pine Beetle Assoc.
Box 1011
Casper, WY 82602

CANADIAN ASSOCIATIONS

CANADA (NATIONWIDE)

Canadian Forestry Assoc.
185 Somerset St. West
Ottawa, Ontario K2P 0J2

ALBERTA

Alberta Forestry Assoc.
218 Alberta Block
10526 Jasper Ave.
Edmonton, Alberta T5J 1Z7

BRITISH COLUMBIA

Canadian Forestry Assoc.
of British Columbia
Suite 410, 1200 W. Pender St.
Vancouver, B.C. V6E 2S9

MANITOBA

Manitoba Forestry Assoc.
Suite 2, 720 Dorchester Ave.
Winnipeg, Manitoba R3M 0R5

NEW BRUNSWICK

Canadian Forestry Assoc.
of New Brunswick
Maritime Forest Ranger
School Campus
R.R. 5
Fredericton, N.B. E3B 4X6

NEWFOUNDLAND

Newfoundland Forest
Protection Assoc.
Pleasantville, Building 810
St. John's, N.F. A1A 1P9

NOVA SCOTIA

Nova Scotia Forestry Assoc.
6070 Quinpool Road
Halifax, Nova Scotia B3L 1A1

ONTARIO

Ontario Forestry Assoc.
Room 209, 150 Consumers Road
Willowdale, Ontario M2J 1P9

QUEBEC

Assoc. forestière
québecoise, inc.
915 ouest, rue st-Cyrille
Quebec, G1S 1T8

SASKATCHEWAN

Saskatchewan Forestry Assoc.
308 Poplar Crescent
Saskatoon, S.K. S7M 0A6

Appendix B
Land Grant Institutions (Extension Services)

Extension Natural Resources
Alabama Coop. Extension Service
M. White Smith Hall
Auburn, AL 36830

Extension Forester
Cooperative Extension Service
University of Alaska
Fairbanks, AK 99701

School of Forestry
Box 4098
Northern Arizona University
Flagstaff, AZ 86001

Extension Forester
Cooperative Extension Service
P.O. Box 391
Little Rock, AR 72203

Cooperative Extension-Forestry
163 Mulford Hall
University of California
Berkeley, CA 94720

Colorado State Forest Service
Colorado State University
Fort Collins, CO 80523

Extension Forester
Box U-87, CANR
University of Connecticut
Storrs, CT 06268

Department of Agriculture
Forestry Section
Drawer D
Dover, DE 19901

Forestry Extension
University of Florida
Gainesville, FL 32661

Forest Resources Department
Cooperatve Extension Service
Room 210, Barrow Hall
Athens, GA 30602

Institute of Tropical Agriculture
and Human Resources
Forestry Extension
University of Hawaii
Honolulu, HI 96822

Extension Forester
College of Forestry,
Wildlife and Range Sciences
University of Idaho
Moscow, ID 83843

Extension Forester
110 Mumford Hall
1301 W. Gregory Drive
Urbana, IL 61801

Forestry Extension Coordinator
Dept. of Forestry and
Natural Resources
Purdue University
W. Lafayette, IN 47907

Forestry Extension
Iowa State University
Ames, IA 50011

Extension Specialist
Dept. of Forestry
University of Kentucky
Lexington, KY 40546

Forestry Extension
Kansas State University
Manhattan, KS 66506

Forestry Extension
Knapp Hall
Louisiana State University
Baton Rouge, LA 70893

Extension Forester
107 Nutting Hall
University of Maine
Orono, ME 04469

Extension Forester
Dept. of Horticulture
University of Maryland
College Park, MD 20742

Extension Forester
Dept. of Forest & Wildlife Mgt.
Univ. of Massachusetts
Amherst, MA 01003

Forestry Extension
126 Natural Resources
Michigan State University
East Lansing, MI 48824

Extension Forestry
102 Green Hall
University of Minnesota
St. Paul, MN 55108

Extension Forestry Department
Cooperative Extension Service
P.O. Box 5426
State College, MS 39762

Extension Forester
1-31 Agriculture Building
University of Missouri
Columbia, MO 65211

Extension Forester
School of Forestry
University of Montana
Missoula, MT 59812

Forestry Extension
University of Nebraska
Lincoln, NE 68583

Division of Renewable
Natural Resources
University of Nevada - Reno
1000 Valley Road
Reno, NV 89512

Cooperative Forestry Programs
Pettee Hall
University of New Hampshire
Durham, NH 03824

Extension Forester
Cook College, Rutgers Univ.
New Brunswick, NJ 08902

Cooperative Extension Service
Box 3AE
Las Cruces, NM 88003

State Coop. Extension Forester
Dept. of Natural Resources
Fernow Hall
Cornell University
Ithaca, NY 14853

Extension Forest Resources
North Carolina State Univ.
P.O. Box 5488
Raleigh, NC 27650

Forestry Extension
North Dakota State University
of Ag. and Applied Science
State U. Station
Fargo, ND 58105

Forestry Extension
2021 Coffey Road
Columbus, OH 43210

Extension Forester
016 Ag Hall South
Oklahoma State University
Stillwater, OK 74078

Coordinator, Extension Forestry
School of Forestry
Oregon State University
Corvallis, OR 97331

Forestry Extension
Penn. State University
University Park, PA 16802

Cooperative Extension
Specialist/Natural Resources
210 C Woodward Hall
Dept. of Forest and
Wildlife Management
Kingston, RI 02881

Extension Forestry
272 Lehotsky Hall
Clemson University
Clemson, SC 29631

Forestry Extension
South Dakota State University
Brookings, SD 57007

Extension Forester
Dept. of Forest Science
Texas A & M University
College Station, TX 77843

Extension Forester
P.O. Box 1071
University of Tennessee
Knoxville, TN 37918

Forestry Extension
Utah State University of
Ag and Applied Science
Logan, UT 84322

Program Coordinator -
Extension Natural Resources
Aiken Center
University of Vermont
Burlington, VT 05405

Forestry Extension
Virginia Polytechnic Institute
and State University
Blacksburg, VA 24061

Extension Forest Resource
Specialist
131 Johnson Hall
Washington State University
Pullman, WA 99164

Forestry Extension
Percival Hall
West Virginia University
Morgantown, WV 26506

Forestry Extension
Department of Forestry
University of Wisconsin
1630 Linden Drive
Madison, WI 53706

No forestry extension at
University of Wyoming. Contact:
State Forester
Wyoming State Forestry Div.
1100 West 22nd Street
Cheyenne, WY 82002

Appendix C
Woodland Suppliers

Fortunately, most of the tools and gadgets for measuring and managing woodlands can be purchased through the mail. A few of the many dealers who welcome mail order business or who will send product information are listed below. Write or phone for a free catalog.

GENERAL SUPPLIERS

Ben Meadows Company
3589 Broad Street
P.O. Box 80549
Atlanta, GA 30366

2601-B West 5th Avenue
P.O. Box 2781
Eugene, OR 97402

(Phone toll-free:	1-800-241-6401;
in Georgia, collect:	404-455-0907
Western Division:	1-800-547-8813;
in Oregon, collect:	503-344-5468)

Forestry Suppliers, Inc.
205 West Rankin Street
P.O. Box 8397
Jackson, MS 39204

(Phone toll-free:	1-800-647-5368;
in Mississippi:	1-800-682-5397;
in Alaska, collect	601-354-3565

TSI Company
P.O. Box 151
Flanders, NJ 07836

NURSERIES

Canale's Nursery
Shelocta, PA 15774
(Phone: 412-354-2801)

Pine Grove Nursery
RD No. 3
Clearfield, PA 16830

Greener 'N Ever Nursery
P.O. Box 222435
Carmel, CA 93922

Vans Pines, Inc.
P.O. Box 735
West Olive, MI 49460
(Phone: 616-399-1620

Fantasy Farm Nursery
P.O. Box 157
Peck, ID 83545

Western Maine Nurseries
Fryeburg, ME 04037
(Phone: 207-935-2161)

Musser
Indiana, PA 15701

CHRISTMAS TREE PRODUCTION EQUIPMENT

Gunnard Company
P.O. Box 516
Lakeville, MN 55044
(Phone: 612-469-2422)
[Stands]

Long Life Chemical
305 University Avenue
Unit F
Los Gatos, CA 95030
(Phone: 408-395-3443)
[Fire retardant]

Horta-Craft
5800 West Grand River
P.O. Box 17099
Lansing, MI 48901
(Phone: 517-323-4200)
[Tree tags]

The Kirk Company
P.O. Box 340
Puyallup, WA 98371
(Phone: 206-845-8893)
[Packaging and plastic netting equipment]

Hughes Manufacturing Co.
15501 South Texaco Ave.
Paramount, CA 90723
(Phone: 213-633-1054)
[Miscellaneous]

MISCELLANEOUS

Alex Emerson
1061 Monument Street
Concord, MA 01742
[Plans for "The Woodchuck" lightweight forwarder]

Traction, Inc.
Troy, VT 05868
[Makers of Quadractor, lightweight forwarder]

Shemin Nurseries, Inc.
P.O. Box 64
Glenville Station
Greenwich, CN 06830
(Phone: 203-531-7352)

Wilbur-Ellis Company
P.O. Box 8838
Portland, OR 97208
(Phone: 503-227-3525)

[Outlets for "Deer Away," a highly effective big game repellent]

Leader Evaporator Co.
25 Stowell Street
St. Albans, VT 05478
(Phone: 802-524-3931
or 524-4966
[Supplies for maple syrup production]

John Voss
RD No. 1
Manlius, NY 13104
(Phone: 315-682-6418
[Boundary signs, wildlife zone signs, etc.]

Woodland Enterprises
Box 3524
University Station
Moscow, ID 83843
[Outdoor books; Smokey Bear and Woodsy Owl products]

Appendix D
State Forestry Laws[1]

State	State Forest Practices Act	State Permits Required to Transport:			Log Scale Used
		Christmas Trees	Firewood	Logs/Pulpwood	(L) = Specified by law (C) = Most commonly used on private land
Alabama	No				Doyle (C) & Scribner (C)
Alaska	Alaska Statutes Title 41, Public Resources Chap. 17, 010-950				Scribner Decimal C (C)
Arizona	No			X	Scribner (C)
Arkansas	No				Doyle (L for purposes of several tax)
California	1973 Div. 4, Chap. 8, Public Res. Code Sec. 4511-4628	X	X	X	Scribner (L for yield tax)
Colorado	No	X		X	Scribner Decimal C (C)
Connecticut	No				International ¼" (L)
Delaware	No				Doyle (C)
Florida	No			X	Scribner (C)
Georgia	No				Scribner Decimal C (L for pines) Doyle (C for hardwoods) Also, weight basis (C)
Hawaii	No				International ¼" (C)
Idaho	Title 38, Chap 13 ICA				Scribner Decimal C (L)
	Title 38, Chap 1 & 4 ICA	X	X	X	
Illinois	No	X		X	Doyle (C)
Indiana	No				Doyle (C)
Iowa	No			X	Scribner (L)
Kentucky	No				Doyle (C)
Kansas	No				Doyle (C)
Louisiana	No				Doyle (L)
Maine	No	X			International ¼" (L)
Maryland	No				Doyle (C)
Massachusetts	Chap 132				International ¼" (L unless otherwise specified in contract)
Michigan	No	X			Doyle, Scribner, International (C)
Minnesota	No	X			Scribner Decimal C (C)
Mississippi	No				Doyle (C)
Missouri	Forest Cropland Law				Doyle and International (C)
Montana	No		X	X	Scribner
Nebraska	No				Doyle (C)
Nevada	Nev. Revised Statutes 528	X	X	X	Scribner Decimal C & International ¼" (C)
New Hampshire	No				International ¼" (C)
New Jersey	No		X		N.J. Modified Doyle (C)
New Mexico	N.M. Statutes Annotated 1968 Chap. 68 & Related Regulations	X	X	X	Scribner (C)
New York	Title 7 of Article 9 of Environ. Conservation Law of 1972				International ¼" (L if none other is specified) Also, Scribner & Doyle (C)
North Carolina	No				Doyle, Scribner & International ¼" (C)

State				
North Dakota	No			International ¼" (C)
Ohio	No	X		Doyle (C)
Oregon	ORS 527.610 to ORS 527.730 and Part 1 of 527.990		X X	Scribner (C)
Pennsylvania	319			Scribner (L) Doyle (C)
Rhode Island	No			
South Carolina	No			Weight factors for pulpwood (L) Scribner (C for pine) Doyle (C for hardwoods)
Texas	No			Doyle (C)
Utah	No			Scribner (C)
Vermont	No			International ¼" and Vermont Rule (L)
Virginia	Scattered under several acts			Doyle and International ¼" (C)
Washington	Wash. Admin. Code 222	X	X	Scribner (C)
West Virginia	No			Doyle (L)
Wisconsin	No	X		Scribner Decimal C (L for disputes) Also, International ¼" and Doyle (C)
Wyoming	No			Scribner Decimal C (C)

[1] This information was obtained in 1983 through a survey of Cooperative Extension forestry specialists in each state.

Appendix E
Some Silvical Characteristics
of Common Forest Trees

Species	Shade Tolerance	Sapling Growth	Potential Longevity	Ease of Reproduction (Natural)	Soil Moisture	Frost Resistance	Drought Resistance	Other
Eastern United States								
Balsam fir (Abies Balsamea)	Very tolerant	Rapid	Short	Easy	Moist to wet	High	Low	
Basswood (Tilia americana)	Intolerant	Rapid	Medium	Medium	Moist	High	Medium	Prolific sprouter
Beech (Fagus grandifolia)	Very tolerant	Slow	Long	Medium	Moist	High	Medium	Prolific sprouter
Birches								
White/Paper (Betula papyrifera)	Intolerant	Rapid	Medium	Easy	Moist	High	Medium	A "pioneer" after land disturbance
Yellow (Betula alleghaniensis)	Tolerant	Medium	Long	Easy	Moist	High	Low	
Black cherry (Prunus serotina)	Intolerant	Rapid	Medium	Easy	Moist	Low to medium	Low	
Black locust (Robinia pseudoacacia)	Intolerant	Rapid	Medium	Easy	Moist to dry	High	High	Good growth on poor soils
Black walnut (Juglans nigra)	Intolerant	Rapid	Long	Difficult	Moist to wet	Medium	Low	Best on deep, fertile soil
Hemlock (Tsuga canadensis)	Very tolerant	Medium	Long	Easy	Moist	High	Low	
Hickories (Carya)	Tolerant	Slow	Long	Medium	Dry to moist	Medium	High	
Holly (Ilex opaca)	Very tolerant	Slow	Medium	Easy	Moist to wet	Low	Low	Male and female trees (Dioecious)
Maples								
Red (Acer rubrum)	Intolerant	Medium	Short	Easy	Dry to wet	High	Medium	
Sugar (Acer saccharum)	Very tolerant	Medium	Long	Easy	Moist	High	Low	
Oaks								
Black (Quercus velutina)	Intolerant	Medium	Long	Medium	Dry	Medium	High	
Live (Quercus virginiana)	Intermediate	Rapid	Medium	Medium	Dry to moist	Low	High	
Red (Quercus rubra)	Intolerant	Rapid	Long	Easy	Moist	High	High	
White (Quercus alba)	Intolerant	Slow	Long	Difficult	Dry to moist	Medium	High	
Pines								
Jack (Pinus banksiana)	Intolerant	Rapid	Short	Easy	Dry	High	High	
Loblolly (Pinus taeda)	Intolerant	Very rapid	Long	Medium	Dry to moist	Low	High	
Longleaf (Pinus palustris)	Intolerant	Rapid	Long	Difficult	Dry to medium	Low	Medium	
Red (Pinus resinosa)	Very intolerant	Medium	Long	Difficult	Dry	High	Medium	
Shortleaf (Pinus echinata)	Intolerant	Rapid	Long	Medium	Dry	Medium	Medium	
Slash (Pinus elliottii)	Intolerant	Very rapid	Medium	Easy	Medium to wet	Low	Low	
White (Pinus strobus)	Medium	Medium	Long	Easy	Moist	High	Medium	
Sassafras (Sassafras albidum)	Tolerant	Slow	Short	Medium	Dry to moist	Medium	Low	Propagation by root suckers
Spruces								
Black (Picea mariana)	Intermediate	Slow	Medium	Medium	Moist to wet	High	Low	
Red (Picea rubens)	Tolerant	Slow	Medium	Difficult	Moist	High	Low	
White (Picea glauca)	Tolerant	Slow	Medium	Difficult	Moist	High	Low	
Sweetgum (Liquidambar styraciflua)	Intolerant	Rapid	Medium	Easy	Moist to wet	Medium	Low	Floodplain species

190

Species	Shade Tolerance	Sapling Growth	Potential Longevity	Ease of Reproduction (Natural)	Soil Moisture	Frost Resistance	Drought Resistance	Other
White Ash (Fraxinus americana)	Intolerant	Rapid	Medium	Easy	Moist	High	Low	
White-cedar (Thuja Occidentalis)	Intolerant	Slow	Medium	Easy	Dry to wet	High	Low	Poorly drained sites
Yellow-poplar (Liriodendron tulipifera)	Tolerant	Rapid	Long	Easy	Moist	Medium	Low	Deep, fertile soil

Western United States

Species	Shade Tolerance	Sapling Growth	Potential Longevity	Ease of Reproduction (Natural)	Soil Moisture	Frost Resistance	Drought Resistance	Other
Douglas-fir (Pseudotsuga menziesii)	Intermediate	Rapid	Long	Easy	Moist to dry; well-drained	Medium	High	
Firs								
Grand (Abies grandis)	Tolerant	Medium	Medium	Easy	Moist	High	Low	Saplings of all four fir species establish well under high canopy.
Noble (Abies procera)	Intolerant	Slow	Long	Easy	Moist	High	Low	
Pacific silver (Abies amabilis)	Tolerant	Slow	Medium	Easy	Moist	High	Low	
White (Abies concolor)	Tolerant	Medium	Medium	Easy	Moist to dry	High	High	
Incense-cedar (Calocedrus decurrens)	Tolerant	Medium	Medium	Easy	Moist	High	High	
Pines								
Lodgepole (Pinus contorta)	Intolerant	Rapid	Medium	Easy	Wet to dry	High	High	Broad ecological amplitude
Ponderosa (Pinus ponderosa)	Intermediate	Medium	Long	Easy	Moist to dry	Medium	High	
Single-leaf Pinyon (Pinus monophylla)	Intermediate	Slow	Medium	Easy	Dry	High	High	
Sugar (Pinus lambertiana)	Intermediate	Medium	Long	Medium	Moist to dry	High	Medium	
Western white (Pinus monticola)	Intermediate	Medium	Long	Easy	Moist	High	Medium to low	
Redwood (Sequoia sempervirens)	Very tolerant	Rapid	Very long	Easy	Moist to wet	Low	Low	Prolific sprouter
Spruces								
Engelmann (Picea engelmannii)	Tolerant	Medium	Medium	Easy	Moist to wet	High	Medium to low	
Sitka (Picea sitchensis)	Tolerant	Rapid	Long	Easy	Moist to wet	Low	Low	Can endure ocean salt spray
Western hemlock (Tsuga heterophylla)	Very tolerant	Rapid	Medium	Easy	Moist to wet	Medium	Low	
Western larch (Larix occidentalis)	Very intolerant	Rapid	Long	Medium	Moist to dry	High	Medium	Drops needles in winter
Western redcedar (Thuja plicata)	Very tolerant	Medium	Very long	Difficult	Moist to wet	High	Low	

Suitability for...

	Clearcutting	Seed-tree	Shelterwood	Coppicing	Single-tree Selection	Group Selection	Notes
							x = Technically feasible. Recommended, but landowner objectives would make the difference in which cutting system to use.
							(F)= Very flexible possibilities. Chioce depends on objectives, existing species, desired species, products sought, etc.
Northeast & Middle Atlantic							
Allegheny Hardwoods (Cherry-Maple)	x		x			x	Heavy deer populations make it necessary to assure extra large numbers of seedlings or sprouts to arrive at adequate stocking. Coppicing is also a possibility, but potentially high timber values suggest other methods.
Appalachian Mixed Hardwoods	x		x	x	x	x	(F)
Northern Hardwoods	x		x	x	x	x	(F)
Oak-Hickory	x			x		x	
Spruce-Fir	x		x		x	x	
White Pine	x	x	x			x	
North Central & Lake States							
Black Spruce	x						Seed-tree and shelterwood are also possible but wind throw would be high.
Jack Pine	x	x	x				
Lake States Aspen	x			x			
Lake States Northern Hardwoods	x		x	x	x	x	(F)
Oak-Hickory	x			x		x	The most widely distributed eastern type.
Red Pine	x		x				
Southern							
Bottomland Hardwoods	x		x	x		x	(F)
Loblolly-Shortleaf Pine	x	x	x				Most widespread type in the South. Group selection is a possibility also, especially in understocked stands.
Longleaf Pine	x		x				
Slash Pine	x	x	x			x	
Oak-Pine	x						Common on upland sites. Options are quite flexible depending on objectives. The usual objective is to convert the stand to faster growing pines, in which case clearcutting and bush control become the primary method.
Tupelo-Cypress Swamps	x			x			
Northern Rockies							
Engelmann Spruce-Subalpine Fir	x		x	x	x	x	Choice depends on many variables. Often no cutting is best. Selection cuts are difficult.
Lodgepole Pine	x		x				Shelterwood not recommended if mistletoe is present. Otherwise may allow conversion to shade-tolerant species.
Ponderosa Pine and Douglas-fir	x	x	x		x	x	(F)
Western Larch	x	x	x			x	Group selection recommended onl if aesthetics are essential.
Western White Pine	x	x	x				Selection cutting may be used t convert to higher percent of shade-tolerant trees in the stand (e.g. grand fir, hemlock, redcedar).

	Clearcutting	Seed-tree	Shelterwood	Coppicing	Single-tree Selection	Group Selection	Notes
Central & Southern Rockies							
Aspen	x			x			
Black Hills Ponderosa Pine			x		x	x	(F)
Engelmann Spruce-Subalpine Fir	x		x		x	x	
Southwestern Mixed Conifers	x				x	x	
Southwestern Ponderosa Pine	x		x			x	
Pacific Southwest							
California Mixed Conifers	x	x	x			x	Single tree selection favors white fir and incense cedar over the pines.
Pacific Ponderosa Pine	x	x	x				
Red Fir-White Fir	x		x		x	x	Dwarf mistletoe infection is a problem with selection methods.
Redwood	x			x	x	x	
Pacific Northwest and Alaska							
Douglas-fir (coastal)	x		x			x	Group selection is difficult.
Interior Alaska Hardwoods	x						
Interior Alaska White Spruce	x		x				Selection systems may also be possible.
Mixed Conifers of Southwestern Oregon	x(coastal)		x(interior)				Wide differences based on slope, frosts and moisture conditions. Selection systems possible on moist, gentle sites.
Mixed Pine-Fir of Eastern Washington and Oregon	x	x	x				
Ponderosa Pine		x	x			x	
True Firs-Mountain Hemlock	x		x			x	Single-tree selection cutting may be appropriate when shade-tolerant Pacific silver fir and hemlocks are present.
Western Hemlock-Sitka Spruce	x		x				Shelterwood will favor the hemlock regeneration.

Appendix G
(Example) Timber Sale Contract

(Note: This is a sample for selling by the unit price method as opposed to a lump sum sale. Many provisions, however, would be applicable in either case.)

This agreement is entered into this _____ day of _____ 19 _____, between _____, hereinafter called the Seller and _____, hereinafter called the Purchaser.

Witnesseth:

Paragraph 1: The Seller, being the owner thereof, covenants and agrees to sell and convey to the Purchaser, and the Purchaser covenants and agrees to purchase from the Seller, upon the terms and conditions hereafter set forth, the marked timber described below, located in _____ County, State of _____, to wit:

_____
_____
_____
_____
_____
_____

Paragraph 2: The purchase price shall be based on the Scribner Decimal C log rule.

Species   *Rate Per Thousand Baord Feet*

a. A deposit, cash bond, or surety bond in the amount of twenty (20) percent of the timber sale value shall be made prior to removal of any timber to be held for the life of the contract for the faithful compliance with each and every term of the contract.

b. All payments to the Seller shall be made on the _____ and _____ day of the month by personal check, and shall be accompanied by true and correct scale tickets. The scaling and measurements shall be made by the Scribner Decimal C log rule. Load ticket numbers shall be indicated on the scale ticket receipt. The Purchaser must maintain consecutive ticket numbers for all loads hauled for the duration of this contract. Any lost or unaccounted for tickets shall be assigned a value equaling the highest value load removed during the life of this contract. The Purchaser shall provide the Seller with one (1) carbon copy of the scale ticket for each load.

c. Title to the timber shall remain the Seller's until cut by the Purchaser, at that time, the Purchaser will obtain title.

Paragraph 3: It is understood and agreed between the Purchaser and the Seller that this agreement begins on the _____ day of _____ 19 _____, and terminates on the _____ day of _____ 19 _____. Any timber or other products covered by this agreement not cut or removed by the termination date shall revert to the Seller. Additional provisions whereby time limits may be extended, are: natural disasters, extreme adverse weather conditions or other just cause as determined by the Seller. Either party may terminate this contract prior to the termination date after eighty-five (85) percent of the estimated sale volume has been removed.

Paragraph 4: The Purchaser shall be responsible for compliance with all State, Federal, and local laws, statutes, rules, regulations, and requirements, which are:
a. Idaho State Slash Compliance and Forest Practices Act Notification.
b. Slash responsibility and disposal.
c. Fire prevention.
Fire loss shall be at the risk of the Purchaser.

Paragraph 5: The Purchaser agrees to cut and remove said timber in strict accordance with the following conditions:
a. ONLY timber marked with blue paint within the sale area will be cut.
b. Every reasonable precaution not to cut or injure any trees or seedlings on the designated sale area must be taken.

c. The Purchaser will be assessed double stumpage rates for cutting unmarked timber.

d. The Purchaser shall use existing roads; new roads and ski trails shall be located only with the consent of the Seller; and roads at all times shall be kept free of logs, brush, and debris resulting from the Purchaser's operations. Any road used by the Purchaser in connection with this sale that is damaged or injured beyond ordinary wear and tear through such use shall promptly be restored by the Purchaser to its original conditions.

e. Young trees shall be protected from unnecessary injury: only dead trees and less valuable species may be used for construction purposes in connection with logging operations. All improvements shall be left in place by the Purchaser.

f. Diligent care shall be exercised at all times by the Purchaser and Purchaser's employees and agents against the starting and spread of fires.

g. The Purchaser agrees not to assign this agreement in whole or in part without the prior written consent of the Seller.

h. The Purchaser shall protect property such as fields, fences, telephone, light and power lines, building, ditches, bridges, etc. against unnecessary injury, and shall repair damaged caused by restoring them to the original condition.

i. As far as practical all logging and hauling shall be in an orderly and progressive manner.

j. The Purchaser and Purchaser's employees and agents shall protect young growth, and shall give due consideration to distrubances which will affect soil movement or impair and aggravate water movement.

k. All roads and skid trails shall be crossed ditched in a manner that will allow continued use by the Seller. This work shall be completed immediately upon cessation of use.

Paragraph 6: The Purchaser agrees to abide by the following utilization standards:

a. All sawlogs which have a net scale of thirty-three (33) percent or more and contain a minimum of ten (10) board feet Scribner log rule are merchantable.

b. Minimum top diameter for all sawtimber will be six (6) inches diameter inside bark (d.i.b.).

c. Minimum scaling length for sawtimber will be ten (10) feet lus trim. Maximum scaling length for sawtimber will be twenty (20) feet plus trim.

d. Minimum trim allowance will be four (4) inches per scaling segment unless otherwise specified by the Purchaser. Logs not having this minimum trim allowance shall be scaled at the next shorter length. trim allowance shall be six (6) inches on logs less than twenty-two (22) feet and twelve (12) inches on logs greater than twenty-two (22) feet.

e. The Purchaser shall specify desired log lengths to facilitate hauling.

f. The Purchaser will be responsible for skidding and hauling all merchantable logs. The Purchaser will be assessed double stumapge prices for any uncut timber or timber which has been improperly utilized as determined by the seller and shall be property of the seller.

Paragraph 7:

a. Special requirements are: All long butting shall be done at the landing to aid in slash disposal. All skidding should be done log length.

b. Any species cut that is unmerchantable for sawlogs but satisfactory for pulp and/or firewood shall be decked at a location designated by the Seller.

c. Subject to the provisions of sub-section (g) Paragraph 5 above, this agreement shall be binding upon and shall insure to the benefit of the heirs, executers, administrators, successors and assigns of the parties hereto.

d. PURCHASER AGREES TO INDEMNITY AND HOLD HARMLESS THE SELLER from any and all damages, claims, or demands upon the part of third parties on account of any acts or omissions of the Purchasers, Purchaser agents, servants, or employees, and furthermore to respect and protect all right-of-way, eastments, and servitudes belonging to any other party or parties, and agrees not to injure, damage, or waste the same in any way whatsoever, and does hereby covenent and agree to indemnity and hold harmless the Seller therefrom.

Paragraph 8: In the event of dispute the Purchaser and Seller agree to accept decision of an arbitration board of three members; one to be selected by the Seller, one by the Purchaser and the third to be selected by the first two. The arbitrators must reach an agreement within thirty (30) days.

Paragraph 9: The Seller covenants that he/she has full power to sell and convey said timber in fee simple, and that said timber is free and clear of all encumbrances, and that the Seller does hereby warrant and will forever defend the title to said timber against all claims of all persons whomsoever.

IN WITNESS WHEREOF, THIS AGREEMENT HAS BEEN EXECUTED BY THE PARTIES HERE TO ON THE DATE FIRST WRITTEN ABOVE.

Witness: _____

_____

Witness: _____

_____

Seller: _____

Purchaser:_____

_____

STATE OF _____

County of _____

On this _____ day of _____, 19_____, before me, the udnersigned, a Notary Public in and for the said State, personally appeared _____

known to me to be the persons whose names are subscribed to the above and foregoing instrument and acknowledge to me that they executed the same.

IN WITNESS WHEREOF, I have hereunto set my hand and notorial seal the date last above written.

NOTARY PUBLIC in and for the
State of
Idaho, residing at

_____

_____ .

Pleasant Acres Farm

Permit To: _____

Address: _____

Phone: _____

Date: _____

    This will acknowledge your assignment for _____ cords of firewood. You may cut this wood from all trees designated with two paint spots, one at base and one on trunk, from the lands owned by David and/or Myra Houston. Area Number _____ Color _____

1. You should understand that producing fuel wood is hard and dangerous work. If you do not have any previous experience with cutting wood, you should seriously reconsider your request.
2. In cutting and removing this wood, you assume all risks for injury to yourself, or other persons, and damage to property, and agree to save the farm harmless from any claims which may result from your operation.
3. All fences and gates shall be kept closed at all times when not entering or exiting fuelwood cutting area.
4. All hauling of wood shall be done between the months of June through Sept., unless permission granted by owner.
5. If you are willing to assume the associated risks and proceed with this operation, please sign the statement at the bottom of this letter and return a copy to owner. You are authorized to remove the wood upon payment of _____ a cord.
6. This permit expires two years from date of issuance, on _____.

                                   Pleasant Acres Farm
                                   David and/or Myra Houston
                                   Box 35
                                   Cabot, Vermont 05647
                                   Phone 563-2578

I hereby certify that I have read and understand the terms of this permit and that I assume the risks involved in obtaining the firewood authorized by this permit.

_____   _____
             Date   Permittee

Appendix I
(Example) Christmas Tree Sale Contract

Agreement entered into on this _____ day of _____, 19_____ between

_____ of _____, hereinafter called the "Seller," and

_____ of _____, hereinafter called the "Purchaser."

Article I: The Seller agrees to sell to the Purchaser, under terms and conditions hereinafter stated, the Christmas trees listed below in the quantities and at the prices set forth:

Species	Height	Grade	Quantity	Price
_____	_____	_____	_____	_____
_____	_____	_____	_____	_____
_____	_____	_____	_____	_____
_____	_____	_____	_____	_____

These trees are on a tract of land in the county and state of _____ and described

as follows: _____.

Article II: The Purchaser agrees not to deposit $_____ of the purchase price and will pay the unit price as each load is removed and, in any event, the balance before the trees are removed from the premises.

Article IIIa: The Purchaser agrees to cut, prepare for shipment, and remove the Christmas trees in strict accordance with the following conditions:

1. Unless an extension of time is granted, all Christmas trees shall be cut and removed from the land between _____

   _____ and _____, 19_____. (In the case of the Purchaser's failure to do so, the Seller, at her/his option and without notice to the Purchaser, may sell the trees for the account of the Purchaser and hold her/him for any deficiency plus a reasonable charge for disposing of same; or she/he may hold the Purchaser for the full purchase price; or she/he may retain the deposit and treat the trees as her/his own property.)

2. Proper care will be used to protect other trees from damage while harvesting the Christmas trees.

3. Christmas trees will be cut off within 6 inches of the ground, or else all green limbs will be cut from the stump if the stump is higher than 6 inches; or above a whorl of living branches where turn-ups are to be grown.

4. Only trees (marked by _____) (within boundaries delineated with _____) shall be cut.

5. No new roads or trails will be created without the written consent of the Seller.

6. Any damage beyond ordinary wear and tear caused to ditches, fences, bridges, roads or any other improvements will be repaired.

OR

Article IIIb: The Seller agrees to cut and convey (or cut, bale, and convey) all trees covered by this contract. She/he further agrees to

deliver the trees to the Purchaser at _____ between _____, 19 _____

and _____, 19_____.

Article IV: It is mutually understood and agreed by and between the parties heretofore mentioned as follows:

1. Title to the trees shall pass to the Purchaser when the same are severed from the stump or when selected by her/him, as the case may be. The Seller shall have a lien thereon for the purchase price and may hold same until it is paid. Risk of loss and damage after severance or selection shall be on the Purchaser.

2. The Purchaser has found the trees selected by her/him to be of acceptable merchantable quality.

3. In case of dispute over the terms of this contract, final decision shall rest with a reputable person to be mutually agreed upon by parties to this contract, and in case of further disagreement, with an arbitration board of three persons, one to be selected by each party to this contract and a third to be mutually agreed upon.

In witness whereof the parties hereto have executed this contract in duplicate this _____ day of

_____, 19_____.

Purchaser: _____

Seller: _____

I. DESIGN THE CRUISE

A. The Total Cruise

To do a total cruise, simply divide your forest into corridors with lines close enough that you can see the sides of each strip. One hundred feet may be a good average distance, but this depends on the thickness of the woods. Start about 100 feet inside one edge of your property and run the first compass line, marking trees or shrubs along this line with chalk or pieces of white toilet paper. Toilet paper is especially good as temporary flagging (in dry weather) because it is cheap, highly visible, and quickly disappears since it is biodegradable.

The lines can be due north, or due east, or in the direction of easiest travel -- any way that is easy, just as long as they are parallel and visible as you later walk down each corridor. Some folks lay out the whole woodlot, then cruise; others find it more prudent to do a few strips at a time (in case it rains and wipes out the toilet paper!).

THE TOTAL CRUISE
PARALLEL COMPASS LINES, MARKED BY CHALK ON TREE TRUNKS OR PIECES OF TOILET TISSUE ON SHRUBS, ORGANIZE THE FOREST FOR 100 PERCENT CRUISE.

If you are interested in more than an estimate of timber volume, you'll need to put each compass line on your map. This way, as you cruise (and pace or otherwise measure distances) you can plot out various features such as changes in cover type, location of openings or plantings, marshes, creeks, wildlife trees, and potential picnic sites.

B. The Sample Cruise

Designing a sample cruise is more complex, but is the faster and more practical method on larger tracts or in homogeneous stands. There are many ways to cruise, but the procedure suggested here is an easy one for non-professionals. After planning your sample cruise, it is a good idea to check with a local forester to see if he concurs.

1. Select a circular plot size.

   Plots are usually
   1/10 acre (37.24 ft. radius)
   or 1/5 acre (52.66 ft. radius)
   or 1/4 acre (58.88 ft. radius)

   Rules of thumb:
   1. Use 1/4- or 1/5-acre plots for trees of sawtimber size; drop to 1/10-acre plots for pulpwood, posts, short trees or other small product wood.

   2. Sample not less than 25% of total acreage on tracts of 50 acres or less, and no less than 10% on areas larger than 50 acres. Above 500 acres, a smaller sample will usually be needed for efficiency. Discuss with a forester.

   SPECIAL NOTE: We are primarily focusing on the inventory of merchantable-sized trees or those soon entering such size classes. Estimates of reproduction (seelings and saplings) are usually made following a similar system but with milacre plots (1/1000 acre, or a 6.6-ft. X 6.6-ft. quadrant or circular 1/300-acre plots with a 6.8-ft. radius).

2. Lay out a plot grid.

   The secret to obtaining an unbiased sampling of the trees in your forest is to pre-determine where each plot should go. One good method is to lay out a uniform grid, that is, the plots will be spaced evenly throughout the stand, like the trees in an orchard. Here's how to determine the distance between plot centers.

   (A) $\dfrac{\text{Total Area}}{\text{Size of Plots}}$ X $\begin{array}{c}\text{Percent}\\\text{Cruise}\end{array}$ = $\begin{array}{c}\text{Number of}\\\text{Plots Needed}\end{array}$

   Example:

   $$\frac{80 \text{ acres}}{.25 \text{ acre}} \text{ X } .15 = 48 \text{ plots}$$

   (B) $\dfrac{\text{Total Area}}{\text{Number of Plots}}$ = $\begin{array}{c}\text{Area Represented}\\\text{by Each Plot}\end{array}$

(C) Go to the "Table of Plot Center Distances" to find distances between plots.

(D) Using the distances between plot centers, lay out lines on your map that distance apart, then add dots along the lines using the same distance figure.

Example:

$$\frac{80 \text{ acres}}{48 \text{ plots}} = 1.7 \text{ acres (represented by each } \tfrac{1}{4}\text{-acre plot)}$$

Extrapolating between 1.5 and 2.0 in the table, we find that the plots and lines should be 271 feet apart.

Table of Plot Center Distances -- "Orchard Method"

Area represented by each plot	Distance between plots[1]
Acres	Feet
1.0	209
1.5	255
2.0	295
2.5	330
3.0	361
3.5	390
4.0	417
4.5	442
5.0	467

[1]Like tree spacing in an orchard or plantation, these may be calculated by multiplying the number of square feet in an acre (43,560) by the area represented by each plot (or tree plus growing space in the case of orchards and plantations), then extracting the square root.

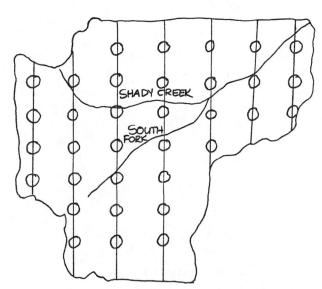

THE PARTIAL OR SAMPLE CRUISE

EXAMPLE OF A DESIGN FOR A PARTIAL CRUISE USING EVEN, BUT ARBITRARILY SPACED LINES WITH EVENLY SPACED PLOT CENTERS. THIS IS AN ALTERNATIVE TO THE ORCHARD LAYOUT SYSTEM WHERE BOTH PLOTS AND LINES ARE EQUALLY SPACED.

This method works best with square or rectangular areas, but with some common sense it can also be put on maps of irregular tracts. Precision is not necessary as long as the plots cover the tract uniformly and come reasonably close to sampling the percent of the stand you have decided upon. What is critical is that once your sampling system is designed, you religiously stick to it. Remember to allow for slope when pacing. Also, if plot centers are 300 feet apart, don't pace 295 feet and stop because there are greenbriars five feet ahead. The goal is to get a random sampling of your forest, but for efficiency, to do it in a systematic manner.

A less structured alternative to the above method is to simply lay out your cruise lines on the map at any distance apart that reasonably covers the tract. They should go across drainage patterns rather than parallel with them so you are more likely to pick up changes in the forest cover caused by elevation, soil moisture or aspect differences. On your map, measure the approximate total length of your cruise lines. Then,

(A) $\dfrac{\text{Total Area to be Cruised}}{\text{Size of Plots}}$ X $\dfrac{\text{Percent}}{\text{Cruise}}$ = $\dfrac{\text{Number of}}{\text{Plots Needed}}$

(B) $\dfrac{\text{Total Length of Cruise Lines}}{\text{Number of Plots}}$ = $\dfrac{\text{Distance Between}}{\text{Plot Centers}}$

II. MEASURE YOUR TREES

After designing an appropriate cruise, measure the trees following the procedures outlined in Chapter 3.

III. KEEP A TALLY

As you cruise your woodland measuring the trees, a systematic method is needed for keeping the count. This is done on *tally sheets*. These come in many varieties, but you can easily make and duplicate your own to fit your particular needs. A sample of one of the simplest but most useful is included in this appendix. A form like this one is flexible in that you can list the species to be tallied any way you like. In a mixed hardwood forest, this may be a species by species listing, or in a young southern pine forest being measured for a pulpwood sale (except for large pines of saw timber size), the column headings might be:

Saw Timber   Other Conifers   Hardwoods

THE FORESTER'S DOT TALLY

.	..	::.	.::	.:.	⌐	⌐	□	◹	⊠	⊠.	⊠..
1	2 3	4	5 6	6	7	8	9	10	11	12	ETC

Where more than seven species or groups of species are to be tallied, more than one sheet will be needed. Often, one sheet or set of sheets will be used per plot on a partial cruise. There is also a blank space in the DBH column for any size above 24 inches. If many merchantable trees in your stand run higher than that, you may want to scratch out and change the DBH numbers accordingly, perhaps having the spread go from 12" to 30", or continue the listing on another page. (See sample at end of appendix for a convenient way to summarize the tally sheets and arrive at total volume.)

To keep from counting a tree twice during a cruise, which is especially easy to do in a total cruise, it helps to mark the tallied ones with chalk or lumber crayon. But that is a lot of extra work. An easier way is to mark the first one in a circular plot so you will know when you have completed the 360 degree sweep of the plot. In a total cruise, mark those on or near the edge of your corridor that is adjacent to the next corridor to be worked. Always mark on the same side (perhaps south) so you quickly know where to look for these helpful reminders.

Since you are making an effort to estimate as closely as possible the actual amount of usable wood that could be sold, you should not tally portions of trees that are obviously rotten, severely crooked or otherwise unusable. There is usually an additional amount of internal decay or other hidden defects that you can expect the buyer to deduct when he scales the sawlogs at roadside or the mill (See Chapter 8). Sometimes an average defect factor is used locally to improve accuracy. On the University of Idaho Experimental Forest, for example, approximately 10 percent of the Douglas-fir volume is subtracted to allow for defect, 20 percent from the grand fir totals, and five percent from ponderosa pine.

IV. ARRIVE AT THE TOTAL VOLUME

You will end the cruise with quite a sheaf of tally sheets. The next step is to convert the tally into useful figures that represent the total volumes of usable wood in your forest. In so doing, you will need to convert cylindrical trees into some unit of wood that is used in sales, the most common being cords and board feet. The problem is further complicated by the fact that if you pile cordwood, much of the pile is air spaces between the round logs. And when logs are sawed, not only is there waste in bark and slabs as the rounded log gets squared, there is also actually taper in what we measured as a perfect cylinder in the woods.

Happily, there are tables that take all these factors into account. Today, the only trick is to get the right table. Many have been developed using dozens of formulas, each with its own strengths and weaknesses for accurately converting standing volume to the amount of merchantable wood in trees. These formulas are called *log scaling rules*. Without going into the math and politics of why different ones are used, the four most common ones are listed below. To find which one is used most in your area, see the chart in Appendix D.

Doyle Rule
The official rule (by law) in some Southern states. Favored by industry log buyers in East. Tends to underestimate true volume, especially on small diameter trees.

International 1/4-inch Rule
The official rule in Connecticut, Maine, Massachusetts, New York, and Vermont. Comes closest to the actual mill tally (what is actually produced from sawlogs). Favored by many public agencies in Canada and the United States.

Scribner Decimal C
The standard used by the U.S. Forest Service and many other United States public land agencies. Widely used in West. Tends to underestimate volume of small diameter logs. Official in Georgia and Idaho. The right hand digit is always dropped by rounding off the next digit to the nearest 10 bf.

Scribner
Widely used in Pennsylvania and California. Retains all digits in expressing board feet.

Another name you will encounter on some volume tables is *Girard Form Class*. This is an expression of taper in a tree; specifically, the ratio between DBH (inside bark) and diameter (inside bark) at the top of the first 16-foot log. Each species has a known form class, but for some species this varies with locale. In other words, a white pine growing in Vermont can be expected to have a different taper to its trunk than a white pine in Michigan. Most sets of volume tables used locally have been developed incorporating form class but it could happen that you might need to first find the form class of your trees before obtaining the table. If so, it is a matter for a local professional.

While all of this may sound complex, it is intended to make you aware of why two people may arrive at different total volumes from your cruise data. In actual practice there is a simple solution. Contact your local extension forester or other public forester to find out what volume tables are commonly used in your area. He will probably be able to give you copies of the tables or you can then write fo them by contacting a government forestry office. It is a good idea to discuss this with the forester *before* you cruise, possibly during the same visit when you show him your cruise design. This is because some tables may make it necessary to tally a certain way, such as lumping several species, or using a minimum DBH, or measuring total tree height instead of logs, etc.

Two volume tables are shown here as examples. From the diameter and height of each tree on the tally sheet, a volume in board feet or cordwood (for pulp, firewood, charcoal, etc.) can be determined. To help speed this summing process, it pays to construct a computing form like the one pictured for board feet totals at the end of this appendix. All the entries come from your tally sheets and the volume tables. Then it's just a matter of multiplying the volume of one tree times the number of trees you had in that *class* (DBH and number of logs), and adding up the totals. If you did a total cruise, the job is done. If you did a partial cruise, you simply multiply the species totals by a correction factor derived from:

$$\frac{\text{Total Area}}{\text{Total Area in Plots}} = \text{Correction Factor}$$

The bottom line is the grand total for each species on your land. This is your merchantable volume and if you are planning a sale, it will be the basis for bargaining with buyers. If you cruised for other purposes, you have an equally valuable record of the composition of your woodland.

TALLY SHEET

Location PENN'S WOODLAND (HWY 55) Date 10/5/85

BUCKSVILLE, PA   Plot Number 4 (SHEET 1 of 2)

DBH	# LOGS	WHITE OAK	RED OAK	HICKORY	BASSWOOD	WHITE ASH	HARD MAPLE	OTHERS
6	.5	⊠		.:	.	..		:.
6	1		:.	..	::		.	▱
8	.5						∟	
8	1					.		
10	.5							
10	1						.	
10	1.5							
12	.5							
12	1					.		..
12	1.5							
12	2							
14	1							
14	1.5		..					
14	2							
14	2.5							
16	1.5							
16	2							
16	2.5							
18	1							
18	1.5							
18	2						.	
18	2.5							
20	1							
20	1.5							
20	2							
22	1.5							
22	2							
22	2.5							.
22	3							
24	1.5							
24	2							
24	2.5							
24	3							
32 =	2.5							.
Total Vol.:								
B.F.								
Cords								

Notes: Excellent spring near here.

202

EXAMPLES OF VOLUME TABLES

For Saw Logs --

Table 3. Second-growth tree volumes[1] (Scribner Decimal C)

DBH (in.)	No. logs	WWP[2]	PP	WL	DF	GF	WRC	WH	ES
				(Board foot volume in tens)					
12	2	5	6	6	6	7	7	7	5
	3	9	9	10	9	11	10	12	9
14	2	7	9	9	9	10	10	11	8
	3	13	14	15	15	17	16	19	12
	4	19		20	22	25	22	26	18
16	2	9	12	10	10	12	11	12	10
	3	16	19	17	18	20	18	22	15
	4	23	25	24	26	29	25	31	22
	5	30		30	33	38	32	41	30
18	2	12	14	12	12	13	12	14	12
	3	19	24	20	21	24	21	25	18
	4	28	32	28	30	34	30	37	26
	5	36	42	35	39	45	38	48	34
20	3	22	29	22	24	28	24	29	22
	4	33	41	32	35	40	34	43	31
	5	44	54	41	45	53	44	56	40
22	3	26	34	26	28	32	28	34	26
	4	39	48	37	40	47	40	50	36
	5	52	62	48	53	62	51	66	47
24	3	31	38	29	32	36	32	39	30
	4	46	56	42	46	54	45	58	42
	5	61	74	55	61	72	59	76	54
	6	76	92	68	75	90	73	95	68
26	3	36	42	34	36	40	36	44	35
	4	54	64	48	52	61	51	66	48
	5	71	86	62	69	83	67	88	62
	6	89	108	77	86	105	83	110	78
28	3	41	46	37	40	44	40	49	49
	4	62	72	54	59	68	58	74	55
	5	82	98	71	78	94	76	100	71
	6	105	124	88	98	120	93	125	89
30	3	47	50	41	45	49	45	54	45
	4	70	80	60	66	77	64	84	62
	5	94	110	79	88	105	85	115	80
	6	115	140	99	110	135	105	145	100

[1]Compiled from U S. D. A. Tech. Bul. 323 and U. of I. Bul. No. 20.

[2] WWP=western white pine   GF=grand fir
PP=ponderosa pine   WRC=western red cedar
WL=western larch   WH=western hemlock
DF=Douglas fir   ES=Engelmann spruce

For Pulpwood --

VIRGINIA PINE

Table 13. Merchantable Volume in Cords, with Bark *
Monongahela National Forest, West Virginia

D.b.h. (in.)	Total height in feet					
	20	30	40	50	60	70
6	0.027	0.033	0.039	0.045		
8	.037	.047	.058	.070		
10	.047	.066	.085	.103		
12		.088	.125	.166		
14		.115	.180	.260	0.35	0.44
16		.147	.245	.360	.48	.62
18		.184	.320	.480	.67	.85
20			.410	.610	.85	1.08

* Stump height, 12 in. on uphill side. Minimum top diameter at limit of merchantability, 4 in. inside bark. Average deviation, volume of individual tree, 14.4 percent. Reduce volumes 15 percent for peeled wood.
Source: Roberts, Monongahela National Forest, 1937.

EXAMPLE COMPUTING FORM FOR TOTALS FROM CRUISE DATA
(BOARD FEET, SCRIBNER RULE)

Species	Size Class		Volume of One Tree	No. of Trees Tallied	Total Volume in Size Class
	DBH	No. 16' Logs			
White Oak	14	1.5	92	40	3,680
	16	1.5	127	8	1,016
	16	2.0	159	23	3,657
	16	2.5	185	18	3,330
	18	1.0	123	25	3,075
Total				114	14,758
Red Oak	12	1.0	47	31	
	12	1.5	61		
	14	1.0	69		

Index

A

Agricultural Conservation Program, 33
Agricultural Stabilization and Conservation Service, 22, 33–35
aerial photos, 21, 22
American Forest Institute, 181–182
American Forestry Association, 17, 41, 178, 180–181
American Tree Farm System, 87, 181–182
annual rings, 12, 64
Arbor Day, 59
arson, 71
aspect, 11
assistance, sources of, 32–37, 186
Association of Consulting Foresters, 35
associations, 5, 35, 178–182, 185
Audubon, 170, 176

B

Barbour, Scott, 104–106
Barrett, John W., 52
basal area, 24–26
Beineke, Walter F., 115
Biltmore stick, 23
binomial nomenclature, 13
biome, 7, 164
board foot, 24–25
boundary signs and marking, 37–38, 187
bridges, 90, 92
Brockman, C. Frank, 17
Brush, W.D., 17
brush control, 55–56, 63, 109–110
Bruun, B., 176
bucking, 97–102
buds, 18
Burroughs, John, 7, 21

C

Callahan, John C., 89
Canadian
    land ownership, 2–3
    maps and aerial photos, 22
    sources of assistance, 35–36, 185
Carlson, Axel, 118
chain, (length), 23
chain saws, 96–99
Chapman, Walter and Ann, 153–157
charcoal, 118-119
Christmas trees, 133-145
    contracts, 198
    equipment suppliers, 187
Clark, Brian F., 115
Clarke-McNary Act, 56
cleaning, 44, 62–63
clearcutting, 47
climax forest, 9–10
Collingwood, G.H., 17
commercial forest land
    defined, 2
    ownership of, 2–3
computers, 27
consulting foresters, 34–35, 37
continuous forest inventory, 27
contracts, 93–95, 194–198
Cooperative Extension Service, 32–34, 186
cooperatives, firewood, 128
coppicing, 51–52
cord, 25, 126
Coulter, J. Bruce, 73

cover types, 7–9
cruising timber, 21, 24, 199–203
cultivars, 148
cunit, 25
cuttings
    clearcutting, 47, 192–193
    diameter limit, 51
    harvest, 43, 45–52, 192–193
    intermediate, 43–45
    improvement, 44
    liberation, 44
    salvage, 44
    selection, 49–50, 159, 192–193
    shelterwood, 48, 192–193
    seed tree, 47–48, 192–193

D

Daubenmire, Rexford and Jean, 10
Dauerwald, 49–50
Decker, Daniel J., 176
Decker, E., 177
defects, 93
Dent, D. Douglas, 104
diameter
    measuring, 23
    –limit cutting, 51
diameter at breast height, 23, 25–27
diseases, 82–84
Draft Horse and Mule Association, 106
drying wood, 129
durability of wood, 120

E

Ebersole, Fred, 150
ecology, 13, 41
economics
    of Christmas trees, 133, 139–140, 145
    of firewood, 126–127, 130–131
    of forestry, 38–39, 68, 89
    of maple syrup, 160
erosion control, 90–91
Eyre, F.H., 8

F

face cord, 25
Federal Land Bank, 33
felling, 96–99
fence posts, 119–120
fertilizers and fertilizing, 60, 62, 136, 148
Fine Hardwoods/American Walnut Assoc., 115
financial maturity, 89
fire and fire fighting, 56, 71–77
fire management, 75
firewood, 110, 115, 123–131, 159–160
    contracts, 197
Firewood Finders, Inc., 128
Fischer, Burnell C., 68
Forbes, Reginald, D., 41
forest (See specific subject)
forest types, 7–10
Forestry Incentives Program, 33
forwarders (See skidders)
Fowells, H.A., 41
Freeman, George, 109–110
Frome, Michael, 179
fruit, 17

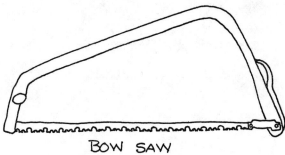

BOW SAW

Personal Notes...

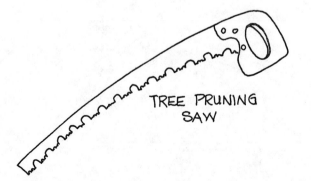

TREE PRUNING
SAW

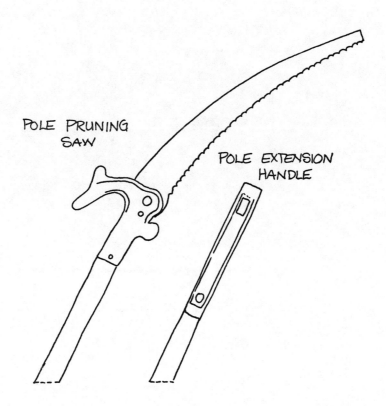

POLE PRUNING
SAW

POLE EXTENSION
HANDLE

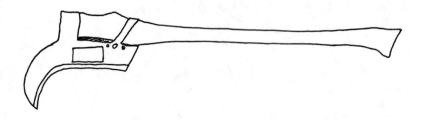

Personal Notes...

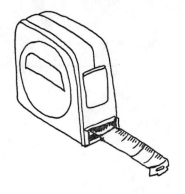